Preface

One of the most important tasks facing editors who put together a yearbook on science and technology is to choose subjects that are most significant and most timely. At the same time, we like to strike a balance in subject matter that reflects the wide range of interests among our readers. We try to have something for everyone.

For this reason, we usually devote only one Special Report to a subject area. But occasionally, significance and timeliness suggest that we make an exception. In *Science Year* 1984 we made the exception twice.

One area is the field of environment/ecology. The disposal of toxic waste continues to be a worrisome thing for more and more people whose backyards and neighborhoods have become a repository for dangerous metals and chemicals. In the Special Report, LAYING WASTE IN AMERICA, the author describes the extent of the problems and outlines some solutions that will require commitment by society along with, of course, the expenditure of lots of money.

This year we also felt it necessary to report on another pollution problem. Certain chemicals put into the atmosphere travel downwind for hundreds of miles to descend as acid rain to despoil lakes, forests, and structures. The Special Report, ACID FROM THE SKY, describes the destruction, what the probable causes are and, again, sees solutions that will be costly and require the cooperation of a great many people.

The other subject area that this edition examines twice is anthropology. In recent years, most of the important fossil evidence of our earliest ancestors has come from a rift junction in Ethiopia called the Afar Triangle. Why this is such a fertile area for such evidence turns out to be a matter of the right geophysical forces combined with the right climatic changes. The author of THE AFAR'S BOUNTIFUL LEGACY describes the evolution of a rift valley and how it serves first to protect—and later to reveal—a wealth of fossil bones.

Meanwhile, a new breed of anthropologists are comparing cells and tissues of animals living in the present, rather than the bones of those that lived in the past. The Special Report MOLECULAR CLUES TO OUR ORIGINS tells how these molecular anthropologists are finding relationships among some species and discovering evolutionary time scales that differ from the classical picture.

There is still room in *Science Year*, of course, for the usual variety of Special Reports on astronomy, animal behavior, medicine, geoscience, and the like. And Science File continues its coverage of the news of the year in the major disciplines. We think there is still something for everyone.   [Arthur G. Tressler]

3

Contents

4

1984

Science Year

The World Book Science Annual

A Review of Science and Technology During the 1983 School Year

World Book, Inc.

a Scott Fetzer company

Chicago London Sydney Toronto

Staff

Publisher
William H. Nault

Editorial
Editor
A. Richard Harmet

Executive Editor
Arthur G. Tressler

Managing Editor
Darlene R. Stille

Senior Editors
David L. Dreier
Marsha F. Goldsmith
Barbara A. Mayes
Jay Myers

Contributing Editors
Gary A. Alt
Sara Dreyfuss
Lynn Gutknecht

Research Editor
Irene B. Keller

Editorial Assistant
Lettie Zinnamon

Art
Executive Art Director
William Hammond

Art Director
Roberta Dimmer

Senior Artist
Nikki Conner

Artists
Rosa Cabrera
Alice F. Dole
Alexandra Kalantzis

Photography Director
John S. Marshall

Photographs Editors
Karen M. Koblik
Sandra M. Ozanick
Randi E. Sherman

Research and Services
Director of Editorial Services
Susan C. Kilburg

Head, Research Services
Mary Norton

Head, Library Services
Mary Kayaian

Head, Cartographic Services
H. George Stoll

Index Editor
Claire Bolton

Product Production
Executive Director
Peter Mollman

Director of Manufacturing
Joseph LaCount

Director of Pre-Press
J. J. Stack

Production Control Manager
Barbara Podczerwinski

Assistant Product Manager
Madelyn Krzak

Film Separations Manager
Alfred J. Mozdzen

Film Separations Assistant Manager
Barbara J. McDonald

Research and Development Manager
Henry Koval

Editorial Advisory Board

Contributors

Adelman, George, M.S.
Free-Lance Consultant Editor
Neuroscience

Alderman, Michael H., M.D.
Professor of Medicine and
Public Health
Cornell University Medical College
Medicine, Internal
Public Health

Alexander, George, B.S.
Science Writer
Los Angeles Times
Molecular Clues to Our Origins

Auerbach, Stanley I., Ph.D.
Director, Environmental
Sciences Division
Oak Ridge National Laboratory
Ecology

Baym, Gordon, Ph.D.
Professor of Physics
University of Illinois
Physics, Condensed Matter

Bell, William J., Ph.D.
Professor of Biology
University of Kansas
Zoology

Belton, Michael J. S., Ph.D.
Astronomer
Kitt Peak National Observatory
Astronomy, Solar System

Bierman, Howard, B.E.E.
Managing Editor
Electronics Magazine
Close-Up, Electronics
Electronics

Black, John H., Ph.D.
Associate Professor of Astronomy
Steward Observatory
University of Arizona
Astronomy, Galactic

Brancazio, Peter J., Ph.D.
Associate Professor of Physics
Brooklyn College
City University of New York
Close-Up, Physics

Brett, Carlton E., Ph.D.
Assistant Professor
Department of Geological Sciences
University of Rochester
Earth Sciences, Paleontology

Clark, G. A., Ph.D.
Professor of Anthropology
Arizona State University
Archaeology, Old World

Cox, Allan, Ph.D.
Professor of Geophysics
Stanford University
The Patchwork Earth

Cromie, William J., B.S.
Executive Director
Council for the Advancement
of Science Writing
Rebuilding Bodies

Dewey, Russell A., Ph.D.
Assistant Professor of Psychology
Georgia Southern College
Psychology

Engebretson, David C., Ph.D.
Assistant Professor and
Research Associate
Western Washington University
The Patchwork Earth

Fishman, Gerald A., M.D.
Professor of Ophthalmology
University of Illinois
Shielding Your Eyes

Fitzpatrick, John W., Ph.D.
Associate Curator and Head
Division of Birds
Field Museum of Natural History
Staying Around the Nest

Gates, W. Lawrence, Sc.D.
Professor and Chairman
Department of Atmospheric Sciences
Oregon State University
Earth Sciences, Meteorology

Geller, Margaret J., Ph.D.
Assistant Professor
Center for Astrophysics
Harvard University
Mapping the Universe

Goldhaber, Paul, D.D.S.
Dean and Professor of Periodontology
Harvard School of Dental Medicine
Medicine, Dentistry

Gore, Rick, M.S.
Senior Writer
National Geographic Magazine
Close-Up, Archaeology

Gump, Frank E., M.D.
Professor of Surgery
Columbia University
Medicine, Surgery

Hartl, Daniel L., Ph.D.
Professor of Genetics
Washington University School
of Medicine
Genetics

Hester, Thomas R., Ph.D.
Professor of Anthropology
and Director
Center for Archaeological Research
University of Texas, San Antonio
Archaeology, New World

Hyman, Richard W., Ph.D.
Professor of Microbiology
Hershey Medical Center
Herpes Is Forever

Jennings, Feenan D., B.S.
Director
Sea Grant Program
Texas A&M University
Earth Sciences, Oceanography

Jones, William G., A.M.L.S.
Assistant University Librarian
University of Illinois, Chicago Circle
Books of Science

Kalb, Jon E., B.Sc.
Associate Research Scientist
Balcones Research Center
University of Texas
The Afar's Bountiful Legacy

Kantor, Thomas G., M.D.
Professor of Clinical Medicine
New York University School of
Medicine
Picking Out a Pain Reliever

Katz, Joseph J., Ph.D.
Distinguished Senior Scientist
Emeritus
Argonne National Laboratory
New Light on Photosynthesis

Katz, Paul, M.D.
Assistant Professor of Medicine
University of Florida College of
Medicine
Immunology

Kay, Robert W., Ph.D.
Associate Professor
Cornell University
Earth Sciences, Geology

King, Lauriston R., Ph.D.
Deputy Director
Sea Grant Program
Texas A&M University
Earth Sciences, Oceanography

Kinne, Harold C., Ph.D.
Senior Vice President
Future Computing, Inc.
*Personal Computers: More for Your
Dollar*

March, Robert H., Ph.D.
Professor of Physics
University of Wisconsin
*Physics, Atoms and Nuclei,
Particles and Forces*

Maugh, Thomas H. II, Ph.D.
Senior Science Writer
Science Magazine
Laying Waste in America

Merbs, Charles F., Ph.D.
Professor
Department of Anthropology
Arizona State University
Anthropology

Merz, Beverly, A.B.
Associate Editor, Medical News
*Journal of the American Medical
Association*
Cancer's Genetic Connection

Miyares, Ben, B.A.
Executive Editor
Food & Drug Packaging Magazine
Close-Up, Drugs

Moore, Mike, B.A.
Assistant Editor
*The Physician and Sportsmedicine
Magazine*
Getting a Good Run for Your Money

Murray, Stephen S., Ph.D.
Astrophysicist
Smithsonian Astrophysical Observatory
Astronomy, Extragalactic

Nash, Edward G., A.B.
Editor, *Economic Perspectives*,
Federal Reserve Bank of Chicago
Science on Display

Nassau, Kurt, Ph.D.
Member of Technical Staff
Bell Laboratories
The Physics of Color

Olson, Maynard V., Ph.D.
Assistant Professor
Department of Genetics
Washington University School
of Medicine
Molecular Biology

Patrusky, Ben, B.E.E.
Free-Lance Science Writer
The Secrets of Living Lights

Pennisi, Elizabeth, M.S.
Free-Lance Science Writer
*Close-Up, Immunology,
Zoology*

Reidenberg, Marcus M., M.D.
Professor of Pharmacology and
Medicine
Cornell University Medical College
Drugs

Salisbury, Frank B., Ph.D.
Professor of Plant Physiology
Plant Science Department
Utah State University
Botany

Sands, Richard D., Ph.D.
Professor of Chemistry
Alfred University
Options for the Soap Dish

Sforza, Pasquale M., Ph.D.
Professor of Mechanical and
Aeronautical Engineering
Polytechnic Institute of New York
The Physics of the Fireplace

Shore, Bradd, Ph.D.
Associate Professor of Anthropology
Emory University
Close-Up, Anthropology

Trefil, James, Ph.D.
Professor of Physics
University of Virginia
New Missions for Magnetism

Verbit, Lawrence P., Ph.D.
Professor of Chemistry
State University of New York
at Binghamton
Chemistry

Vietmeyer, Noel D., Ph.D.
Professional Associate
National Academy of Sciences
Norman E. Borlaug

Visich, Marian, Jr., Ph.D.
Associate Dean of Engineering
State University of New York
Acid from the Sky, Energy

Westman, Walt, Ph.D.
Professor of Ecosystem Analysis
and Conservation
Department of Geography
University of California, Los Angeles
Environment

Wheatley, John, Ph.D.
Staff Member
Los Alamos National Laboratory
Close-Up, Energy

Wittwer, Sylvan H., Ph.D.
Director, Agricultural Experiment
Station
Michigan State University
Agriculture

Woolfenden, Glen E., Ph.D.
Professor of Zoology
University of South Florida
Staying Around the Nest

Young, Eleanor A., Ph.D.
Associate Professor
Department of Medicine
The University of Texas Health
Science Center at San Antonio
Nutrition

Special Reports

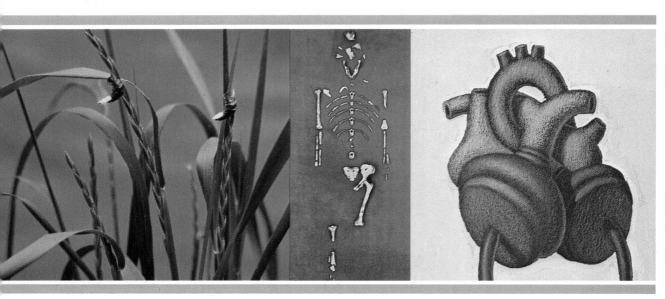

The Special Reports give in-depth treatment to the major advances in science and technology. The subjects were chosen for their current importance and lasting interest.

Staying Around the Nest

By John W. Fitzpatrick
and Glen E. Woolfenden

Florida scrub jays cope with a crowded habitat through cooperative breeding, in which the young put off their own reproduction to further the family.

It is early on a misty spring morning in central Florida. Within the dense cover of low oak shrubs, a blue and gray bird — a type of jay — sits quietly on her camouflaged nest of interwoven sticks and fibers. Uttering a soft guttural sound, she watches as her mate glides into the nest, carrying the remains of a large green grasshopper in his bill. Pausing momentarily on the rim of the nest, the male bird stuffs the grasshopper into the gaping mouth of one of three baby jays that are clamoring to be fed.

Soon, a third jay, bearing a dismembered caterpillar, alights on the nest and feeds another of the ravenous nestlings. From a few yards away, a fourth jay watches the activity at the nest. Suddenly, this onlooker points her bill to the sky and utters a series of loud clicking sounds — an alarm signifying that she has spotted some neighboring jays intruding on the family's territory. Instantly, all four jays take to the air. Flying in low, rhythmic patterns toward their threatened boundary, the jays drive away the trespassers with harsh, angry cries.

Another day has begun in the life of a family of Florida scrub jays. The first two jays we spotted have been mates for four years. The third jay is their 3-year-old son, who is still helping at home rather than striking out on his own. The fourth jay is their daughter, born the previous spring. She was raised by the other three jays working together and now, like her older brother, works as a "helper" at her parents' nest.

This unusual social system, in which some birds apparently forgo breeding their own families to assist others in raising their young, is known as cooperative breeding. It is practiced by only a few hundred of the nearly 9,000 known species of birds in the world. In North America, only a handful of bird species are cooperative breeders. Of these, the Florida scrub jay has been one of the most closely studied by scientists.

The scrub jay, like most other varieties of jays, is about the size of a robin and is predominantly blue. It differs from other jays in lacking a crest and having a pale-gray belly, a light-tan back, and a broad white eyebrow over its dark facial mask. It is a member of the family *Corvidae*, which includes crows, ravens, and magpies as well as about 50 species of jays. All these birds are known for their superior intelligence and their mischievous behavior around humans.

Scrub jays thrive in thousands of square miles of the Western United States and Mexico. On the other side of the continent, the Florida scrub jay lives in total isolation from its relatives to the west. This separation probably took place over a period of several million years as climatic changes gradually eliminated habitats acceptable to scrub jays between Florida and Texas.

The Florida scrub jay inhabits the austere but beautiful scrub oak terrain in the central part of the state. Most of us think of Florida as a land of beaches, palms, citrus groves, and cypress bottom lands. In fact, much of central Florida is prairie grassland, dominated by cattle ranches. Down the middle of the peninsula runs a narrow, elevated ridge of sand dunes left from an ancient period when the ocean blanketed most of the state. Citrus groves now flourish on most of the ridge. But here and there, where water drainage is especially good and the land is undeveloped, one of North America's rarest and most endangered natural environments—the Florida scrub oak habitat—clings to life. This terrain—often called simply the scrub—consists of a variety of shrubs interspersed with patches of gleaming white sand. The plants, which include many found nowhere else in the world, are mostly brushy, stunted oak trees rarely more than 6 feet in height. This rare, vanishing habitat is the only home of the Florida scrub jay.

We have come to know the Florida scrub jay quite well since 1970, when we began a long-term study of its fascinating behavior. Over the years, we have followed the births, daily lives, movements, matings, and deaths of hundreds of jays.

Our study encompasses a "neighborhood" of some 25 scrub jay families—about 120 birds in any given year. Each family lives within the boundaries of its own territory. These territories, which together cover about 1½ square miles, are located within one of the

The authors:
John W. Fitzpatrick is director of the bird division of the Field Museum of Natural History in Chicago. Glen E. Woolfenden is a professor of zoology at the University of South Florida in Tampa.

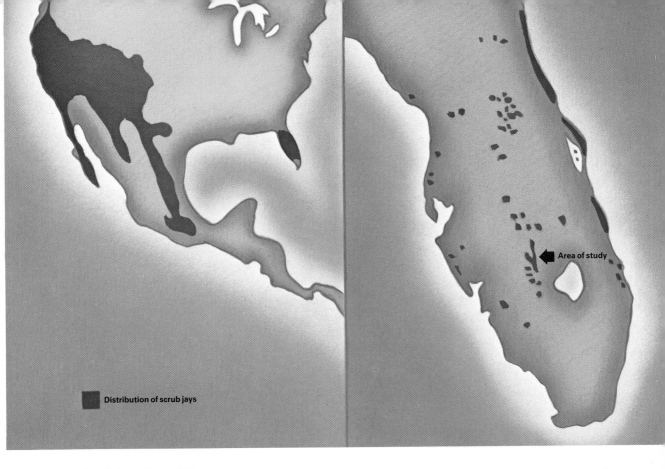

Scrub Jays Far and Near
Scrub jays range across large areas of the Western United States and
Mexico. But an isolated group inhabits a vanishing scrub oak habitat in
central Florida, like that at the Archbold Biological Station, *below*.

Distribution of scrub jays

Area of study

largest remaining tracts of virgin oak scrub left in Florida, owned and protected by the Archbold Biological Station, a privately operated research preserve dedicated to the scientific study of ecology and natural history.

We undertook this study of scrub jay sociobiology — the study of the evolutionary basis of social behavior among animals — to learn why Florida scrub jays are cooperative breeders. We hoped that such knowledge would shed light on the entire phenomenon of cooperative breeding among birds.

The Florida scrub jay is an ideal research subject because, although it is the same species as the Western scrub jay, it regularly breeds cooperatively. The Western jay never does, and so serves as a sort of control group for our study. The Florida scrub jay has one other characteristic that makes it an excellent study subject — it never migrates. Most Florida scrub jays spend their entire life within a mile of their birthplace.

We are fortunate to be able to watch these birds from extremely close range. Florida scrub jays become unusually tame when they are not bothered by humans. We often are first aware of the presence of a jay when it suddenly lands on someone's head. We have taken advantage of this amiable trait by taming the jays, mainly by giving them small peanut bits. After a while, they not only accept food from us, but also start to demand it. If we refuse to give them

A male helper, *above,* watches for hawks, as part of his family duties. A mother scrub jay, right, and her helper daughter, *below,* sit in the nest with the baby birds while the father stands guard.

a peanut morsel, certain of our jays will peck our hands or heads out of apparent frustration.

In our ongoing project to learn the intricacies of the scrub jay social system, our most crucial field procedure is to continually make sure that every jay in our study area is wearing a set of colored plastic and aluminum leg bands. These bands, each set of which has a unique pattern, are our only means of positively identifying individual jays. We band baby birds 11 days after they hatch. At that stage they are still nearly as "naked as jaybirds," but their legs are almost full-sized and can tolerate the bands.

Our second most important task is to locate and monitor every one of the jays' nests during the spring breeding season. This is not quite as simple as it sounds. There is a constant danger from predators, such as snakes, bobcats, raccoons, and other birds — even other scrub jays. Thus, the jays hide their nests well in the dense brush and do all they can to keep the location a secret known only to the family.

However, by patiently studying and following the birds, we are able to find their nests, often before any eggs have been laid. One of our favorite tricks works only when a jay pair have nearly completed their nest. The nest is lined with tough fibers taken from a small palm called the sand palmetto. So we pluck a few fibers ourselves and offer them by hand to the jays. Because they are tame, they take

At a feeding device used to test dominance among scrub jays, *below left,* a male helper, on ground, eats peanut morsels while his sister waits her turn. A baby jay, *below right,* is banded for future identification.

With a Little Help from Their Kin

An extended scrub jay family cooperates in the breeding of offspring. At the nest, lower right, an adult couple feed their hungry baby birds while, above them, a male helper waits with another insect for the fledglings. To the left of the nest, another male helper threatens a predatory snake. Behind him, a female helper spots jays that are intruding on the family's territory and emits a cry of alarm.

In the background, upper left, a jay couple from another family build a nest in the adjacent territory.

How Scrub Jay Generations Grow

Scrub jay families expand by "budding" – offspring inherit part of their parents' territory or take over adjacent territory from other families. A jay family begins the process with two adult mates (M and P), their adult helper son (A), and a fledgling son (B).

In the spring of the following year, the family has expanded its territory. Son A, now with a mate, has inherited a section of it. His parents, with a new daughter (C), are still being helped by son B.

The third spring, daughter C leaves home to find a mate. Neither the original pair (M and P) nor son A and his mate produce any offspring this season. Son B continues to help his parents.

the fibers from us. Once the jays are carrying fibers, their nest-building instinct takes over and they fly directly to the nest, revealing its location to us.

Being able to monitor nests without disturbing the jays is a tremendous advantage to us. We can stand quietly a few yards from the nest and record the comings and goings of the birds, noting which family members are feeding the young and often what they are feeding them. The jays simply ignore us. Indeed, to check the contents of a nest, we frequently have to lift the mother bird off the nest by hand.

With all jays banded and all nests located, we can monitor the changes within each family through the years. We watch the young grow up, help their parents, move away from the family territories to establish territories of their own, and finally die. We keep a continuous record of the number of birds in our study group by counting them every month. Each census requires us to tramp through the entire study tract, visiting every territory, until we have accounted for every bird. During most seasons, the jays will fly to us, looking for a piece of peanut. If a jay is missing, we keep checking back until we find it — or until we have convinced ourselves that it has either died or gone elsewhere to live. Because of their tameness, we can usually account for every living jay.

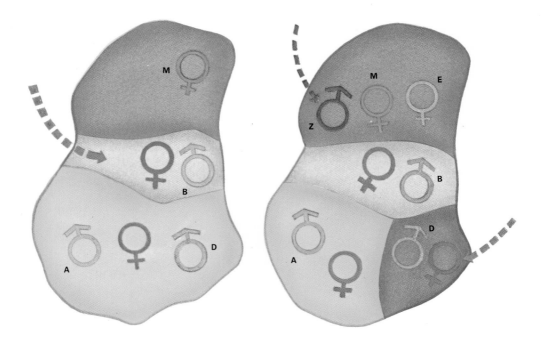

The fourth spring, son B brings home a mate and inherits some of his parents' territory. P died during the past year, and M is now without a mate.

Four years have now passed. The male of the original pair has been replaced by another male (Z). The couple have a daughter (E). The families of A and B produce no offspring this season. D — the son of A and his mate and the grandson of the original pair — has found a mate and expanded the family's territory for the second time.

By constantly counting the bird population and mapping the territory controlled by each family, we have established an important feature of Florida scrub jay ecology. A breeding pair live in essentially the same patch of scrub — an average of 20 to 25 acres per couple — throughout their existence, and the habitat is completely saturated with these permanently occupied and defended territories. Moreover, we have learned that the number of breeding jays varies by less than 5 per cent per year. This is the most stable breeding population ever recorded for any land bird, and it reflects the fact that habitable terrain is in short supply. Clearly, the "housing shortage" must be considered a major factor in any explanation of Florida scrub jay behavior.

Scrub jays become helpers as soon as they reach maturity. Each spring, between March and June, a mated couple attempt to raise a new brood of fledglings. Any young jays that survive to adulthood do not leave home as do most other birds. Instead, they remain in their parents' territory where they participate in territorial defense and predator harassing. During the next breeding season, they also help with certain nesting activities — mainly bringing food to the baby birds. In any given year, about half the scrub jay pairs have at least one helper, others have two or three, and a few may even have four or more.

Of the hundreds of helpers we have seen, 64 per cent were helping both their parents. When one parent dies, a bird from a different territory usually takes its place, thus becoming a "stepparent" to any young jays still at home. Twenty-six per cent of our helpers were assisting a parent and a stepparent. The remaining 10 per cent were helping a variety of more distantly related jays, and sometimes a pair of jays that were entirely unrelated. Florida scrub jays never live alone. Orphaned jays attempt to join other families, where they may eventually be accepted as subordinate members.

We have found that during the breeding season a pronounced division of labor exists between the members of a pair. The female performs the incubating and brooding, while the male delivers most of the food. Helpers also divide the workload according to sex — males bring much more food to the nest than do females, with older male helpers the most active. By decreasing the amount of food that the breeders must deliver to the nest, helpers make life easier for the breeders and enable them to devote more time to other activities, such as guarding the nest.

The value of having helpers is immediately evident from one extraordinary statistic: Scrub jay pairs with helpers produce 50 per cent more young that survive to adulthood than those without helpers. Plainly, helpers provide an evolutionary benefit to breeding pairs, because producing more surviving offspring than one's competitors is the most important evolutionary measure of success.

Helpers increase the survival rate of the offspring mainly by spotting and chasing away nest robbers. The parents can provide all the food needed by baby birds, but helpers enhance their ability to protect the nest against predators that are after their eggs and nestlings. When a predator is spotted, all the adult birds in the family fly at and around it at close quarters, an activity known as mobbing. Even a large animal like a bobcat, fearing for its eyes, can be intimidated by this swirl of beaks and claws.

Helpers not only improve the survival rate of offspring, but also often enable the breeders to make it to their next birthday. We found that pairs without helpers suffer an annual mortality rate of about 23 per cent, compared with about 15 per cent for pairs with helpers. The reason, once again, is that helpers aid in detecting and escaping from predators, primarily hawks.

Hence, breeders derive great evolutionary benefits from having helpers. But what about the helpers — what is in it for them? The answer is protection, food, and sometimes even a permanent home. By dwelling in a family group on its home territory, a helper is less likely to be caught by a predator. And, since it is on familiar ground, it knows where all the food sources are. Also, a male helper may eventually be able to claim part of the family's territory as his own and become a breeder there. A female helper, on the other hand, must eventually go outside the home territory to breed, and thus has

What Is Sociobiology?

Why do lions live in prides, while most other big cats live alone? Why do colonies of bees have thousands of sterile workers and only one breeding queen? Why do many Florida scrub jays postpone having offspring of their own while they help to raise other scrub jays' young? These are the kinds of questions being studied within the new scientific field of sociobiology.

Such questions seem innocent enough on their own, but in the late 1970s they ignited one of the most heated scientific and philosophical debates of the century. The emotional storm was triggered by biologist Edward O. Wilson of Harvard University in Cambridge, Mass., in his book *Sociobiology: The New Synthesis* (1975). In the first 26 chapters of this monumental work, Wilson describes the various levels of social organization found throughout the animal world. But in the 27th and final chapter, Wilson extended his observations and speculations to the human species. By suggesting that we humans are, at least in part, ruled by our evolutionary past, Wilson opened the door to a host of criticisms about how much of human behavior is governed by genetic factors we cannot control.

The science of sociobiology began to take form about 20 years ago. It brings together three scientific disciplines — ethology, the study of animal behavior; ecology, the study of how living things relate to one another in nature; and evolutionary biology, the study of the genetic process by which living things change over many generations. All these fields are founded on the British naturalist Charles Darwin's theory of natural selection — genetically more "fit" individuals are superior at survival and reproduction.

The boundaries between these fields began to crumble in the 1960s. Seemingly unrelated aspects of social behavior among animals — such as courtship, defense of territory, and even parental care — were tied together by one simple conclusion — that the social behavior of animals is subject to molding by natural selection.

For example, in certain environments, an animal with genes that promote aggressiveness may prevail over its timid rivals in the contest for mates. The next generation will therefore receive more aggressiveness genes than timidity genes, and aggressiveness will become a more common trait in this species.

Aggressive behavior can increase an animal's chances of surviving and reproducing. But what about traits such as altruism? Could seemingly unselfish devotion to the welfare of others be favored by evolution? Sociobiologists argue that it could because the contest among individuals to contribute the greatest number of genes to future generations can take indirect routes. Even when an animal puts itself in danger for the sake of others — such as when a scrub jay helper warns the family of an approaching hawk and thereby calls attention to itself — it might be doing so for unconsciously selfish reasons. By protecting other members of its family, the helper increases the likelihood that the family genes, many of which the helper shares, will be passed on.

But what of human beings? Are we, too, slaves of our genetic past? Few scientists doubt that human beings and apes descended from the same primate ancestor. Furthermore, we are, like most other primates, an extremely social species. For these reasons, sociobiologists argue, we might better understand human society by studying the societies of other animals.

On the other hand, many scientists vehemently object to the application of sociobiological theories to humans. The most frequent objection is that humans rely on intelligence and learning more than any other animal. We even developed spoken and written language as a way of transmitting knowledge to future generations. Even Wilson has said that our genetic tendencies can often be overcome by the need to conform to the customs of a civilized society. Through culture, we humans might indeed be escaping our animal past.   [J.W.F. & G.E.W.]

23

Tamed scrub jays
perch on the fingers
of zoologist
Glen Woolfenden
at the Archbold
Biological Station.

less to gain by staying at the nest. Perhaps for this reason, virtually all female scrub jays try to leave home to find a mate by the time they are 2 or 3 years old.

A year-old female scrub jay, just after her first spring as a helper, starts making brief flights away from the home territory in search of a mate. These forays away from home are dangerous. A wandering bird, separated from the protection of its family, is twice as likely as one of its homebound brothers and sisters to be killed by a predator.

Mated pairs apparently keep their helpers from breeding through a form of behavior control based on dominance. By observing jays both in their natural setting and at an experimental feeding device, we have found that a definite dominant-subordinate system holds throughout all scrub jay families. Males dominate females, breeders dominate helpers, and older helpers dominate younger ones. Even among siblings of the same sex and age, one becomes dominant.

In families with more than one male helper, it is usually the dominant helper that becomes the next breeder. He often does this by a process called territorial budding. A dominant helper, nearly always the one who has helped the longest — perhaps as long as five years — will start confining his activities to just one segment of the family's territory. Eventually, he attracts a mate from another territory. The new pair gradually become the sole occupants of this small piece of scrub. By the next breeding season, their holdings are secure, their pair bond is established, and they build a nest together. If the mates produce young who survive until the following breeding season, they gain helpers — and so the cycle continues.

By comparing the size of different territories through the years, we discovered that as scrub jay families grow, so do their territories. A new, lone pair usually control about 10 acres of scrub. These holdings tend to increase as the pair gain breeding experience, so that mates who have been together for several years control an average of 17 acres. If the pair successfully raise some helpers, the average territory expands to about 25 acres. The biggest families can control 40 or more acres.

Because the scrub habitat is constantly filled with breeding pairs, certain territories can grow only if others shrink. Most territories are bounded by five or six other territories, and a few of these are always occupied by pairs that have failed to raise any young. Sometimes such a pair is broken up by the death of one of the mates. These less successful families, waning in numbers, lose ground to the growing families. Thus, a neighborhood of scrub jays is in constant, gradual change. These territorial fluctuations are not characterized by extensive warfare among families, but rather by frequent, mild skirmishes as families continually test one another along their mutually defended boundaries.

As successful families grow, and expand their landholdings, the dominant helpers one by one inherit small segments. Sometimes, such as when both breeders die, a helper will inherit their entire territory. Through their system of territorial growth and inheritance, families are able to hold large areas of scrub and pass them on through many generations. Helpers, by improving the survival rate of baby birds, help to enlarge the family and subsequently the territory. This increases their chances of eventually gaining their own breeding space.

We think that the importance of territorial inheritance among Florida scrub jays explains the differences in behavior between scrub jays in western North America and those in Florida. Helping apparently evolved in the Florida scrub jay population because of the tremendous crowding within the rare and patchy Florida habitat.

In the West, habitats acceptable to scrub jays cover thousands of square miles. With so much scrub available, many areas, even if only marginal in quality, are always open. This means that young jays can always find an acceptable space in which to breed.

In evolutionary terms, animals exist for one purpose — to pass on as many of their genes as they can to future generations. The most direct way for an animal to do that is to produce a great number of surviving offspring. This is not a conscious decision, of course. Instead, animals whose genes make them superior at reproducing simply come to outnumber animals that are less successful at producing offspring. In this way, evolutionary "strategies" come about that produce the maximum number of offspring within a species.

Such strategies can be indirect as well as direct. For example, if an animal increases the reproductive success of its close relatives, such as parents or siblings, it thereby contributes the genes it shares with its relatives to succeeding generations. Florida scrub jay helpers benefit indirectly from this strategy, known as kin selection, by helping to raise siblings during the period of several years when they are not reproducing directly.

But, as contradictory as it may seem, male scrub jays are also directly advancing their own reproductive success by staying home for several years and helping. In an environment constantly saturated with breeding couples, what can a young would-be breeder do to enhance his chances of contributing genes — not just the family's genes, but his own — to future generations?

The answer appears to be to "work from the inside." Instead of risking the dangers of leaving home to search for breeding space, a young jay stays in the safety of his family's territory, which he helps to defend and enlarge. During his years as a helper, he receives a slight, indirect genetic benefit from improving the survival of his younger brothers and sisters. But more important, he enlarges the family's territory and can eventually inherit the space he needs to start his own nest. The faithful helper thus becomes the direct beneficiary of the territorial "land bank" in which he has invested so much of his life.

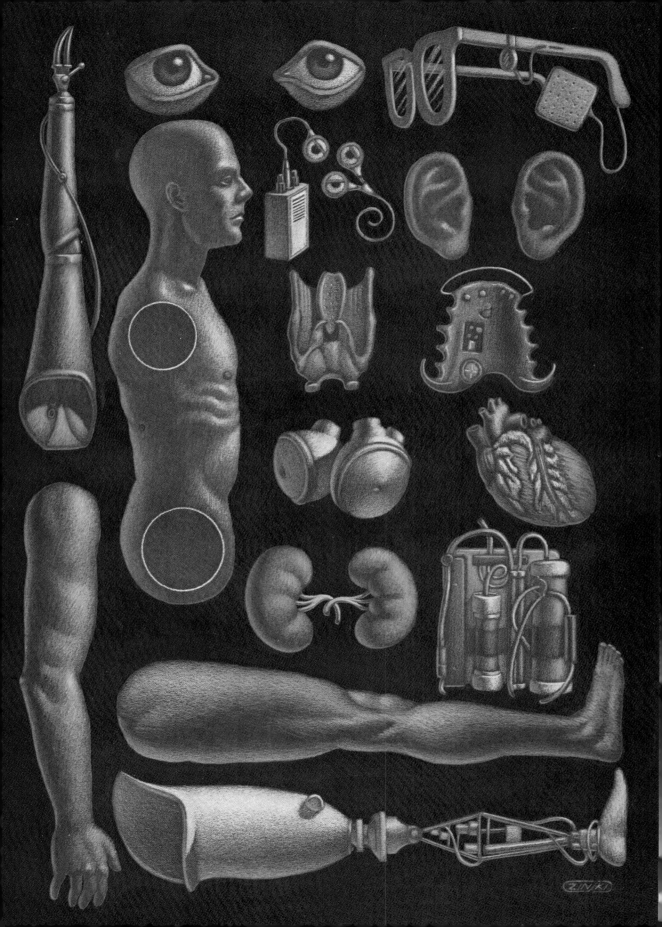

Rebuilding Bodies

By William J. Cromie

From metal knees to plastic hearts, motorized elbows to electronic ears, artificial parts are replacing a great many damaged or missing pieces of the human body.

"**W**hen I first got the hand, my mind rejected it because I knew it was not supposed to be there. Now I'm accustomed to it, and feel natural wearing it." Alice Olson of Westfir, Ore., was talking about the bionic limb that replaces the arm and hand she lost in a factory accident more than five years ago. In 1982, she became the first amputee fitted with a new type of electronic arm-hand combination that has more power than the limb it replaces.

"At first, I wanted the arm and hand just for cosmetic reasons," said 33-year-old Alice. "But I've found that it's useful for things I do every day, like opening jars, slicing vegetables, putting on makeup, or holding a cup of coffee."

Alice received her motorized arm and hand at the University of Utah in Salt Lake City where teams of scientists, surgeons, and engineers have been making remarkable advances in bionics. This is the science that combines biological knowledge of anatomy with developments in new materials and electronics to create artificial limbs and organs. Utah researchers also have developed an artificial heart, artificial kidney, and electronic ear for the deaf. At other medical centers in the United States and abroad, researchers are constructing electronic legs and eyes; metal jaws, joints, and bones; and replacements for the lungs, pancreas, liver, and blood. "If we find the right material, we can replace virtually any part of the body," declares Donald J. Lyman, professor of materials science and engineering at the University of Utah.

With few exceptions, artificial parts do not work as well as the natural ones they replace. They relieve pain, restore function, and prolong life, but they do not turn the handicapped into superpeople.

Russie Berndt is a good example. People kid the plucky 34-year-old victim of rheumatoid arthritis about being a bionic woman because she has had a hip, wrist, elbow, and two finger joints replaced by metal and plastic parts at Rush-Presbyterian-St. Luke's Medical Center in Chicago. She expects to have more artificial joints implanted in her body to replace those crippled by the disease. But Russie will never leap over tall buildings or put a crushing hold on a burly badman. She is happy to be able to hold a pencil or climb a few stairs.

Nevertheless, hundreds of thousands of people benefit from artificial parts. "Replacements exist for almost all joints in the body," says Chicago orthopedic surgeon Steven Gitelis. Pelvic, leg, foot, shoulder, arm, wrist, and finger bones can be replaced by metals and other materials when enough muscles and tendons remain functional for support and control. Even sections of the backbone destroyed by cancer have been rebuilt with metal and plastic. Chins are made from silicone rubber and jaws from titanium. Surgeons are experimenting with a "putty" made from the bones of cadavers to reconstruct noses, foreheads, and cheeks, and to correct deformities of the face and head. Physicians make silicone toes, complete with toenails, and attach them to the foot with adhesives. Bioengineers also have developed artificial skin, a spare part for burn victims.

When not enough nerves, muscles, or tendons remain to support artificial bones and joints, an entire limb can be replaced. Tens of thousands of people wear artificial arms and legs, but almost all such limbs are heavy, clumsy, difficult to operate, and liable to fall off. The wearer must move the arm or leg by a complex manipulation of cables attached to the "stump," or intact part of the limb.

Microelectronics and synthetic materials have become the foundation of a new technology to replace parts of the human body with bionic devices that come close to working like the real thing. Orthopedic surgeons agree that the best of these is the so-called Utah arm, which replaces awkward and difficult cable-operation with muscle-controlled motors. The arm was invented by a University of Utah team headed by bioengineer Stephen C. Jacobsen, director of the Center for Biomedical Design. Amputees who use this model can purchase any combination of a plastic shoulder, upper arm and forearm, motorized elbow, or motorized metal hand consisting of two pincerlike hooks.

The three dozen wearers of Utah limbs operate them by tightening and relaxing remaining upper-arm, shoulder, or chest muscles. The movements generate tiny electrical currents, which are picked up by electrodes attached to the muscles and sent to a microcomputer implanted in the elbow. The microcomputer translates the

The author:
William J. Cromie is executive director of the Council for the Advancement of Science Writing.

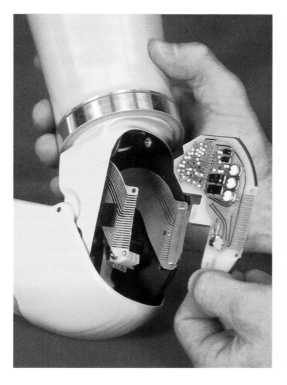

Electronic circuitry in the elbow of the Utah arm, *above,* controls motion via muscle signals, letting a man use the hook hand part for work, *right.*

electrical currents into commands to a battery-operated motor that controls elbow and hand motions. Wearers can hold loads as heavy as 50 pounds. Alice Olson demonstrates the strength of her grip by cracking walnuts—a startling sight when the arm's metal pincers are covered with a plastic glove resembling a normal hand, complete with cosmetic fingers, nails, and creases. The Utah arm costs at least $17,000—three to four times the cost of standard cable-operated artificial limbs.

Amputees cannot yet buy a bionic leg as good as the Utah arm, but development of computer-controlled knees and legs is underway at various laboratories. At the Moss Rehabilitation Hospital in Philadelphia, for example, Timothy Fitzpatrick, an above-knee amputee, walks on a prototype electronic leg. Electrodes on his thigh and hip muscles relay electrical signals generated by contractions and relaxations to a large stationary computer. The machine's program recognizes different patterns of signals for raising or lowering the leg and moving it forward and back. The computer then sends appropriate electrical impulses to operate a pneumatic, or air-driven, device that provides much greater control than does a conventional artificial leg. For Fitzpatrick to use the leg outside a laboratory, it

The arm's cosmetic hand lets its wearer grip a walnut strongly enough to crack it, *top,* or hold a tomato gently.

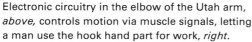

will have to be connected to a portable microcomputer. This does not represent a major technical obstacle, and the Moss researchers expect to have their legs on the streets by 1987.

Paralyzed people with intact limbs that do not function because of injured muscles or nerves may someday walk again with the same type of electrical signals that move Fitzpatrick's bionic leg. At Michael Reese Hospital in Chicago, *paraplegics* (people with the lower half of the body paralyzed), like 35-year-old Joaquin Burgos, move muscles on their upper back to tell a computer what they want to do with their legs. The system was designed by electrical engineer Daniel Graupe of Illinois Institute of Technology (IIT) in Chicago and is being tried out by physician Kate Kohn, head of rehabilitation medicine at Reese.

Healthy people walk when the brain sends signals along the nerves to the legs. The IIT system uses a microcomputer to by-pass injured spinal nerves and send movement signals directly from back muscles to the legs. Someday, such systems may allow paraplegics to leave their wheelchairs.

Meanwhile, Burgos and other patients stand with the aid of parallel bars as they learn to control their own walking movements. For example, a forward motion of Burgos' left shoulder becomes an electrical signal picked up by electrodes on his back and sent to the computer. The computer signals his left leg to move forward by means of electrodes positioned on the leg muscles. For the paralytic, a computer generates the impulses that the nonfunctioning nerves cannot provide. The system will not work where there is widespread muscle and nerve damage.

At Wright State University in Dayton, Ohio, physiologist Jerrold S. Petrofsky of the Biomedical Engineering Laboratory promised two paraplegics and two *quadriplegics* (people with all four limbs paralyzed) that he would have them standing by Christmas of 1982. Petrofsky made good his promise with a system in which movement is started by signals from a computer, not by moving undamaged muscles. Petrofsky programs the computer with standing, bicycle pedaling, and walking sequences. These act as a brain, sending the electrical equivalent of nerve impulses to electrodes taped to the skin over the major leg muscles. Sensors in a leg brace provide the computer with constant readings of hip, knee, and ankle positions. This feedback tells the electronic circuits which muscles to stimulate to keep the movement going.

Petrofsky uses the system to exercise paralytics and prevent deterioration of their muscles. The Wright State patients — who are all students at the university — raise weights with their legs and pedal a stationary bicycle to build muscle strength and mass. After three months of such conditioning, 22-year-old Nan Davis pedaled around the campus on an adult-sized tricycle equipped with a battery-powered computer small enough to fit in its wire basket. In November

1982, Petrofsky connected Nan to a computer programmed to stimulate a walking motion. She "walked" for the first time since she was injured in an automobile crash four years earlier.

To make a system practical enough to liberate people from wheelchairs, Petrofsky has constructed a computer small enough to fit into a backpack. He also plans to miniaturize the sensors and electrodes, then implant them under the skin along with the necessary wires. "With the progress in miniaturization of electronics components, we should also be able to build a computer and long-lived batteries small enough to be implanted under the abdominal skin," he says.

Miniaturized electronic devices can be implanted in the body because — like metal joints and bones, and plastic heart valves — they are biologically inert. The body's immune system does not recognize them as foreign invaders, such as viruses or bacteria, and reject them. This is not the case with spare parts that come into direct contact with the blood, such as artificial hearts and kidneys. In these devices, special *polymers* (synthetic materials that include plastic and rubber) are used to combat blood clotting and rejection.

Almost all such artificial organs were still experimental in 1983. Most were still being tested in laboratory animals.

The artificial kidney is an exception. As long ago as 1913, scientists thought of making a device that would remove wastes from

An experimental leg governed by the will of the wearer enables him to simulate normal leg movements. Signals he sends to his upper leg muscles are sensed by electrodes in the artificial leg. These are connected to a computer, which then processes them to signal the leg to react.

Paraplegics Nan Davis, *top,* and Joaquin Burgos, *above,* try out two computerized electrical stimulation-feedback systems to help them walk, as the inventors watch.

the body using a filtering system, as the natural kidney does. They visualized doing this by taking the blood out of an artery, removing the impurities through a filter or membrane, then putting it back into a vein. Willem J. Kolff, then a 29-year-old physician in the Netherlands, attempted to do this in 1939 after watching a young man die from the build-up of wastes in his blood. Kolff used cellophane sausage casings as a filter to separate impurities from the blood. After experimenting with many models, he finally built a successful artificial kidney in 1945. Modern versions of this dialysis, or blood-cleaning, machine keep about 50,000 Americans alive today.

Some of these people maintain machines at home, but most travel to hospitals or dialysis centers where they spend four or five hours, three times a week, hooked up to an artificial kidney. The procedure is fatiguing, psychologically punishing, and expensive — costing about $25,000 per patient per year. Kolff, now director of the Institute for Biomedical Engineering at the University of Utah, urged his inventive colleagues to develop a machine that patients could wear. Stephen Jacobsen and his team took up the challenge and constructed a battery-powered device that is worn like a large chest pack. Called the Wearable Artificial Kidney (WAK), it weighs about 14 pounds with batteries. "WAKs will allow more people to dialyze at home," a Utah physician comments. "We expect approval from the Food and Drug Administration in 1983, then they should be available commercially for about $7,000." WAKs should ease the lives of many kidney patients.

Kidney failure is one complication of diabetes, the third leading cause of death in the United States. Diabetes results from failure of the pancreas — a gland near the stomach — to secrete enough insulin to control high levels of sugar in the blood. To treat the problem, researchers around the world experiment with artificial devices that they hope will be more effective than the traditional treatment of self-administered injections of insulin. William Chick, now professor at the University of Massachusetts Medical School in Worcester, and Pierre M. Galletti, professor of medical science at Brown University in

Providence, R.I., for example, designed an artificial pancreas that functions in much the same way as an artificial kidney. In the pancreas device, blood flows through porous plastic tubes inside a chamber containing live insulin-producing cells. Blood sugar passing through the tube walls signals the cells to produce insulin at the rate needed to balance the sugar. The insulin then moves through the tube walls and into the bloodstream.

Galletti and his team worked with French researchers to conduct the first human test of an artificial pancreas at Hôtel-Dieu Hospital in Paris in September 1982. That device, kept outside the body, was connected to the same type of artery-vein shunt used for dialysis. The volunteer's blood ran through the artificial pancreas for about five hours, after which his blood sugar level was normal. This substitute pancreas represents a new concept in human spare parts—an organ that is not entirely a biological transplant and not entirely artificial. Diabetic rats have survived for six months with such bio-artificial, or hybrid, organs, and the U.S.-French team plans longer-term tests with human beings.

Until a hybrid pancreas is proved safe and effective, many diabetics seeking an alternative to insulin shots use a device called an insulin pump. About 5,000 diabetics in the United States wear battery-powered pumps the size of small transistor radios. The pumps provide a continuous flow of insulin, through slender nylon tubes, to needles inserted under the abdominal skin.

While hybrid-organ technology matures, bioengineers and others will continue to fashion body parts from a wide variety of synthetic materials. Galletti, for example, uses coils of Teflon tubing to make artificial lungs. When healthy people breathe in, air enters the nose or mouth, then passes through the windpipe to the lungs. Inside the lungs, oxygen in the air enters the bloodstream while carbon dioxide leaves the bloodstream and enters the lungs to be breathed out. The diaphragm, a powerful muscle between the chest and abdomen, moves down and up to make breathing possible.

Galletti's book-sized spare part consists of two Teflon coils with plastic tubes that connect to the pulmonary artery and vein, which carry blood to and from the heart and lungs. When he puts these artificial lungs in an experimental sheep, the animal's heart pumps blood through the tubing while oxygen circulates through a plastic bag covering the outside of the Teflon. Oxygen enters the blood and carbon dioxide is removed through the walls of the tubes. At present, the oxygen comes from pressurized tanks. Future plans for these devices call for tapping air directly from the windpipe and using the pumping action of the diaphragm muscle as in normal breathing. A workable artificial lung could prolong the lives of some of the estimated 90,000 people in the United States who die each year of respiratory problems. The artificial devices will first be used as "boosters" to take over breathing while weakened natural lungs heal.

Heart boosters have been used since 1965. They take over for the right ventricle of the heart, which pumps blood to the lungs, or the left ventricle, which pumps it to the rest of the body. Since the latter does about 80 per cent of the heart's work, left ventricular assist devices (LVAD) are more common. About 200 people have received LVADs to keep them alive while their hearts heal.

Many heart failures, however, involve both ventricles. The NHLBI estimates that about 30,000 Americans could benefit from a totally artificial heart. Kolff began working on such a device in the 1950s. He put his first model in a dog in 1957, but the animal died 90 minutes later. When Kolff went to work at the University of Utah in 1967, he assembled a team to keep working on the project. By late 1982, a calf had survived 260 days on a plastic, air-driven heart that the Kolff team developed, and the Food and Drug Administration approved the device for experimental use in human beings. Robert K. Jarvik, who as a medical student had designed a mechanical heart that kept a calf alive for 268 days, was the principal inventor of the device. It is called the Jarvik-7 heart.

Early on Thursday morning, Dec. 2, 1982, surgeons at the University of Utah Medical Center cut out most of the natural heart of 61-year-old dentist Barney B. Clark and replaced it with a 10-ounce

A kidney patient enjoys the new vistas open to people equipped with a portable dialysis system — the wearable artificial kidney (WAK). The battery-powered device ends the need for thrice-weekly visits to a dialysis center.

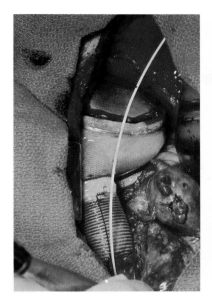

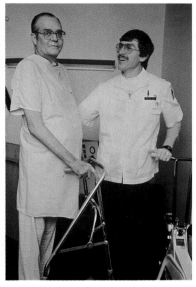

The first artificial heart to be implanted in a human being, *far left,* beat in the chest of Barney Clark, *left.* It replaced diseased parts of his natural heart, *below left,* with right and left ventricles of plastic, *below,* that substituted electrically driven pumping action for the real heartbeat.

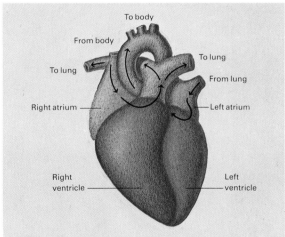

To body
From body
To lung
To lung
From lung
Right atrium
Left atrium
Right ventricle
Left ventricle

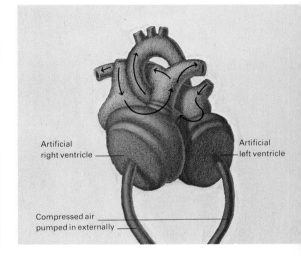

Artificial right ventricle
Artificial left ventricle
Compressed air pumped in externally

double pump 15 inches in diameter and 12 inches long. The device fits into cuffs sewn onto the remaining lower part of the natural heart and two large arteries — the pulmonary artery supplying blood to the lungs and the aorta leading from the left side of the heart to the other parts of the body.

Air pumped from outside the chest moves thin elastic diaphragms that pull blood into the heart then pump it into the arteries. The air comes from a 375-pound assembly of a compressor, vacuum system, air tanks, batteries, and monitoring instruments that fits into a wheeled cart about the size of those used in supermarkets. Two 6-foot-long plastic tubes connect the patient with this complicated and cumbersome life supply.

Clark said in February 1983 that such an encumbrance was preferable to being dead or too sick to put on his own pants. Clark survived 112 days with an artificial heart, then he died of other medical problems on March 23. The heart still functioned perfectly at the time of his death. See MEDICINE (Surgery).

To replace the heavy and unwieldy 375-pound assembly, Utah scientists are now testing a 9-pound unit small enough to be carried on a shoulder strap. The new device, which is about the size of a camera case, was invented by Peter Heimes of the Helmholtz Institute in Aachen, West Germany.

The smaller unit can be used with the Jarvik-7, or more advanced hearts that the researchers expect to build. Jarvik already has implanted a new electrohydraulic model in calves. It consists of a reversible motor and propeller pump, the size of a large cigar butt, which pumps a small amount of hydraulic fluid from one artificial ventricle to the other. This action pushes blood alternately to the aorta and pulmonary artery. Blood and hydraulic fluid are separated by a plastic diaphragm. In human patients, the 0.25-inch-diameter air tubes and shopping cart required by the Jarvik-7 heart would be replaced by four thin wires leading from the motor through the chest to a belt-mounted battery pack.

Clark died of circulatory-system failure, dramatically illustrating that for the heart to get blood to all parts of the body, an extensive network of blood vessels must be healthy. Since the early 1950s, surgeons have used Dacron tubes to substitute for blood vessels that become clogged or damaged, usually by atherosclerotic disease. These tubes work only if their diameter exceeds 0.3 inch. Smaller artificial vessels become blocked by blood clots. This involves a critical problem because about 75 per cent of our blood vessels are smaller than 0.25 inch. After 10 years of hard work, Lyman and his

Older artificial blood vessels made of Dacron, *below,* left, dwarf the very narrow new one of polyurethane, right. About as wide as a straw, the small blood vessels can replace 75 per cent of those blocked in the human body. A new electronic larynx, *below right,* can be mounted on a removable prosthesis fitted to the roof of the mouth or on an upper denture. It can be switched on and off with a flick of the tongue, permitting people with useless vocal cords to speak without using a hand to activate their artificial "voice box."

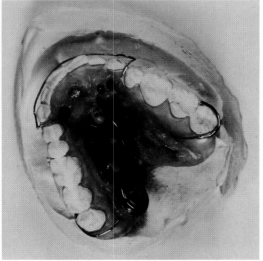

Utah colleagues designed a polyurethane tube that resisted blood clotting in laboratory tests. When they implanted the plastic vessels in dogs, however, all of them became blocked.

Lyman found that the blockage occurred at the junction of natural and artificial vessels. "The plastic was as stiff as a steel pipe compared to the elasticity of the natural vessels," he explains. "Flexing at the junction set up stresses that caused scar tissue to form and occlude [block] the opening. We solved the problem by developing a plastic as flexible as the natural vessels. Dogs with the new vessels have survived as long as three years." Lyman now is ready to implant them in people who face amputation because blood cannot circulate through their limbs. He estimates that as many as 300,000 Americans each year can benefit from the plastic blood vessels, including those who need new coronary arteries to keep alive their heart muscles.

Meanwhile, thousands of others may be kept alive by a temporary replacement for blood itself. Red blood cells carry oxygen, minerals,

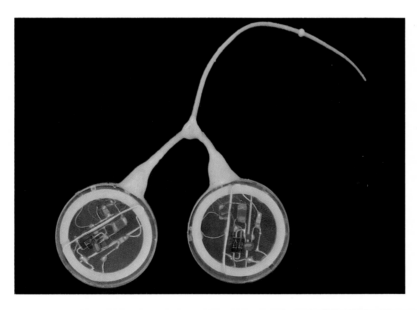

A cochlear electrode implant enables profoundly deaf people to hear most common sounds and understand many words. An electrode is threaded through the ear canal into the cochlea, *below,* and connected to a pair of internal receivers, *below left,* implanted under the scalp behind the ear. Sound from a microphonelike sound processor is conveyed through an external transmitter placed over the internal receiver.

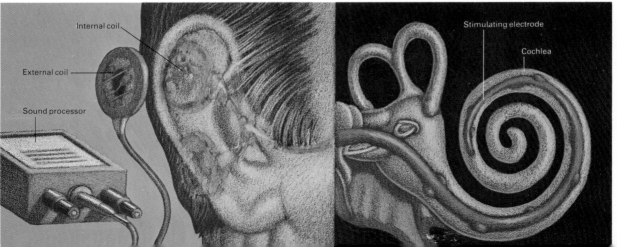

and proteins through the body, while the white blood cells fight infection. A colorless mixture of fluorine and carbon called Fluosol can be substituted for blood until bone marrow replaces natural red blood cells that have been lost. Fluosol has helped to save hundreds of people, including Jehovah's Witnesses whose religion prevents them from accepting transfusions of natural blood. Strictly speaking, Fluosol is not artificial blood because it carries only oxygen, but those who are alive because of it do not quibble about terms.

Despite its present limitations, synthetic blood in the future may be better than the real thing. "Normal blood carries disease-causing organisms as well as substances that promote clogging of arteries and lead to heart attacks and strokes," notes physician Leland C. Clark of Children's Hospital in Cincinnati. "Synthetic blood could be custom-made and mixed with natural blood to transport the drugs to treat such problems."

No part of the body that can be disabled by disease or accident has been overlooked by bioengineers. Some of their more imaginative and startling inventions include electronic speech, hearing, and even sight.

Voiceless individuals must now make do with the flat mechanical sounds produced by various substitutes for nonfunctioning vocal cords. One of the most advanced devices is a battery-powered artificial larynx devised by researchers at Thomas Jefferson University in Philadelphia. It consists of a thin wafer of plastic and microcircuits fitted to the roof of the mouth and turned on and off by the tongue. This leaves both hands free, a considerable advantage over conventional devices that require users to press their fingers against the throat in order to speak.

Speech is simpler than hearing to restore electronically. In normal hearing, sound waves strike the eardrum, causing it to vibrate. The vibrations move delicate ear bones, which transfer the sound to some 25,000 microscopic hair cells in a spiral structure called the cochlea. The hair cells convert the sound vibrations to nerve impulses that travel along the auditory nerve to the brain. When disease or injury destroys the hair cells, a person becomes deaf. To restore hearing, bioengineers stimulate the auditory nerve directly with electrodes implanted in the cochlea.

Totally deaf persons participating in an electronic hearing program at the University of California, San Francisco, wear a combination battery and microphone in a chest pouch. The microphone converts sound vibrations to electrical pulses, and the pulses travel over a thin cable to a small coil antenna worn behind one ear. The antenna sends the signals through the skin to a receiver implanted in the skull along with a wire going to eight pairs of electrodes in the cochlea.

With this system, Lee Yount, a retiree in his 60s, could hear as much as 50 per cent of the words in simple spoken sentences and 65 per cent of a series of two-syllable words. When Yount could also read the speaker's lips and gestures, he understood 100 per cent of what was said. Biophysicist Donald Eddington of the University of Utah obtained similar results with much the same kind of system. As many as 300,000 totally deaf people may benefit from such research as well as hundreds of thousands of others who barely hear even with the strongest hearing aid.

Bioengineers could not make such progress in conquering deafness without also trying to light up the darkness for the blind. Since 1975, William H. Dobelle, now head of the private Institute for Artificial Organs in New York City, has been experimenting with a technique by which electrodes implanted in the brain enable a blind person to "see." To someone with this kind of electronic vision, the world looks like the animated scoreboards in major-league ball parks. A blind person hooked to a large computer has seen bluish dots and lines. To make such a system portable requires connecting a television camera small enough to fit behind an artificial eye with a microcomputer built into a battery-holding eyeglass frame.

A computer small enough to fit into an eyeglass frame is not unrealistic at a time when researchers believe they can put 10 million switches and other electronic components on a silicon wafer the size of a postage stamp. The density of single units of information stored in a computer memory already is a hundred times higher than comparable units in the brain. "With further shrinkage," says Stanford University electrical engineer Robert L. White, "the dimensional advantages of electronic intelligence over nervous tissue can only increase. It is now possible to contemplate the replacement of defective nervous tissue by synthetic intelligence. . . . " In other words, White believes that we are not far away from replacing defective parts of the brain with microcomputers.

If researchers get this far, could they go all the way to replacing the entire brain, or to building a computer as versatile and intelligent as the human brain? "No reason why not," replies computer expert Marvin Minsky, Donner Professor of Science in the Artificial Intelligence Laboratory at Massachusetts Institute of Technology. But Minsky is known for daring to think the unthinkable. Others doubt that the brain is intelligent enough to duplicate itself. "The artificial devices we construct seldom perform as well as the natural systems they are designed to replace," Jacobsen comments. "We never will have the ability or economic incentive to build a bionic person that will enjoy a sunset or lead a nation."

"When you replace an arm or a heart, you still have an injured person or a heart patient," Lyman says. "The more you replace, the more you lose the human qualities of life. No serious bioengineer is trying to make a bionic man or woman. When you see all the suffering around, it's enough to try to increase the quality of life for sick and injured people."

Acid from the Sky

By Marian Visich, Jr.

An airborne by-product of industrial society is killing lakes, defacing buildings, threatening human health — and turning neighbor against neighbor.

Big Moose Lake is a 1,268-acre lake in the Adirondack Mountains of New York state. It was the setting of Theodore Dreiser's novel *An American Tragedy*, which recounted the real-life drowning of a young woman by her lover in 1906. Today, a tragedy of another sort is occurring in Big Moose Lake — the lake itself is dying, from acid deposited by rain and snow. The lake water became 30 times more acid during the 1970s, resulting in the decline or disappearance of fish and wildlife.

William Marleau, a New York state forest ranger for more than 30 years, remembers that during the 1940s he could catch a basketful of trout in one day on Big Moose Lake. In those days, the lake teemed with trout, perch, sunfish, and smallmouth bass. Otters, deer, raccoons, and other mammals were plentiful around the lake, as were such birds as loons, blue herons, and ospreys.

In 1983, only a few trout and perch survive in the acidic lake. Most of the birds and mammals that depend upon the fish as a source of food have gone away. Even mosquitoes, and the bullfrogs that feed upon them, are scarce. The lake, which once resounded with life, now stands eerily silent.

Big Moose Lake serves as the source of drinking water for local residents. In 1980, Chester V. Bowes, owner of Covewood Lodge, became concerned about the water's strange taste. An analysis showed that the water contained five times the amount of lead and three times the amount of copper regarded as safe by the New York State Department of Health. The water from the lake was so acid that it was leaching lead and copper from the lodge's plumbing.

Half a world away, in Athens, Greece, acid rain has taken its toll on one of the world's greatest architectural treasures. Through more than 23 centuries of war and weather, six marble statues stood on the south porch of the Erechtheum of the Acropolis. The statues survived until 1977, when they were replaced by fiberglass reproductions. Acid deposits had eaten away the surface of the statues.

In the forests of central Europe, treetops are dying and conifers are losing their needles. According to biochemist Bernard Ulrich, director of the Institute for Soil Sciences and Forest Nutrition of Göttingen University in West Germany, the tree damage is the result of the soil becoming increasingly acid.

The common thread in this tapestry of damage is acid deposition — or acid rain, to use its popular name. Acid deposition refers to processes that remove acidic materials from the atmosphere and deposit them on the earth's surface. Acid deposits may be either wet or dry. In wet deposits, acids are collected from the atmosphere by rain, fog, snow, or other forms of precipitation. Dry deposits come from acid-forming particles and gases that fall from the atmosphere during dry periods.

Wet or dry, acid deposits are causing worldwide concern. This concern is felt most keenly in North America and Europe, where burning fossil fuels to provide power for industry and transportation appears to be causing large deposits of acid. The regions of North America and Europe that lie downwind of major industrial areas are the most affected. This aspect of the problem — pollution created by one region apparently causing damage to another — has made acid rain a source of regional and international friction.

What exactly is acid rain, and how acidic is it? To answer these questions, we must become familiar with the pH scale used to measure the acidity or alkalinity of a solution. The letters *pH* stand for *potential of hydrogen;* pH values indicate the concentration of hydrogen ions. The pH scale ranges from 0 to 14. Pure water is neutral and has a pH of 7. Acidic solutions have a pH below 7; alkaline solutions have a pH above 7. The scale is logarithmic, so a decrease of one pH number corresponds to a tenfold increase in acidity.

The author:
Marian Visich, Jr., is associate dean of the College of Engineering and Applied Sciences at the State University of New York at Stony Brook.

Rain from a clean atmosphere is mildly acidic, with a pH of 5.6. This is due to carbonic acid, a weak acid that forms from the combination of atmospheric carbon dioxide with water vapor. Acid rain, therefore, is defined as precipitation with a pH below 5.6. Today, many parts of the world regularly receive precipitation with a pH far below 5.6. These levels are caused almost entirely by two strong acids — sulfuric acid and nitric acid.

Sulfuric acid forms in the atmosphere primarily from the oxidation of sulfur dioxide gas. Nitric acid forms mainly from the oxidation of nitric oxide and nitrogen dioxide, two gases that are usually lumped together under the term nitrogen oxides. Sulfur dioxide is converted to sulfuric acid in the atmosphere by a combination of reactions involving sunlight, water vapor, and various catalysts, substances that initiate or change the speed of chemical reactions. These processes are complex and depend on time, temperature, and the amount of sunlight available. Nitric acid forms from nitrogen oxides in a similar way. Once formed, these acids are carried to earth in rain or snow. Sulfur dioxide and nitrogen oxides also come from the atmosphere in the form of dry particles or gases. On the ground, the particles and gases react with water to form acids.

Sulfur and nitrogen compounds enter the atmosphere from both natural processes and human activities. Natural sources of atmospheric sulfur and nitrogen compounds include volcanic eruptions, forest fires, hot springs and geysers, decay of organic matter, and sea sprays containing sulfate salts.

Natural processes account for at least half of the global sulfur and nitrogen emissions. However, living systems have evolved in the presence of natural emissions and have learned to tolerate them. This is not true of man-made emissions. They have come upon the scene in a relatively short period of time. Furthermore, man-made emissions are highly concentrated, meaning that some regions receive extremely large amounts. For example, more than 95 per cent of the atmospheric sulfur compounds found over the Northeastern United States probably come from human activities. Most of these are in the form of sulfur dioxide

The pH Scale

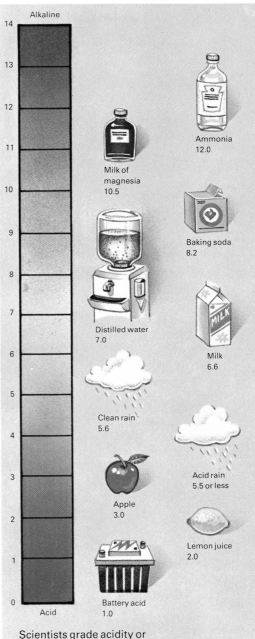

14 Alkaline

13

12

11 — Milk of magnesia 10.5

10

9

8

7 — Distilled water 7.0

6

5 — Clean rain 5.6

4

3 — Apple 3.0

2

1

0 Acid — Battery acid 1.0

Ammonia 12.0

Baking soda 8.2

Milk 6.6

Acid rain 5.5 or less

Lemon juice 2.0

Scientists grade acidity or alkalinity on the pH scale, which ranges from 0 to 14. A pH of 7 is neutral. Values below 7 indicate acidity; those above 7, alkalinity. There is a tenfold difference between each whole number.

Wind direction

Sulfur dioxide and
nitrogen oxides

Sulfur dioxide

Sulfur dioxide

Nitrogen oxides

Dry deposition

What Goes Up . . .

Sulfur dioxide (SO$_2$)
and nitrogen oxides
(NO$_x$) are the chief
acid-forming compounds
put into the atmosphere.
Some of these gases
enter the air from
natural sources,
such as forest fires
and volcanoes. Large
amounts also come from
emissions produced by
the burning of fossil
fuels by industry
and in automobiles.

generated by the burning of fossil fuels. Emissions from electric utilities and from metal-smelting and other industrial processes rank as
the major sources. Burning fossil fuels also accounts for most of the
gaseous nitrogen — in the form of nitrogen oxides. Almost half of the
nitrogen oxides are emitted by automobiles and other vehicles. The
rest comes from factories and electric utilities.

The man-made emissions of sulfur dioxide and nitrogen oxides in
North America are concentrated in the densely populated and heavily industrialized eastern half of the continent. The 31 states bordering on and east of the Mississippi River produce 75 per cent of the
total sulfur dioxide emissions in the United States. In fact, the utility
power plants in the Ohio River Basin, which burn high-sulfur coal
from the Appalachian and Midwestern states, account for more than
33 per cent of the U.S. total. Eastern North America also produces
about 85 per cent of the combined U.S.-Canadian emissions of nitrogen oxides.

Several factors influence where and in what form the acid deposits
will fall. Chief among these are the height at which the emissions
are released into the atmosphere and the prevailing wind patterns.
If sulfur dioxide and nitrogen oxides are emitted near ground level,
they normally spend only a day or so in the atmosphere, and they
generally descend as dry deposits near the emission source. But if
they are discharged from tall smokestacks, sulfur dioxide and nitrogen oxides generally remain in the atmosphere up to four days. During that time, prevailing winds can transport the pollutants over
continents and oceans. And during this time aloft, the sulfur dioxide

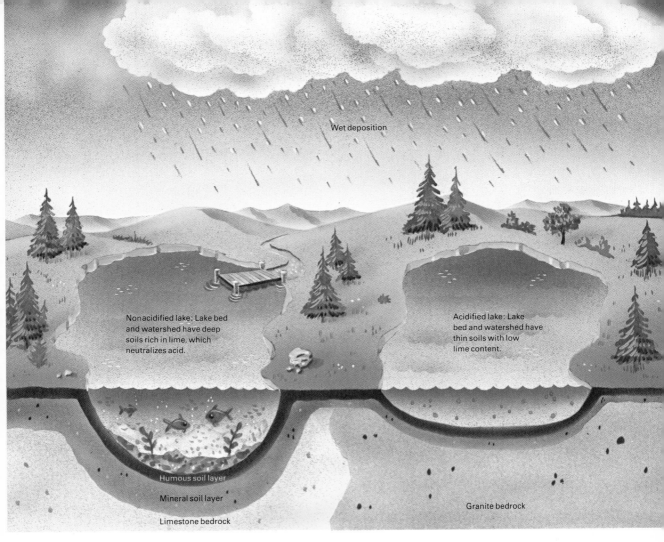

Wet deposition

Nonacidified lake: Lake bed and watershed have deep soils rich in lime, which neutralizes acid.

Acidified lake: Lake bed and watershed have thin soils with low lime content.

Humous soil layer

Mineral soil layer

Limestone bedrock

Granite bedrock

and nitrogen oxides are largely converted to sulfuric acid and nitric acid, so that they descend as acid rain or snow.

Ironically, numerous tall stacks were erected in North America and Europe during the 1970s as a solution to local air-pollution problems. Theoretically, pollutants released high in the atmosphere would disperse so widely that their harmful effects would dissipate. In reality, the tall stacks seem to have moved the problem hundreds or thousands of miles downwind.

From 1973 to 1977, 11 nations in Western Europe participated in a program to measure the long-range transport of air pollution. The study showed, for example, 70 to 80 per cent of the sulfur deposited in Sweden came from sources outside that country. Since the prevailing winds in northern Europe blow from the southwest, France, East and West Germany, and Great Britain were implicated as the major contributors to Sweden's pollution.

In North America, the prevailing summer winds over the northeastern part of the continent are steady and strong from the south-

Must Come Down
Some SO_2 and NO_x fall to earth as gases and particles in dry deposition. These deposits can combine with water on the ground to form sulfuric and nitric acids. Other SO_2 and NO_x gases react with water vapor to form acids aloft. The acids descend as wet deposition in rain, snow, or fog. A lake becomes acidic according to the chemistry of its lake bed and watershed.

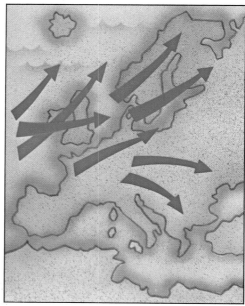

Summer winds

Winter winds

On Wings of Wind
Acid-forming pollutants can travel hundreds of miles downwind. The prevailing winds of eastern North America carry emissions from the Midwest to the Northeastern United States and southeastern Canada. Similarly, prevailing winds deposit pollutants from Great Britain and western Europe on Scandinavia.

west. These winds carry pollutants discharged by power plants in the Ohio River Basin for hundreds of miles, transporting them to the Northeastern United States and southeastern Canada. The U.S. Environmental Protection Agency (EPA) estimated in 1980 that the United States sent to Canada 2 to 4 times as much sulfur dioxide and 11 times as much nitrogen oxides as it got back from its northern neighbor.

Climate plays a major role in determining the amount and the effects of acid rain. For example, in the Western United States, where the climate is dry, large amounts of alkaline dust are blown into the atmosphere from the surface of the soil. This tends to neutralize acid compounds in the atmosphere. In the Eastern United States, where rainfall is more abundant and regular, there is little such neutralization.

Furthermore, climate can produce seasonal patterns of heavy acid rain. This is important because large amounts of acid rain falling over a short period of time can be far more damaging than the same amount of acid deposited evenly throughout the year. This seasonal effect is especially pronounced in cold climates that receive large deposits of acid snow. Here, the major impact occurs when snow melts in the spring. The sudden doses of acid released then can produce disastrous effects on the environment. This phenomenon is called *acid shock*.

What, if anything, can be done to lessen the impact of this unwelcome fallout from technology? Nature has provided some defenses of its own. For example, a lake can withstand the effects of acid rain by what scientists call its natural buffering capacity. This is influenced by many factors. Chief among these is the soil chemistry of the lake bed and the surrounding watershed — the area that drains into the lake. If the soil is rich in limestone or other alkaline material, the lake and its watershed will contain compounds that can neutralize the acid. If the soil around the lake is thin and lies on top of hard, crystalline bedrock, such as granite, there is very little buffering. Unfortunately, between 50 and 80 per cent of the world's freshwater lakes are in regions with low buffering capacity.

It takes several years for a lake to become acidic. Chemist Arne Hendriksen of the Norwegian Institute for Water Research has divided the process into three stages. During the first stage, the alkalinity decreases, but the lake still has sufficient buffering capacity to maintain pH levels of 6.0 to 5.5. In the second stage, the buffering capacity declines and the pH of the lake decreases rapidly. This leads to a radical decline of aquatic life. The final stage — an acid lake — is reached when the lake has no more buffering capacity and the pH level falls below 5.0. The acid water flowing into the lake leaches metals from the surrounding soil. As a result, toxic metals, especially aluminum, build up in the lake water.

Few species of fish can survive in an acid lake, primarily because of interference with the reproductive cycle. Calcium levels drop so low in an acid lake that female fish may be unable to develop eggs. If eggs are developed, they often are not laid. If they are laid, they may not hatch. And if they hatch, the new fish may not survive. Sensitive species, such as smallmouth bass, stop reproducing at a pH of 6.0 to 5.5. More acid-tolerant species, including lake herring and yellow perch, cease reproducing at a pH of 4.7 to 4.5. Below a pH of 4.5, no fish reproduce.

Adult fish may even begin to die at pH levels above 5.0. Biologist Carl Schofield of Cornell University in Ithaca, N.Y., has discovered that aluminum leached from soil into lake water irritates the fish's gills, the organs that regulate the animal's intake of oxygen and salt. The fish responds by secreting a protective mucus that coats the gills. Unfortunately, the mucus also clogs the gills, and eventually the gill filaments erode. As a result, the salt level in the fish decreases, leading to destruction of its protein and its eventual death.

High acid levels and toxic metals also kill pondweeds, reeds, and other large plants in the lake. Plankton — the tiny, free-floating plants and animals that form the base of aquatic food chains — decline dramatically. A lake with a pH of 7.0 typically has between 30 and 80 species of plankton plants. The number of species drops to 12 at a pH of 5.0, and none survive at a pH below 4.5. Ironically, with the loss of fish, plants, and plankton, most acid lakes become crystal clear.

Many lakes in the Adirondack Mountains are victims of acid rain. During the summer of 1975, Schofield made a detailed study of the water chemistry and fish populations in 214 lakes in the Adirondacks. He found that 111 lakes had a pH level below 5.0, and 82 per cent of those were too acidic to support life. In a larger study, aquatic biologists Martin Pfeiffer and Patrick Festa of the New York State Department of Environmental Conservation measured the pH levels of 849 lakes in the Adirondacks during the late 1970s. They found 212 lakes that had a pH below 5.0.

Hundreds of lakes in eastern Canada have lost their fish because of acid water. Ontario's Ministry of the Environment has warned that many of the province's 48,000 susceptible lakes could lose much of their aquatic life over the next 20 years if the 1980 levels of acid rain remain constant or increase.

Scandinavia has suffered severe losses of aquatic ecosystems. More than 18,000 lakes have been acidified in Sweden, and plant and animal life in approximately 4,000 of these has been damaged very seriously. In southern Norway, lakes covering more than 3.2 million acres contain no fish, and fish stocks have decreased in lakes covering another 5 million acres.

In areas that receive large amounts of acid snowfall, even well-buffered lakes and streams can suffer damage during the acid shock associated with the spring thaw. For example, the Syterbacken stream in Sweden normally has a pH of 7.0. During the 1979 spring thaw, the pH fell as low as 4.85 before it began returning to normal in June. Since spring is the time when fish eggs hatch, such an acid surge can eliminate an entire year's hatch of fish. A large acid surge can also raise the aluminum content of water to levels that kill adult

A sandstone statue, erected in 1702 in the Ruhr Valley of West Germany, still had most of its features in 1908, *left.* Exposure to acid deposition over the next 60 years had almost obliterated the figure by 1969, *right.*

The leaves, on the left, of a snap bean plant, *above left,* exposed to simulated acid rain with a pH of 3.2 show white damaged areas. Leaves on the right exposed to simulated normal rain with a pH of 5.6 are unblemished. Young brown trout hatched in water with a pH of 5.5 are normal, *top,* but those hatched in water with a pH of 5.0 are grossly deformed, *above.*

fish. In Norway's Tovdal River, for example, all the trout died following the melting of snow with a pH of 4.5 in spring of 1975.

The effect of acid rain on building materials has also been widely studied. Limestone, marble, and sandstone are widely used for statues, monuments, and buildings. These building materials contain calcium carbonate and are seriously affected by sulfur-polluted air. When acid falls on such materials, the calcium carbonate is converted to gypsum, or calcium sulfate, which dissolves in water. Rain washes the gypsum away grain by grain. Ironically, statues sheltered from rainfall may suffer even more damage than those that are not. For on surfaces protected from precipitation, dry deposits of sulfur dioxide produce a crust of gypsum. Eventually, this crust falls off in layers or chunks. Some of the world's greatest architectural treasures, including the Colosseum in Rome and the Taj Mahal in India, are suffering the effects of acid rain. Martin Weaver, technical director of the Canadian historical society Heritage Canada, has estimated that acid rain causes annual damage of $1 billion to Canadian buildings.

Scientists studying the impact of acid rain on forests have reported both favorable and adverse effects. Göttingen's Ulrich conducted extensive studies on the forests of the Solling Plateau in West Germany. He concluded that acid damage to forests occurs in several stages. At first, trees may actually benefit from acid rain because the deposits supply nitrates and sulfates, plant nutrients that many soils lack. Then the damage begins. Sulfates combine with the natural nutrients of the soil, particularly calcium and magnesium, and eliminate them as a source of plant food. Spruce needles turn yellow and fall off from lack of magnesium. A deficiency of calcium causes the tree to draw upon its stored calcium. Crown dieback—that is, the dying of the tree downward from the top—is often the first outward sign that the internal supply of calcium is used up.

Finally, aluminum and heavy metals are leached from the soil. These toxic metals destroy the tiny feeder roots, which supply the tree with nutrients and water. The tree becomes vulnerable to parasites and insects, and gradually dies of starvation and disease.

Crown dieback has been reported in many countries in central Europe. Scientists have concluded that more than 2.5 million acres of forest in central Europe have been damaged by wet and dry acid deposits. In North America, Canadian tree specialist George H. Tomlinson has reported the crown dieback and death of red spruce in the Adirondack Mountains and Green Mountains of the United States and the Laurentian Mountains of Canada.

The most disturbing aspect of acid rain may be its potential to harm human beings. It can affect human health indirectly by causing metals to contaminate water. Acidified water can leach toxic metals from soil or from plumbing. When such water is used for drinking or cooking, the metals are taken into the body. Copper pipes are widely used in European and North American plumbing systems. Water with a low pH level can leach copper from the pipes and lead from the soldered joints. According to the EPA, the maximum safe level of copper in drinking water is 1 milligram per liter. In Sweden, much of the tap water comes from shallow wells. In regions of heavy acid rain, copper levels as high as 45 milligrams

A helicopter deposits lime on acidified Horn Lake in the Adirondack Mountains of upper New York state. Liming can neutralize an acidified lake, but its effects are not permanent.

per liter have been recorded in hot water that had been standing in copper pipes overnight.

Fish caught in acidified lakes and streams also contain toxic metals. The elevated mercury level of fish caught in two remote Adirondack lakes prompted the New York State Department of Health to recommend that residents not eat freshwater fish more than once a day, and that pregnant women and nursing mothers avoid freshwater fish entirely.

Efforts to control the problems caused by acid rain have taken two directions. One is to neutralize the acid deposits; the other is to curb the emissions of acid-forming pollutants. Swedish scientists are experimenting with lime added to acidified waterways. They have found that the addition of lime to lakes increased the number of fish and plankton plants. However, toxic levels of aluminum remained for several months before settling to the bottom of the lake. And if the surrounding watershed is not limed, new aluminum will enter the lake after being leached out of the soil by the acid deposits that continue to fall. Furthermore, even limed lakes can be affected by acid shock during the spring snowmelt. In any case, liming is not a practical solution for the thousands of threatened lakes that lie in hard-to-reach wilderness areas.

Reducing the emissions of acid-forming pollutants offers the best hope for controlling acid rain. To date, scientists have concentrated on sulfur dioxide emissions, because there are no practical methods of limiting nitrogen oxide emissions. The use of low-sulfur coal is one way to reduce sulfur dioxide emissions. Coal from the Western United States has a much lower sulfur content than coal from the Midwest and northern Appalachia. If Midwestern power plants were to switch to Western coal, their emissions of sulfur dioxide would drop substantially. However, the switch would hurt the economy of those states where high-sulfur coal is mined, and would drive up the cost of generating electricity in the Midwest. As an alternative, high-sulfur coal can be crushed and washed to reduce its sulfur content by up to 40 per cent. But this also increases fuel costs.

A different approach to reducing sulfur dioxide

A Bath for a Gas

In one type of gas scrubber, dirty exhaust gas from a coal-fired boiler enters at the top, where it is mixed with a souplike slurry of water and lime. The gas and slurry then pass through a circular opening created by raising a cone-shaped valve. The slurry is broken into a mist as it passes through this opening. As the gas circulates through the central portion of the scrubber, the sulfur dioxide in the gas reacts with the lime to form calcium-sulfur compounds. These are trapped in the mist droplets, which fall to the bottom of the scrubber. From there, the wastes are pumped out for disposal. The cleansed gas leaves the scrubber and is released to the atmosphere through the smokestack.

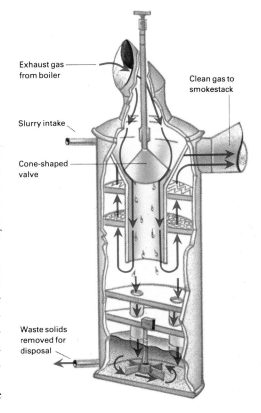

Exhaust gas from boiler

Clean gas to smokestack

Slurry intake

Cone-shaped valve

Waste solids removed for disposal

Acid rain research ranges from simple collection of rainwater to measure local pH levels, *above,* to an elaborate greenhouse rainmaker, *above right,* that simulates rainfall of varying pH levels. It is used to determine the effects of acid rain on plant growth.

emissions involves removing the compound from exhaust gases. Flue gas desulfurization, or "scrubbing," can remove more than 90 per cent of the sulfur dioxide from the exhaust gases of a coal-fired boiler. In a wet scrubber, a slurry, or semifluid mixture, is sprayed into the exhaust gases. The slurry consists of water and an alkaline compound, such as limestone or calcium hydroxide. Sulfur dioxide in the exhaust gas reacts with the slurry to form either calcium sulfite or calcium sulfate. These sulfur compounds are then disposed of, either as a wet sludge or as a solid when mixed with fly ash. A typical wet-scrubber system for a power plant uses from 3 to 5 per cent of the plant's energy output.

Unquestionably, the reduction of sulfur dioxide from the emissions of power plants and industrial sources is enormously expensive. Thus, it is no surprise that the affected industries have fought against the imposition of more stringent emission standards. They have disputed the link between their emissions and downwind acid deposits. And they have challenged the accuracy of studies that show there have been increases in the acidity of the precipitation in eastern North America.

Industry representatives also point out that the U.S. Clean Air Act of 1970 and the amendments of 1977 already limit emissions of sulfur dioxide. However, these regulations were drawn up with the goal of reducing local, ground-level concentrations of pollutants. This is underscored by the fact that older power plants could meet the regulations by raising the height of their smokestacks.

Industry appears to have found an ally in the Administration of President Ronald Reagan. Under the Reagan Administration, the EPA has taken the position that not enough is known about the causes and effects of acid rain to warrant additional controls now. Kathleen M. Bennett, assistant administrator for Air, Noise and Radiation at the EPA, testified at a Senate hearing in October 1981 that it was very important to study the problem for at least three to five more years.

The opposite position is taken by the Committee on the Atmosphere and the Biosphere of the National Research Council. In its 1981 report, the committee stated that "continued emissions of sulfur dioxide and nitrogen oxides at current or accelerated rates, in the face of clear evidence of serious hazard to human health and to the biosphere, will be extremely risky from a long-term economic standpoint as well as from the standpoint of biosphere protection."

Relations between the United States and Canada have become seriously strained over the issue of acid rain. In 1979, President Jimmy Carter's Administration initiated talks with the Canadian government to develop a bilateral agreement that would deal effectively with transboundary air pollution. In August 1980, the two governments agreed to attack the problem through reductions of pollutant emissions. Later, representatives of both countries endorsed a 50 per cent reduction in the sulfur dioxide emissions of each nation.

After the Reagan Administration came to power, the United States delegation reversed its position and argued against new emissions limits. As the talks bogged down, the Canadians sought to break the deadlock. In October 1982, the Canadian government set standards for decreasing the sulfur dioxide emissions of its major industrial offenders by 25 per cent. Canada was willing to increase the standards to attain a 50 per cent decrease, if the United States would match this reduction. American officials declined, leading to further friction between Canada and the United States.

United States citizens also have expressed anger over the federal government's perceived foot-dragging on the acid rain problem. In March 1983, nearly 200 New Hampshire communities held town meetings at which citizens voted on an acid rain resolution. The resolution asked the federal government to impose a 50 per cent reduction in acid-forming emissions from Midwestern utilities and industries. It was passed by 195 towns, many by unanimous votes. Two towns set the resolution aside, but none voted it down.

Such demonstrations of public concern may eventually force the U.S. government to require further reductions in sulfur dioxide emissions. It would, of course, be comforting to know that costly emission reductions would definitely decrease the amount of acid rain that falls. Yet it would be tragic to forestall action, only to discover that irreversible ecological damage had taken place during the delay. Governments must frequently make decisions based on incomplete data, in the knowledge that failure to act could lead to great harm. Those who ask if we can afford to reduce emissions must themselves answer this question: Can we afford not to?

The Secrets of Living Lights

By Ben Patrusky

**Studies of bioluminescence are revealing
the ways in which fireflies and other luminous
organisms flash and glow — and why.**

Lost in the darkness, his fuel nearly gone, the young fighter-pilot desperately scanned the waters of the South Pacific. Somewhere in the blackness below was the aircraft carrier, its lights off to conceal it from the enemy. Where was that blasted ship? Unless the pilot spotted it soon, he'd have to crash-land on the water.

Suddenly, just off the plane's left wing tip, a narrow strip of ocean surface began to dance with a diamondlike sparkle. Heading toward this ribbon of shining sea, the pilot soon caught sight of the carrier and landed safely.

World War II naval lore is filled with such tales — true stories of fliers finding their way back after missions by fixing on a ship's glittering wake. These pilots had come to rely on millions and millions of one-celled light makers — marine organisms called dinoflagellates. When disturbed, as by a ship's passing, these tiny creatures shine like blue-green sparks — a sight the Scottish poet and novelist Sir Walter Scott described as "the mimic fires of ocean glow, the lightning of the waves."

The phenomenon is called bioluminescence, the ability of certain living things to give off light. An amazing variety of organisms, both on the land and in the sea, emit their personal light.

Bioluminescence has intrigued not only poets but also scientists, who have long puzzled over the secrets of the various flashing, glittering, and glowing lights produced by various creatures. Most investigators have been trying to discover how the phenomenon works. Biochemists have been working to discover the chemicals involved in generating this natural light. Physiologists have been trying to uncover the network of cells and organs that make up the light-emission system.

Beginning in the early 1960s, some researchers began to take a close look at why organisms give off light. These biologists and animal behaviorists are conducting studies in the field and in the experimental laboratory to find out how luminescent organisms use light in their daily lives. The scientists' search is based on the idea that evolution, guided by natural selection, keeps only what works. In other words, if organisms are emitting light, they must be using it for a purpose.

Scientists used to think that light emission was simply an accidental by-product of metabolism, the chemical processes vital to life. This notion stemmed, in part, from the erratic, almost random way in which the phenomenon occurs in living things. It seems to have played a kind of evolutionary peekaboo, turning up often in certain related groups of animals; seldom in other groups; and in some groups, not at all. For instance, scientists have found luminous species of shrimp but no luminous crabs. Some varieties of millipedes and centipedes give off light, but scorpions and spiders do not. Of the more than 800,000 species of insects, only about 3,000 luminesce. About 2,000 of these luminous species are fireflies — beetles of the family *Lampyridae*. And, although all fireflies emit light as larvae, only about two-thirds of the species continue to do so as adults.

One of the most remarkable bioluminescent creatures is the railroad worm, a beetle native to Central and South America. It has a fiery red "headlight" and 11 "windows" of bright green light along each side. As the glowing insect crawls through the night, it resembles a tiny lighted train.

Another light-producing insect, the New Zealand glowworm, is actually the larva of a fly. The glowworms dwell in shaded areas along streams and in ravines, but their best-known habitat is the Waitomo Cave on the North Island of New Zealand. Attached to the ceiling of the cave, the larvae spin sticky threads that dangle

The author:
Ben Patrusky is a free-lance science writer and a media consultant to several scientific institutions.

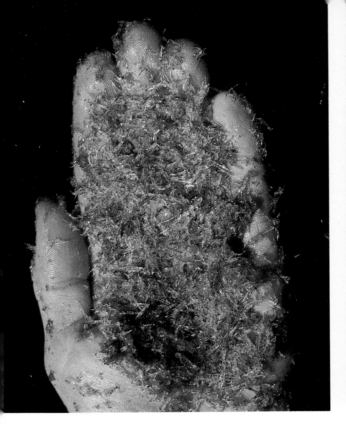

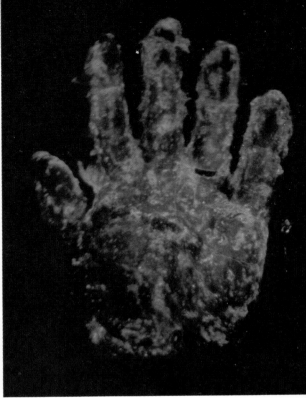

below them like fishing lines. Small insects, which are attracted by the lights of the glowworms, get trapped on these threads. The larvae then reel in their lines and devour their helpless prey. The glowworms thrive in such numbers at Waitomo that the cave ceiling is ablaze with their combined glow.

The oceans house the greatest diversity of bioluminescent organisms, including various species of fish, jellyfish, shrimp, octopus, and squid. The only known light-emitting freshwater species is the New Zealand limpet — a type of mollusk. One of the best-known luminous sea creatures is *Cypridina hilgendorfi*, a tiny crustacean found in Japan's coastal waters. During World War II, Japanese soldiers used these crustaceans for light at night. They poured cool water on a handful of crushed *Cypridina*, producing a faint blue light that enabled them to read messages and maps without revealing their position to the enemy.

Some of the most interesting arrangements of natural lights are found in fish. For example, several species of a fish called the midshipman dwell in the Pacific coastal waters of the United States. Each fish has hundreds of tiny lights on its underside, arranged like the rows of ornamental brass buttons on a naval officer's uniform. In one species of deep-sea lantern fish, only the male has a light, located on top of its head. When a school of these fish is attacked, the males swim off in all directions, flashing their lights like miniature police cars. The predators follow the flashing males, leaving the females behind, safe in the darkness.

Hundreds of the marine crustaceans *Cypridina,* each about the size of a tomato seed, fit on a human hand, *above left*. When these tiny creatures are crushed and mixed with cool water, their light-producing chemicals react, creating a ghostly blue image, *above*.

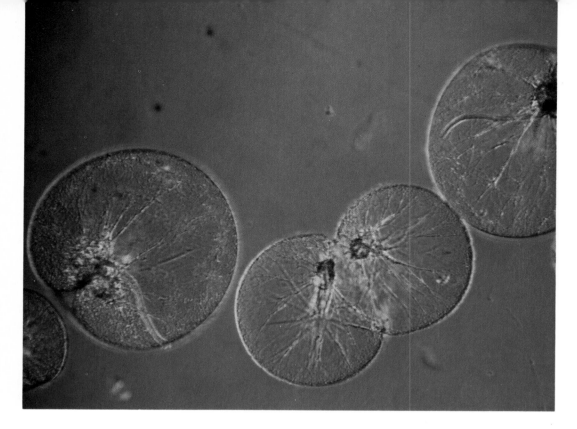

Delicate one-celled dinoflagellates, which float on the surface of the sea, glow in response to direct physical stimulation, such as the passing of a ship or the crashing of a wave.

Fish are the only bioluminescent *vertebrates* (animals with backbones). No amphibians, reptiles, birds, or mammals emit light. Nor, for that matter, do any green plants. However, about 40 species of land-dwelling fungi do luminesce. If you have spent any time in deep forests, you may have encountered will-o'-the-wisp, or foxfire, the eerie light produced by various species of fungi that live on rotting logs and stumps. There are also luminous mushrooms that look like small glowing lampshades. During World War II, a U.S. reporter on the island of New Guinea told of writing a letter to his wife by the light of five mushrooms.

To many observers, this scattershot distribution of bioluminescence suggested that the phenomenon played a minor role, at best, in an organism's survival. But as behaviorists began to study the variety of bioluminescent species, they found that virtually all luminous organisms have one feature in common. All are creatures of the "twilight zone"—they glow and flash only when the surrounding light grows dim. Fireflies do not light up their tails before dusk. Bioluminescent shallow-water fish give off light only after the sky begins to darken. Dinoflagellates, no matter how disturbed, do not start to sparkle until the light around them diminishes. Bioluminescence seems to have evolved in species in which light for survival in the darkness is an advantage.

Not surprisingly, the realm of eternal twilight—the ocean's midwaters—houses the greatest abundance of luminous organisms. At depths of 300 to 3,000 feet, more than 90 per cent of all sea creatures luminesce, compared with only 1 to 2 per cent in shallow coastal waters. The only exceptions to the twilight-only pattern are luminous bacteria and fungi. They shine all the time.

"Mimic fires," Scott's poetic phrase, proved an apt metaphor for bioluminescence, not only visually but also chemically. In fire, oxygen joins with other substances to produce light and heat. Bioluminescence also depends on oxygen, an observation first credited to the 17th-century English scientist Robert Boyle. Boyle showed that the glow of fungi and bacteria faded in a vacuum but reappeared in the presence of air. Unlike fire, however, bioluminescence does not feel hot. Hold a firefly in your hand and you will find its flickering tail cool to the touch.

The key to understanding the chemical mechanism of this cold light came in 1887, about two centuries after Boyle. Experimenting with luminous beetles and clams, the French biologist Raphael DuBois discovered two substances involved in bioluminescence. He named both after *lucifer*, the Latin word for *light-bearing*. One of the substances, luciferin, is the compound that reacts with oxygen to produce heatless light. The other, luciferase, is an enzyme that promotes this chemical reaction.

In the late 1950s, scientists learned how to isolate, purify, and synthesize the molecules that make up the machinery of light emission. They found that there are many different kinds of luciferin and luciferase. Different species may have different forms of the chemi-

Railroad worms of Central and South America put on a spectacular lighting display. Each insect has a fiery red "headlight," as well as 11 "windows" of light along each side.

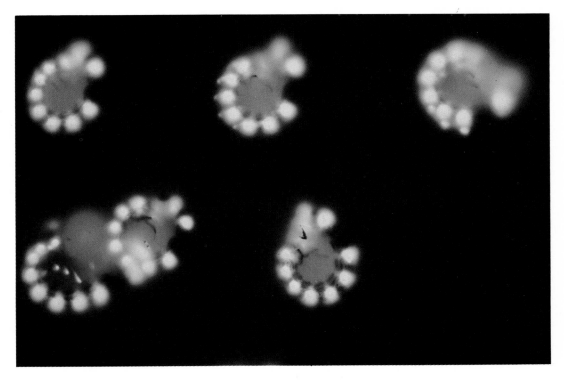

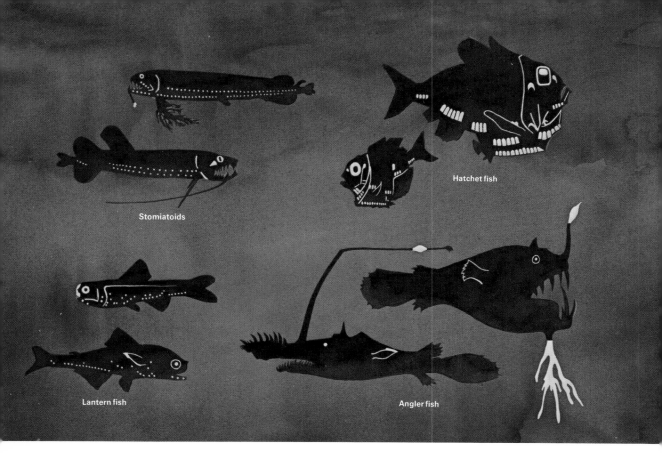

Stomiatoids

Hatchet fish

Lantern fish

Angler fish

Beacons of the Deep

Luminous deep-sea fish, *above,*
display a variety of light
arrangements — from the simple to
the bizarre. The lights are used
to locate and catch prey, ward
off predators, or attract mates.
An angler fish, *right,* lures its
victim with a glowing light
attached to a thin flexible tube
on its head. The luminous
"chin whisker" on a stomiatoid,
below, also acts as a lure.
Numerous small lights on the
sides and belly may aid in
locating and attracting prey.

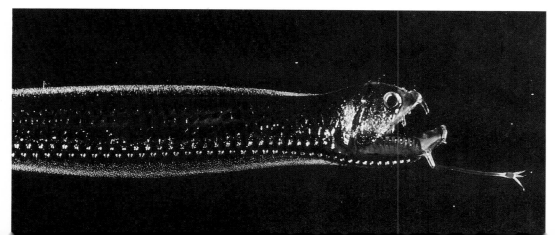

cals. However, although the composition of the substances varies, the basic chemical reaction of bioluminescence is the same. During this reaction, oxygen combines with luciferin — in the presence of luciferase — to form an "excited" molecule. This means that the molecule is highly energetic and unstable because it has temporarily absorbed energy generated by the reaction. The molecule quickly becomes stable when it releases this energy in the form of tiny packets of light called photons. This light always lies in the visible part of the electromagnetic spectrum. The color varies from species to species — from the deep blue of shrimp and other midwater dwellers, to the blue-green of bacteria, the green of mushrooms, the yellow of fireflies, and the red and green of railroad worms.

Some systems of bioluminescence require more than just luciferin, luciferase, and oxygen. In fireflies, for example, luciferin must first react with adenosine triphosphate (ATP), a compound found in the cells of all living things. The product of this reaction then combines with oxygen to produce the excited light-emitting molecule. Other bioluminescent species make use of a single molecule, called a photoprotein, for light emission. The first photoprotein was detected in the jellyfish *Aequorea* and was named aequorin. Aequorin combines with calcium to produce light.

Since its discovery in 1962, scientists have learned that aequorin is really luciferin and luciferase joined together as one molecule. Oxygen is "prepackaged" within the heart of the photoprotein. Calcium releases the oxygen, triggering the bioluminescent reaction.

One of the most startling discoveries that researchers have made about bioluminescence chemistry is that some widely diverse species have identical luciferin. Before the 1950s, many scientists believed that only very closely related creatures would possess similar forms of the compound; all others would have their own distinctive kind. However, the luciferin from certain species of *coelenterates*, a group of soft-bodied animals that includes jellyfish and sea pansies, has been found in several varieties of bioluminescent fish, crustaceans, octopus, and squid. When scientists mixed luciferin isolated from any one of these species with luciferase from another, light was produced. Another type of luciferin, the kind found in *Cypridina*, has been discovered in several species of fish.

Scientists are trying to explain how such diverse, independently evolved species could have identical forms of this chemical. A current theory is that some of these species do not actually produce their own luciferin. Instead, they obtain the compound from luminous organisms in their diet. For example, the species of fish that have luciferin identical to that of *Cypridina* eat these crustaceans regularly. It seems likely that these fish developed a bioluminescence system that makes use of luciferin obtained from their prey.

Scientists have also been looking at how bioluminescent organisms switch their lights on and off, or adjust the amount of light emitted.

A grotesque deep-sea viperfish lies in wait for unwary prey attracted by its lights. Photophores inside the fish's gaping mouth help lure victims within striking distance of its long, sharp teeth.

They have found that the regulatory apparatus depends, in part, on whether the organism "borrows" or manufactures its light.

The "borrowers" get their light by acting as hosts to colonies of luminous bacteria. Numerous varieties of bioluminescent fish, crustaceans, and squid take in these bacteria from the environment and store them in special light organs. The hosts feed the bacteria; the bacteria, in turn, supply the hosts with light.

Since luminous bacteria glow all the time, hosts have had to develop ways to control the light. Often, the control is mechanical. For example, flashlight fish house glowing bacteria in pouches under their eyes. One group, *Photoblepharon*, turns off the lights by raising black lids located beneath the pouches. Another group, *Anomalops*, extinguishes the lights by rotating the bacterial pouches out of sight into pockets below the eyes.

Some luminescent "borrowers," such as reef-dwelling pony fish of Indonesia and the Philippines, can control the amount of light they emit. The bacterial light organ is inside the animal, near its digestive tract. A network of translucent muscle and other tissue guides and filters the bacterial light, which appears as a diffuse glow from the abdomen of the fish. Pigment cells within the translucent tissue expand and contract to regulate brightness.

Control of bacterial light may also be a matter of how well the host species treat their "guests." At Scripps Institution of Oceanography, researchers have conducted studies on the bacterial light organ of the Japanese knightfish. They have found that the intensity of light emitted may depend on the amount of nourishing glucose that reaches the bacteria through the network of blood vessels leading to the light organ.

Organisms that make their own light can be divided into two basic types, those that secrete light-producing chemicals and those

that produce light in special structures in or on their bodies. The secretors release luciferin and luciferase into the surrounding environment, where the bioluminescence reaction occurs at a distance from the organism. *Cypridina*, for example, stores luciferin and luciferase in separate glands. When disturbed, it simply secretes both chemicals into the water. A cloud of brilliant blue luminescence results when the substances meet and mix.

Some species of midwater fish and squid have light-producing organs deep inside their bodies. The light passes through translucent tissue and pigment cells that regulate its intensity. In other luminous organisms, the light-making structures lie directly on the surface. For instance, special light-producing cells called photocytes lie on the surface of many simple bioluminescent creatures, such as jellyfish and other coelenterates. Photocytes give off light in response to direct physical stimulation. The single-celled dinoflagellates are, in effect, photocytes.

More complex light-manufacturing organisms, including fireflies and certain varieties of deep-sea fish, squid, and shrimp, have highly specialized surface organs called photophores. These organs consist of intricate arrangements of photocytes, lenses, filters, and reflectors, which work together to control the color, direction, and intensity of the emitted light.

The central nervous system usually controls the photophores. Scientists have mapped the neural network that regulates the activity of firefly light organs, or lanterns. They have identified what seems to be the chemical messenger that helps convert nerve impulses into photophore flashes. It is a hormonelike chemical called octopamine given off by the nerve endings. Researchers think that octopamine comes into contact with photocytes in the firefly lanterns, triggering a reaction involving a second messenger inside the light-producing

The dazzling array of lights on a sea gooseberry, *top,* a jellyfishlike creature, probably serves to scare attackers away. The shallow-water reef squid, *above,* may also use its glowing photophores to ward off predators.

cells. In some way, this second chemical, called cyclic AMP, sets off the bioluminescence reaction.

As knowledge about the chemistry and the control of bioluminescence has increased, scientists have begun to speculate about the function of this natural light. Why do organisms emit light? How does bioluminescence contribute to survival? Answers to the questions were first sought in the early 1960s, when behaviorists began to document the link between luminescence and life style.

The best evidence of the purpose of bioluminescence has come from the study of fireflies, largely through field work by entomologist James E. Lloyd of the University of Florida. Lloyd discovered that fireflies use their lights to find mates. In other words, those flickers you see in meadows and fields on a summer evening are signals of courtship. Each species has its own distinct code. About 130 such codes have now been deciphered, including those of the species that make up the two main groups of fireflies in the United States, *Photinus* and *Photuris*.

In most cases, the male firefly takes to the air to advertise his sexual availability. Sometimes the signal is a single flash, while in other species it may be a group of flashes. "Like TV commercials," says Lloyd, "males repeat their commercial messages over and over again until they get a buyer." The male flash pattern is only half of the code. The other half is the female response, usually a simple blink. But timing is important. Her answer comes at a definite moment following the male's flash pattern.

In *Photinus pyralis*, for example, the most common species in the Eastern United States, the male flashes at intervals of about seven seconds, each pulse lasting about half a second. The female gives an answering flash about two seconds later from her position on the ground in low vegetation. *Photinus* females do not fly during courtship. The courting male and female continue their dialogue of flashes for several exchanges until the male finally descends, and the couple meets and mates.

Using a small penlight to imitate male flashes, Lloyd found that females of different species of *Photinus* living together in the same meadow responded only to males of their own species. He also demonstrated how the timing of the flash codes changed with temperature. An insect's body chemistry slows down in cold weather. Thus, the colder it is, the longer the interval between the male's flashes, and the longer the delay between the male's signal and the female's response. When Lloyd put a little heater under a captive female, her flash responses speeded up, becoming too fast to attract males of her species flying overhead.

Most adult fireflies are plant eaters, but there are exceptions. Females of the *Photuris* group, which has more than 60 species, are cannibals. They attract and devour males of other firefly species by mimicking the flashes of the females of those species. Lloyd has

Resembling stars in the clear night sky, thousands of shining glowworms cling to the ceiling of New Zealand's Waitomo Cave, *opposite page*. The tiny luminescent insects are fly larvae.

dubbed these predatory *Photuris* "femmes fatales" and what they do "aggressive mimicry." Lloyd has seen females of *Photuris versicolor*, the best known of the femmes fatales, mimic the responses of as many as seven different species. And they switch from one proper answer to another depending on the species of male flying overhead.

One of the most spectacular displays of firefly sexual communication involves the *Pteroptyx* species of Southeast Asia. In these species, the males stay put, signaling in concert to attract flying females. The males cluster on trees in dense swarms and pulse in perfect unison at intervals that range from one-half to three seconds, depending on the particular species. However, according to Lloyd, all is not harmony and cooperation among the insects. Once females get close, cooperation breaks down into intense competition among the males for the females' attention.

Scientists are less certain about the purpose of the light of firefly larvae. Larval lanterns do not flash; they only glow. Moreover, removing the photophores from larvae does not keep them from developing adult lanterns. This means that larval lights do not develop into adult photophores. In the 1970s, neurobiologist Albert B. Carlson of the State University of New York at Stony Brook proposed one possible explanation for the larval lights. They may be a warn-

A flashlight fish, belonging to the group *Anomalops,* forages for food with the help of the glowing bacterial pouches beneath its eyes, *right*. In brighter waters, the fish no longer needs its beams and rotates them out of sight into pockets below the eyes, *below right*.

ing to predators that the larvae have a most unpleasant taste. In one experiment, Carlson fed gelatin capsules containing meal worm or glowing firefly larvae to mice. The mice that bit into the larvae rejected them furiously. The mice flung the larvae away and spent several minutes wiping their mouths with their forelegs.

While fireflies are relatively easy to study, other bioluminescent organisms are not. Most of these dwell in the sea where it is far more difficult to make the necessary close-range studies. Behavioral information obtained from experiments in an aquarium is inconclusive, because scientists cannot be sure that what is happening there is going on in the sea.

Despite the relative scarcity of data, marine biologist James E. Morin of the University of California, Los Angeles, believes that the function of all oceanic bioluminescence fits into four categories: communication, including finding mates and defending territory; keeping predators at bay; finding or attracting prey; and advertisement — one species attracting another species to the benefit of both. Morin says that many organisms, particularly those with more advanced light-making systems, appear capable of using their luminescence for more than one purpose.

Only luminous organisms with well-developed nervous and visual systems, such as fish, octopuses, squids, and some varieties of marine worms, use their light to find mates. For example, during the first few nights after each full moon, the inch-long marine fireworms *Odontosyllis*, found in waters off the Bahamas, leave their burrows in

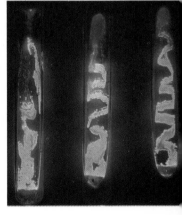

Bioluminescent mushrooms look like small glowing lampshades on the forest floor, *top*. Colonies of light-emitting bacteria illuminate the test tubes that contain them, *above*. Unlike most other luminescent organisms, luminescent mushrooms and bacteria glow all the time.

coral reefs and swim to the surface. For up to an hour, males and females cavort in small circles, the females giving off a green glow and the males flashing periodically. Eventually, the females deposit batches of eggs that the pursuing males quickly cover with sperm. The fireworms then return to the reefs. (Christopher Columbus may have witnessed the mating ritual of *Odontosyllis* when he reported seeing candles burning in the water.)

Morin has charted complex blinking patterns among flashlight fish that also suggest courtship. And once a male and female form an alliance, they may use the light to protect their territory. Morin observed an intruder, another flashlight fish, enter an area inhabited by such a pair. The female shuttered her beams, swam toward the intruder, and then flashed them back on. The would-be competitor was frightened away.

This "flash-and-startle" strategy is very common among bioluminescent marine creatures who want to keep predators at bay. Most shallow-water organisms flash when touched or brushed. They ward off predators in one of three ways: by frightening — what Morin calls the "boo" effect; by temporarily blinding or disorienting — the "flashbulb" effect; or by attracting organisms that prey on the predator — the "burglar alarm" effect. The flashbulb effect may also be used for catching prey. In this case, the luminescent organism emits a flash of light to stun its prey just long enough to capture it.

Lights that glow rather than flash also play a part in defense and in predation. Some bioluminescent organisms seem to use their glowing lights as decoys to confuse would-be attackers. For example, the luminescent cloud that *Cypridina* secretes can act as a smoke screen, allowing the little crustacean to escape. Decoys can also take the form of sacrificial lures, as in the case of the brittle star, a sea animal related to the starfish. The brittle star has long, thin arms that stick up out of its burrow in the sandy seabed. If a predator pokes the arms, they flash. If it persists in poking them, the brittle star will throw off one of the arms. The freed arm glows and twists about like a snake, apparently to draw the predator away from the burrow. Meanwhile, the brittle star goes dark and retracts its remaining arms into the sand. Later, it regenerates a new limb to replace the lost one.

Glowing lights may also serve as a form of camouflage. Many crustaceans, fish, octopuses, and squid emit a diffuse light from their bottom surface that exactly matches the intensity of the sunlight coming down through the water. In this way, they avoid creating a silhouette that might attract predators lurking below. This form of concealment, known as counterillumination, is a two-way street. It allows camouflagers not only to make themselves invisible to predators, but also to sneak up on prey.

Some marine creatures glow to draw prey to them. One group of predatory glowers are deep-sea angler fish. An angler fish has a glowing lure attached to a thin flexible tube on its head. The angler fish whips the lure back and forth like a fishing rod until a curious victim ventures close enough to be caught. Another group of deep-sea fish, the stomiatoids, have luminous "chin whiskers" that also act as lures. Numerous small photophores on the sides and bellies of the stomiatoids may function both in finding and attracting prey. Flashlight fish are also believed to use their beams in detecting and attracting prey. There's a possible drawback—the glowing lights make the fish itself a target for predation. To avoid being nabbed, the flashlight fish can convert its slow glow to a rapid blink while swimming in a zigzag fashion. This "blink-and-run" tactic makes it difficult for a predator to track the fish.

Some glowing may be for advertisement, or what Morin calls "mutualism." One example of mutualism involves bioluminescent fungi that Lloyd studied in the early 1970s. His findings suggest that the light produced by luminous mushrooms and other fungi serves to attract insects. The insects crawl into the fungi to lay their eggs and depart carrying the fungal spores. The insects benefit by laying their eggs in a place that ensures an adequate food supply for the developing offspring. The fungi, in turn, benefit by having the insects scatter their spores.

As scientists unravel the mysteries of bioluminescence, they are also exploring ways in which this natural light-making process can help us. Luciferin and luciferase from fireflies are already being used in a sensitive biochemical test for ATP. This test can measure the amount of infectious bacteria in blood or urine samples. The more bacteria present, the greater the amount of bacterial ATP and the brighter the light generated by the firefly chemicals. The chemicals are also used in unmanned spacecraft that have been equipped with automated devices for performing the ATP test on samples taken from other planets. Light produced by these tests would indicate the presence of a type of life similar to that found on earth.

Firefly luciferin and luciferase may also be used to detect cancer. Scientists have found that the intensity of light produced by the firefly chemicals decreases in the presence of cancerous cells.

Other bioluminescent creatures may also yield useful information. Research biochemist Milton J. Cormier of the University of Georgia in Athens has been studying luminous coelenterates that require calcium to make light. He hopes to develop a method for measuring calcium levels in human cells. Other researchers are taking a close look at the flashlight fish, whose immune system does not attack the bacteria housed in its light organs. Such studies may provide clues to the human immune system. Eventually, the chemical techniques of luminous organisms may even lead to more efficient means of energy production. As the years go by, our fascination with these living lights — and our attempts to discover their secrets — will undoubtedly prove increasingly valuable.

Herpes Is Forever

By Richard W. Hyman

Scientists are struggling to penetrate the secrets of the elusive herpesviruses, which cause untold suffering by creating lifelong, recurring infections.

Genital herpes, an ominous venereal disease, is sweeping the United States today. There is no cure for genital herpes; an infected person can expect to have the disease for life. The Centers for Disease Control (CDC) in Atlanta, Ga., declared in 1982 that the disease has reached epidemic proportions and estimates that at least 500,000 new cases are added each year to the total of about 20 million Americans suffering from this herpes infection.

Most people have heard of genital herpes and are aware that it is caused by the herpes simplex virus 2 (HSV-2). But did you know there are four other viruses in the human herpesvirus family? They are responsible for a variety of common — and not so common — afflictions. Herpes simplex virus 1 (HSV-1), a close relative of HSV-2, causes the fluid-filled lip sores commonly called cold sores or fever blisters. Varicella zoster virus is a herpesvirus responsible for chicken pox and shingles. Epstein-Barr virus, another herpesvirus, causes mononucleosis. Cytomegalovirus infection in fetuses can result in serious birth defects.

In addition, herpesviruses are widespread in the animal world. Every *vertebrate species* (animals with backbones) that scientists have examined has at least one herpesvirus. For example, horses can be afflicted with a herpesvirus that causes pregnant mares to abort. This can pose serious problems in the race-horse-breeding business. In March 1983, an epidemic hit the breeding farm of Austria's famed Lipizzan horses, killing 7 mares and 27 foals. Cattle packed together in feed lots are susceptible to a herpesvirus transmitted through saliva. This infection causes the cattle to lose weight, just the opposite of what should happen in the feed lot.

Whether found in humans or other animals, herpesviruses and the way they cause disease tend to be rather mysterious. Our current understanding has accumulated over centuries of clinical observation and less than one century of research. The name *herpes* in classical Greek meant *the creep*. Almost 2,500 years ago, the ancient Greek physician Hippocrates used the term *herpes* to describe various diseases of the skin that were of a "creeping" or "creepy" nature. Many of these probably were not caused by herpesviruses, and Hippocrates could not have known there were such things as viruses. The concept of a virus was not developed until the late 1800s and early 1900s and viruses were not observed until the electron microscope was developed in the 1930s. Only within the past 20 years have scientists begun to understand some of the secrets of the elusive class called herpesviruses.

My own interest in herpesviruses began in 1970, when I suffered an attack of shingles, a painful rash of fluid-filled sores. Shingles is one of the oldest recognized herpes conditions. The term *shingles* comes from the Latin word *cingulus*, meaning *girdle*, which accurately describes how the shingles rash commonly encircles the torso. During the two months of pain the shingles caused me, I was very annoyed that doctors could do nothing to help me. So I began to read about herpesviruses, at first merely to find out why shingles was so hard to treat. But my interest in the subject grew, and eventually I devoted my full-time research career to the study of herpesviruses.

The first known research into the relationship between chicken pox and shingles was undertaken from about 1890 to 1910 by Physician-in-Chief János Bókay at the Stephanie Children's Hospital in Budapest, Hungary. Bókay noticed that children who had close contact with adults with shingles often developed the fever and itchy rash of chicken pox about two weeks later. He deduced that it was possible for a child to catch chicken pox from an adult with shingles. Two questions arose from Bókay's observations: (1) What was causing chicken pox and shingles? (2) Was the same substance or agent responsible for both diseases?

The answer to the second question came first, in the late 1920s and early 1930s. It was a result of experiments on human subjects in Germany and Norway—experiments that for ethical reasons

The author:
Richard W. Hyman is professor of microbiology at Pennsylvania State University's Milton S. Hershey Medical Center in Hershey, Pa.

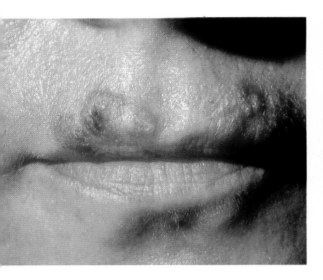

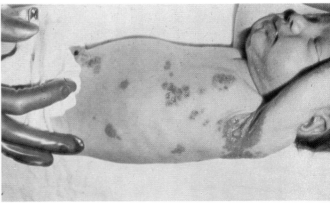

Lip sores, *left,* are caused by herpes simplex virus-1. Sores that cover an infant born to a mother with genital herpes, *above,* are caused by herpes simplex virus-2.

would not be permitted today. Both the German and the Norwegian doctors took fluid from the rash of patients with shingles and injected it into groups of children selected for the experiment. About 50 per cent of the children developed chicken pox two weeks later. These studies showed that the agent causing shingles was the same as that causing chicken pox.

The answer to the first question did not come until 1953, when research biologist Thomas H. Weller of Harvard University in Cambridge, Mass., finally isolated the culprit responsible for chicken pox and shingles in cell culture. Weller, who shared the 1954 Nobel Prize for physiology or medicine for this work, found that the infectious agent is a virus, which was later named varicella zoster virus.

The story of the other herpesviruses is much the same; their isolation and identification were made possible in the 1950s and 1960s by the development of cell culture techniques. Research since then has progressed slowly, however, in part because these viruses grow poorly in culture. Nevertheless, as the result of persistent and dedicated work by many scientists, portraits of the five human herpesviruses and how they cause disease have begun to emerge.

All herpesviruses have certain features in common. First of all, they look alike when viewed through a high-powered electron microscope. Their overall diameter is between 1,500 and 2,000 angstroms. (One angstrom is 0.000000004 inch.) The outer shell of a herpesvirus is composed of proteins, sugars, and fats. Inside is a structure called a capsid containing deoxyribonucleic acid (DNA), the genetic material of the virus.

Herpesviruses are sneaky viruses. They usually get into you when you are young and stay for as long as you live, hiding out somewhere in your body, safe from your immune system. Thus they have the potential for becoming active once again and causing recurring outbreaks of disease. This is especially true of oral or genital herpes infections. But most herpesviruses just hang around without causing any symptoms. It is not unusual for a doctor to test the blood of an adult and find that he or she is playing the unwitting host to four, or even all five, human herpesviruses simultaneously.

Human herpesviruses can be divided into two basic types—those that attack and hide out in nerve tissue and those that are carried in the bloodstream. HSV-1, HSV-2, and varicella zoster virus infect nerve tissue. HSV-1, in addition to causing fluid-filled sores on the lips and sometimes the genitalia, produces keratitis, a dangerous infection of the eye that afflicts about 300,000 to 400,000 people in the United States each year. The disease damages the cornea of the eye and is a major cause of blindness in the United States. Persons with an outbreak of oral herpes—particularly contact lens wearers—can easily spread the infection to their eyes by touching their lip sore and then—without washing—placing the finger in or near their eye. HSV-1 also causes herpes encephalitis, an infection of the brain that is difficult to diagnose and nearly always fatal. Fortunately, herpes encephalitis is very rare.

HSV-2 is the principal cause of genital herpes infection, whose symptoms are painful fluid-filled and highly contagious sores on the genitals, thighs, and buttocks. HSV-2 is also the cause of a rare form of meningitis as well as an often-fatal infection in newborns. Like HSV-1, a genital herpes outbreak can recur at any time. This can have dire consequences since the disease is spread through sexual contact. A woman, for example, may have infectious HSV-2 in her urogenital tract without having any symptoms of genital herpes. Unknowingly, she will pass the HSV-2 infection to any sexual partner. If a pregnant woman delivers her baby while HSV-2 is present in the birth canal, the baby can become infected with the virus. HSV-2 infection of newborns is always serious and often fatal.

The growing prevalence of herpes simplex virus infections has given rise to fears that HSV-1 can be passed along on drinking glasses or that HSV-2 can be contracted from toilet seats, but neither is true. Scientists are virtually certain that these viruses cannot exist outside the body—unless in cell culture—and can only be transmitted by intimate contact.

The third human herpesvirus that attacks nerve tissue, varicella zoster virus, provides a good example of how a herpesvirus causes lifelong infection. It first appears in the young, causing chicken pox. Then it hides in the body, but can reappear at any time—even more than 50 years later—to cause shingles in the adult.

For a healthy child, chicken pox is an annoying, but not a dangerous, disease. For a child whose immune system is not functioning properly, however, chicken pox is always dangerous and sometimes fatal. This is particularly true of children being treated for leukemia, a cancer of white blood cells, or Hodgkin's disease, a lymphoma or cancer of the lymph nodes. Today's treatments, a combination of drugs and radiation, are very effective in controlling these childhood cancers. However, both the cancer and the treatments suppress the immune system, making these children extremely vulnerable to varicella zoster virus infection.

The two herpesviruses that involve blood cells, the Epstein-Barr virus and the cytomegalovirus — produce no symptoms if they are first encountered in childhood. However, if the Epstein-Barr virus is not encountered until the victim is a young adult, then the virus will cause infectious mononucleosis, commonly called the "kissing disease." This happens when healthy people, who have active Epstein-Barr virus in their throat from a childhood infection, pass on the disease by mouth contact. The symptoms of infectious mononucleosis, which include sore throat, fever, and fatigue, result from a large number of abnormal white blood cells and usually last from three to six weeks.

If a person encounters the cytomegalovirus for the first time as a young adult, the infection often produces symptoms similar to Epstein-Barr virus mononucleosis — fever and lethargy that can last for several weeks. But there is a darker side to the cytomegalovirus. It is one of the few human viruses of any type known to cross the placenta, the membrane through which a developing fetus receives nourishment from its mother and eliminates waste.

If a pregnant woman has a cytomegalovirus infection — either a first encounter or a recurrent infection — there is a chance that the virus will cross the placenta, infect, and damage the fetus. Although some congenital infections are mild and produce no detectable damage to the infant, cytomegalovirus is still a leading cause of birth defects. An average of 1 baby in every 100 contracts a cytomegalovirus infection in the womb.

Another group with the risk of getting serious cytomegalovirus infections are organ-transplant patients. Before an organ-transplant

A child with chicken pox, *below left,* will harbor the varicella zoster virus, which causes it, for the rest of his life. It may plague him many years later as an adult with the sores of shingles, *below*.

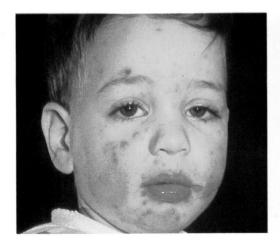

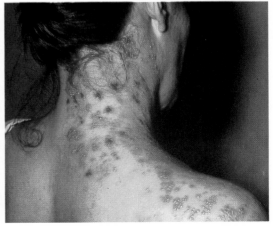

operation is performed, the doctor gives the patient drugs to suppress the immune system. This treatment is necessary so that the new, transplanted organ will not be rejected as a foreign invader. However, when the immune system is suppressed, a cytomegalovirus infection can go wild—just as chicken pox can in leukemia patients. At its worst, the cytomegalovirus causes a fatal pneumonia in organ-transplant patients.

In probing the secrets of herpesviruses, researchers have tried to find which parts of the body provide safe hiding places for the viruses while they wait for the opportunity to break out and cause these recurring infections. From both human and animal studies, scientists have found hints about where the herpes simplex viruses are and in what form while they are silently hiding.

In the early 1970s, neurologist J. Richard Baringer, then of the University of California Medical Center, removed the trigeminal ganglia, a group of nerve cells at the base of the brain, from human cadavers. He examined the nerve tissue for signs of HSV-1, but he could not see the virus in the electron microscope or find any evidence of it through chemical tests. After he kept the nerve tissue in culture for 7 to 10 days, however, the virus appeared. This probably means that the tissue harbors the latent HSV-1 but in a form that may not be infective. Thus, the HSV-1 could be present not as a complete virus but as, for example, a complex mixture of viral DNA and protein.

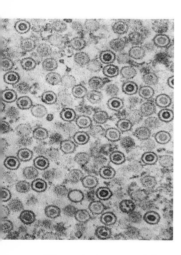

Through the powerful eyes of the electron microscope, all herpesviruses look alike. (Magnified 78,500 times.)

Researchers are now reasonably sure that HSV-1 hides in the trigeminal ganglia; HSV-2, in spinal nerve tissue called the sacral ganglia. They do not yet know what causes the virus to leave its hiding place and travel down nerve fibers to infect cells in the lips or genitals, but they suspect that stress, fever, or sunlight play a role in triggering outbreaks. Scientists believe that the varicella zoster virus hides out in sensory nerve cells—nerves that convey impulses from sense organs—but they are not certain of where.

Scientists believe the Epstein-Barr virus and the cytomegalovirus are blood-borne because they have found these viruses or viral DNA in circulating blood cells. However, it seems unlikely that blood cells are the primary hiding places of these two herpesviruses. Unlike nerve cells, blood cells have short, fixed lifetimes. Also, scientists have found these viruses outside of blood cells. Epstein-Barr virus appears in the throats of healthy individuals and cytomegalovirus in the urine, salivary gland, cervix, and sperm cells. The actual hiding place—or places—of the blood-borne human herpesviruses still remains to be determined.

One of the most important areas of current herpesvirus research focuses on their possible role in causing various kinds of cancer. We know that certain animal herpesviruses can cause cancer in the wild. One well-studied example is Lucké renal adenocarcinoma of the leopard frog. This cancer and its transmission by a "cell-free agent"

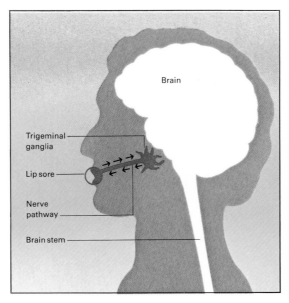

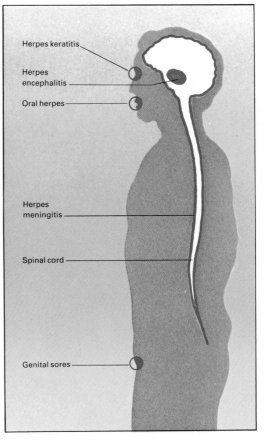

The Herpes Game of Hide-and-Seek
After first infecting the lip, *above,* the herpes simplex virus retreats along nerves to the trigeminal ganglia, where it hides, safe from the body's defenses. Eventually, some of the virus retraces its steps to cause another outbreak. Herpes simplex viruses also cause genital sores, rare forms of encephalitis and meningitis, and herpes keratitis, *right.*

was first described in the 1930s by pathologist Baldwin Lucké of the University of Pennsylvania in Philadelphia. We now know that the "cell-free agent" is a herpesvirus that causes a frog cancer.

Perhaps the best-known example of a herpesvirus causing cancer under natural conditions is Marek's disease, a lymphoma of chickens first described by Hungarian veterinarian Josef Marek in 1907. This chicken herpesvirus, and the cancer, can spread quickly through domestic flocks. It causes high mortality among the chickens and dire economic consequences for the poultry farmer.

We cannot yet make such certain connections between human herpesviruses and human cancers. But we strongly suspect that a connection does exist in a number of instances. For example, researchers believe Epstein-Barr virus is related to two human cancers — Burkitt's lymphoma, a cancer of the lymph nodes that usually strikes children; and nasopharyngeal carcinoma, a cancer of the neck and throat. Scientists have found evidence of the Epstein-Barr virus in tumor tissue from victims of both these diseases. Both of these cancers show a striking geographic distribution. Burkitt's lymphoma is found principally in sub-Saharan Africa; nasopharyngeal carcinoma, in southeastern China. This probably means that these two cancers are caused by a combination of several factors. These include: the Epstein-Barr virus; something in the local environment; and, possibly, genetic factors in the high-risk population. See CANCER'S GENETIC CONNECTION.

HSV-2 has also come under suspicion of causing cancer. Since the early 1970s, many studies have shown that there is at least 10 times more cancer of the cervix among women with a history of genital herpes infection than among women without the infection. Since HSV-2 is now appearing in teen-agers and young adults, this may be a time bomb for women. Twenty to 30 years in the future, the number of urogenital cancer cases among women may rise dramatically as a result of earlier HSV-2 infection. Women with genital herpes should have regular Pap tests to spot possible problems at an early, treatable stage.

An even more ominous connection between cancer and the cytomegalovirus has arisen since 1979, when a new and often fatal disease called acquired immune deficiency syndrome (AIDS) made itself known. The immune system of an AIDS victim is almost completely ineffective in warding off infections. The patient falls victim to infections that a healthy person would fight off without even having symptoms. The AIDS patient often dies of a rare form of pneumonia usually seen in patients whose immune systems have been suppressed by anticancer drugs. Another risk to the AIDS victim is the equally rare skin cancer called Kaposi's sarcoma. The main symptom of the sarcoma, first described by dermatologist Moritz Kaposi at the University of Vienna in 1872, is purple or bluish spots, usually appearing on the legs.

Kaposi's sarcoma is far more common in men than women. Until recently, it was relatively common among both young and older men

Animal cancers, such as kidney tumors in a frog, *below,* and malignant growth of Marek's disease in a chicken, *below right,* are caused by animal herpesviruses.

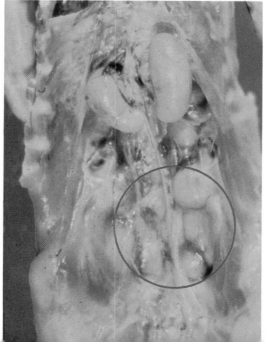

in sub-Saharan Africa but rare in the United States, usually appearing in elderly men of Mediterranean or Jewish descent. In general, the cancer progressed slowly.

Then in 1979 and 1980, the Centers for Disease Control began receiving reports of an increased number of Kaposi's sarcoma cases in Los Angeles, New York City, and San Francisco. At the same time, cases of the rare pneumonia increased. Most of the victims were young, promiscuous, homosexual men, who were also usually drug abusers. None had any other underlying disease that would have damaged their immune system. So investigators began to look for other factors in the victims' life styles that could provide clues to how they contracted what then came to be called AIDS.

By 1982, investigators had identified four main groups afflicted by AIDS—male homosexuals; male and female heroin addicts; Haitians; and hemophiliacs, males prone to hemorrhages because their blood does not clot properly. Hemophiliacs regularly require transfusions of whole blood or clotting factor made from blood products.

In late 1982, several children of Haitian or drug addict parents were suspected of having AIDS. Another child contracted the disease after receiving a blood transfusion from a person later found to have AIDS. All of this evidence points toward some infectious agent as the cause of the disease. The cytomegalovirus has become a leading suspect. It can be transmitted through sexual contact, by the unsanitary needles shared by drug addicts, and through blood transfusions. In 1981, virologist Gaetano Giraldo and his associates at the Memorial Hospital-Sloan Kettering Cancer Center in New York City reported evidence for cytomegalovirus involvement in Kaposi's sarcoma. They analyzed tissue from the sarcoma tumors and found cytomegalovirus DNA.

If cytomegalovirus infection is involved, it is probably only one part of a complex series of events that leads to Kaposi's sarcoma or other diseases related to AIDS. The deadly combination of factors might include multiple sexual partners, cytomegalovirus infection, and the use of illicit drugs.

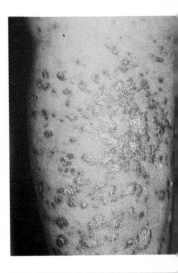

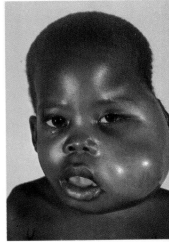

Kaposi's sarcoma, characterized by bluish patches on the leg, *top,* has been linked to a herpesvirus, the cytomegalovirus. Lymph node tumors of Burkitt's lymphoma, *above,* contain evidence of another herpesvirus, Epstein-Barr virus.

Meanwhile, scientists in government and university laboratories as well as at drug companies are urgently searching for ways to prevent the diseases caused by herpesviruses. Some are exploring the possibility of a vaccine. Vaccines have been successful in preventing other viral infections. For example, we have no specific treatment for polio, but we do have vaccines to prevent polio. These vaccines consist of killed or weakened viruses that prime the immune system. If the vaccinated person later encounters natural poliovirus, the previous priming causes the immune system to respond rapidly by producing antibodies, special proteins that call up other molecules to attack and render the invading poliovirus harmless. This same principle works in vaccines against other viral diseases, such as measles. Unfortunately, herpesviruses do not behave the same way.

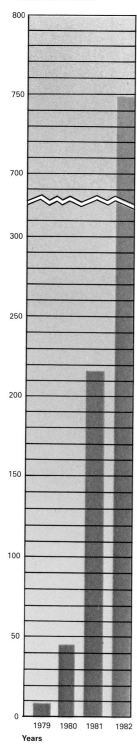

Tracking a New Disease

Number of AIDS cases

800	
750	
700	
300	
250	
200	
150	
100	
50	
0	

1979   1980   1981   1982

Years

Antibodies against herpesvirus do not appear to protect against recurrent infection. Repeatedly, doctors have found that patients with recurrent oral or genital herpes have high levels of antiherpesvirus antibody in their blood. But the infection recurs anyway. Worse, studies on children with African Burkitt's lymphoma have shown that the higher the antibody level to the Epstein-Barr virus, the larger the tumor. Therefore, it appears that traditional approaches to developing vaccines are unlikely to work for herpesviruses. Morever, injecting a person with a live herpesvirus vaccine will cause a lifelong infection by a virus that may play a role in causing cancer.

Nevertheless, attempts are being made at creating vaccines against certain herpesviruses. For example, virologist Michiaki Takahashi and his associates at Osaka University in Japan developed a live, but weakened, chicken pox vaccine in the mid-1970s. Since 1976, they have tested this vaccine on a wide range of children, including children with weakened immune systems. Trials of the vaccine have shown that it provides short-term protection, but the long-term effects of the vaccine have yet to be proved.

Researchers are also trying to develop safe vaccines against herpes simplex virus infections. These vaccines do not contain either whole virus or viral DNA, because of the potential cancer connection. Instead, they consist of outer pieces of the virus that would be capable of triggering a strong antibody response should a herpesvirus invade. Such a vaccine might protect against an initial infection, but would probably have little effect on recurring infection. So far, this approach has not provided very good protection against the virus in test animals.

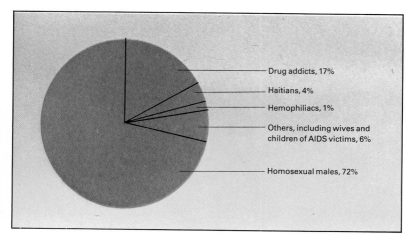

Drug addicts, 17%

Haitians, 4%

Hemophiliacs, 1%

Others, including wives and children of AIDS victims, 6%

Homosexual males, 72%

Acquired immune deficiency syndrome (AIDS) cases rose dramatically after 1979. The many cases among homosexual males, drug addicts, and hemophiliacs suggest a virus that can be transmitted sexually or introduced into the bloodstream. The Haitian link remains unclear.

Doctors have found a simpler way of preventing cytomegalovirus infection in kidney transplant patients. They screen both the donor and recipient of the kidney for prior cytomegalovirus infection. In late 1982 and early 1983, blood-collecting organizations took similar action to guard against the spread of AIDS. They began to screen potential donors for risk factors that may be involved in the development of the disease.

Just as herpesvirus infections are very difficult to prevent, they are also difficult to treat. Since these viruses elude the body's defenses, they also elude drugs that might destroy them. However, there are effective treatments for the cancers related to Epstein-Barr virus — Burkitt's lymphoma and nasopharyngeal carcinoma. The treatment for nasopharyngeal carcinoma involves a combination of surgery, radiation, and anticancer drugs. Burkitt's lymphoma is treated only with anticancer drugs.

Most research on herpesvirus treatment today centers on herpes simplex virus infections. There are three very toxic drugs available that provide reasonably effective treatment for herpes keratitis. They are applied directly to the eye. One of these drugs, given intravenously, has proved effective against herpes encephalitis if the disease is diagnosed early enough. But studies have shown that none of these drugs works against either oral or genital herpes.

For the treatment of genital herpes, a chemical called acyclovir was approved for sale by prescription in 1982. This chemical is somewhat successful in treating the first HSV-2 infection, but is less effective in treating recurrent infection.

The reason for its initial success is also the cause of its eventual failure. In the first infection, HSV-2 DNA codes for an enzyme absent from the uninfected cell. The enzyme chemically reacts with acyclovir and converts it to a form that becomes incorporated into the DNA of a newly formed virus. Once inside the viral DNA, it prevents the virus from reproducing. However, about 1 in 1 million herpes simplex viruses are mutants that do not code for this enzyme and are therefore resistant to acyclovir. After one treatment of the drug, the enzyme-producing virus is killed off and all that is left are these resistant mutants. When the resistant virus emerges from its hiding place to cause recurrent infection, acyclovir is useless. Overall, the picture for vaccination against or treatment of genital herpes as of summer 1983 was not encouraging.

Researchers will continue to seek a better understanding of herpesviruses and ways to prevent the diseases they cause. Meanwhile, people should remember that having multiple sexual partners increases the risk of contracting venereal diseases, including AIDS and genital herpes. Drug abuse, because it can lead to a weakened immune system, may also play a role in AIDS. The only sure way these diseases can be controlled is through common sense about personal health.

Laying Waste
in America

By Thomas H. Maugh II

The technology exists to dispose of hazardous wastes, but where will we put them and who will pay?

Christmas 1982 was not a very happy time for residents of Times Beach, Mo., a small community just southwest of St. Louis. At the beginning of December, the United States Environmental Protection Agency (EPA) had announced that soil samples from Times Beach contained as much as 350 parts of dioxin per billion parts of soil. Dioxin — a by-product in the production of pesticides — is one of the most toxic chemicals known. Exposure to more than 1 part of dioxin per billion parts of soil is dangerous.

The town was contaminated in May 1971 when the local government hired a salvage contractor to spray dirt roads with oil to keep down dust. Unknown to the residents, the oil had been mixed with dioxin-containing industrial sludge, a thick semisolid waste mixture, from a plant that manufactured pesticides and disinfectants. The contaminated oil was sprayed on as many as 100 different sites throughout Missouri. Many animals died and people became ill in 1971, but no one knew why — then.

Ten years of efforts by a few concerned citizens finally persuaded the EPA in November 1982 to make the soil tests. They revealed the presence of dioxin. Then, on December 5, the Meramec River flooded Times Beach and other areas. Authorities feared that the dioxin-contaminated soil might have been spread all over town, depositing the poison inside flooded dwellings and on people's household goods, especially furniture and clothing.

EPA scientists returned to Times Beach and retested the soil. The EPA found that, according to its standards, the flood-deposited silt in the streets was uncontaminated. But officials of the Centers for Disease Control in Atlanta, Ga., warned Times Beach residents to stay away from the town. By Christmas, a few people were trying to clean out their houses, but most of the 2,000 residents were living temporarily at other locations. In February 1983, EPA offered to buy the entire town — the first such offer in the agency's history. It would also relocate the residents of Times Beach in an uncontaminated, less flood-prone site upriver — at a cost of $33 million.

The Times Beach experience may be repeated in the United States or in other industrialized countries. Disposal of toxic and hazardous wastes is a severe and growing problem. They may be hidden or dumped illegally by independent, unlicensed waste haulers known as gypsy haulers and midnight dumpers. Or they may be handled carelessly at legitimate disposal sites, or simply released inadvertently into the environment. Strictly speaking, *toxic* means *poisonous* and *hazardous* means *dangerous*, but the terms are used interchangeably to describe all wastes that threaten health or safety. Such materials can produce fires and explosions, contaminate surface and underground waters, pollute the air, and cause poisoning, birth defects, and tumors.

In December 1982, EPA released a list of 418 waste disposal sites in the United States that represent the greatest potential hazard and should thus be the first to be cleaned up. But EPA has estimated that there may be as many as 14,000 sites that represent potential hazards because they are located near population centers or water supplies. The cost of cleaning up those sites could be as high as $44-billion, so EPA's $1.6-billion Superfund — a special allocation to be spent cleaning up extremely hazardous sites — is clearly only a drop in the cleanup bucket.

The technology to dispose of future wastes safely is available, but it too is expensive. It would be about $686 million per year by EPA estimates, even more by industry estimates. Cost is not the only problem. In many cases, local resistance has delayed or halted the installation of facilities necessary for safe disposal, such as incinerators or landfills. This is forcing industries to use less desirable methods of disposal. Many people familiar with the problems of waste disposal argue that EPA must take a more active role in finding new sites, perhaps pre-empting local regulations that restrict their use.

The author:
Thomas H. Maugh II
is senior staff writer
for *Science* magazine.

Waste disposal has always been something of a problem. Primitive human beings handled it by throwing bones and other scraps onto the ground, leaving them for modern archaeologists to find. When people moved into huts, the first open window was probably also the first outlet for trash disposal. Even when huts were grouped into villages or cities, such informal methods persisted. In Europe, until only a little more than a century ago, kitchen slops and toilet wastes were routinely tossed into open sewers running through city streets. The practice lasted even longer in less developed parts of the world.

When it became clear that these practices were spreading disease in addition to causing foul smells, organized garbage-collection systems were begun. At first, trash was simply carted to a pit outside town and dumped. Today, it is buried or incinerated. There are now some 18,500 sites in the United States for disposal of municipal solid wastes — ranging from old newspapers to junked cars. Another 23,000 sites are used for disposal of sewage sludge — the sediment resulting from treatment of human waste matter in sewage systems.

Throughout most of human history, Mother Nature tolerated people's wastes. Most were, after all, substances that were biodegradable — that is, they were derived from natural products. Nature had ways to deal with them by degrading, or breaking down, their parts and returning them to the air, water, or earth. Helpful bacteria decomposed organic wastes. Sunlight and air killed harmful bacteria and viruses. Soil filtered out harmful bacteria and contaminants from subsurface, or ground, water before it seeped into aquifers — natural underground layers of porous earth and rock that store water that has accumulated for centuries.

When the industrial era began in Great Britain in the 1700s, the nature of wastes began to change. Factories making textiles and steel also created tons of wastes that despoiled much of the countryside while they rotted or rusted. But those wastes also eventually vanished into the soil or air. Then, in the mid-1800s in the United States, chemists began to synthesize strange new molecules. These were the plastics that could not be degraded by bacteria or air and water and that would outlast the pyramids. By the mid-1900s, an expanding population's need for more food led to increased use of chlorinated pesticides. These persist in the environment for long periods and are toxic to microorganisms, birds, and animals as well as to the insects for which they were intended.

Further advances brought us polychlorinated biphenyls (PCBs) — poisonous chemicals used as electrical insulators and in plastics. Their resistance to breakdown was prized in industry but became a major problem in the environment. As many as 35,000 compounds now in use might be considered hazardous by the EPA definition. They are either *ignitible* (can be set on fire); *corrosive* (can eat into things); *reactive* (can combine with other things to become dangerous); explosive; or toxic.

Workers clearing away
debris from flooding at
Times Beach, Mo., *above,*
wear safety garments
because the trash may
be soaked with dioxin.
Meanwhile, scientists
test soil, *right,*
to determine if the
earth is contaminated
with the toxic chemical.

Industries also use great quantities of toxic metals such as mercury, lead, and cadmium. These metals accumulate in microorganisms. They are transmitted up the food chain as larger animals devour smaller ones until they reach concentrations in fish and animals that cause nervous disorders and other problems in the people who eat them.

Such metals are a permanent source of danger. They are a particular problem at a site not far from Meadowlands Sports Complex in East Rutherford, N.J. A plant producing fungicides and other mercury compounds operated there for years under several different owners. During the manufacturing process, according to EPA, as much as 5 pounds of mercury per day was slopped onto the floor and washed into the swampy area outside the plant. Much of it eventually entered nearby Berry's Creek, which flows into the Hackensack River. Surveys of the site have shown that the soil and ground water contain as much as 123,000 parts per million of mercury. A dose of only 160 parts per million is lethal, and EPA warns that the concentration in drinking water should be less than 1 part per billion.

Not only have the types of wastes changed, but the volume has vastly increased. In 1941, the United States petrochemical industry produced about 1 billion pounds of synthetic chemicals derived from petroleum, or oil. That number grew to well over 350 billion pounds by 1982. The volume of wastes has grown proportionately. An EPA survey in 1982 estimated that 115 billion pounds of toxic or hazard-

A mobile incineration system developed by EPA is mounted on three semitrailers. It can travel to toxic-waste dumps throughout the United States, treat the wastes on-site, and leave after the job is done. Primarily designed for use in emergencies, the new mobile unit may be a waste-disposal solution for communities that object to permanent treatment plants.

ous wastes are created as manufacturing by-products each year and that the volume will grow to 176 billion pounds by 1990.

EPA estimates that about 760,000 firms in the United States produce hazardous wastes. Most of them, about 695,000, produce less than 2,200 pounds of wastes per month. They are exempt from most controls unless their wastes, such as those from pesticides, are especially hazardous. Small firms that create toxic wastes range from the shop that electroplates your automobile bumper to your local exterminator and the neighborhood dry cleaner.

In recent years, only about 10 per cent of all hazardous wastes were disposed of in accordance with current EPA regulations. That is true even when they are disposed of on-site — that is, on the property of the companies that create them. EPA estimates that there are at least 50,000 such sites.

Fully 50 per cent of all hazardous wastes have been dumped into lagoons or unlined shallow ponds. There, the wastewater and easily vaporized chemicals can evaporate into the air and other chemicals can seep into the ground. Another 30 per cent were buried in unsecured landfills, or unlined earth pits, where they could also seep into the soil. "We didn't understand," says former EPA Administrator Douglas M. Costle, "that every barrel stuck into the ground was a ticking time bomb, primed to go off." As much as 10 per cent more of these wastes were simply dumped into sewers, spread on roads, injected into deep wells or highly porous underground rock formations, burned in the open, or stored on vacant off-site lots.

One such lot, in Elizabeth, N.J., was owned by a company called Chemical Control, Incorporated. Just before 11 P.M. on April 21, 1980, some 30,000 rusted and leaking barrels of industrial wastes stored there exploded and burst into flame. The wastes had been entrusted to the company — one of about 300 legally regulated hazardous-waste disposal firms in the United States — for safe disposal. But the firm's owners had simply allowed the barrels to accumulate on a 3.4-acre site near the waterfront. Fortunately, 10,000 barrels of the most hazardous wastes had already been removed from the lot by state authorities, and prevailing winds blew the toxic smoke out to sea rather than over nearby New York City. Even so, 100 people were treated for nausea and throat, eye, and lung irritation.

Such serious mishaps are unusual. Disposal areas are more likely to pose threats to water supplies. For example, heading EPA's list of the 418 most hazardous sites is a leaky landfill in the small town of Fridley, Minn., where the FMC Corporation has dumped its solvents, paint sludge, and chemical wastes. The dump is not a major problem for Fridley; residents are hardly aware of its existence. But the chemicals could leak into the Mississippi River and threaten the water supply of nearby Minneapolis.

Many of the other sites on the EPA list threaten or have already contaminated the underground water supply in aquifers. Such aqui-

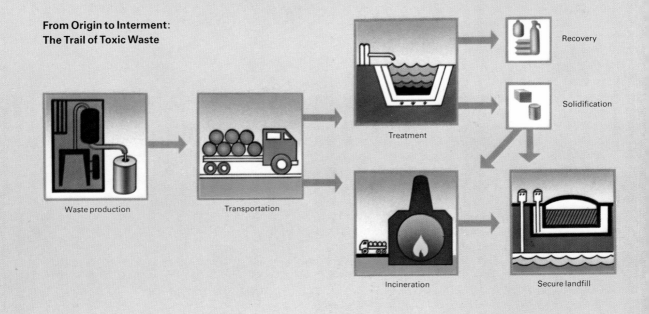

From Origin to Interment:
The Trail of Toxic Waste

Waste production

Transportation

Treatment

Recovery

Solidification

Incineration

Secure landfill

fers are a particular concern because they are the primary water sources for at least one-fourth of the U.S. population, and there is no practical way to clean an aquifer once it has been contaminated. The only realistic possibility, therefore, is to prevent chemicals from reaching underground water by cleaning up the sites.

The U.S. Congress began attacking the problem with passage of the Comprehensive Environmental Response, Compensation and Liability Act of 1980. This act established the Superfund, earmarked for cleaning up sites where ownership or responsibility cannot be established or where the responsible parties have insufficient money. For example, at the Salisbury Laboratories site in Charles City, Iowa, which is grossly contaminated with arsenic, cleanup is expected to cost $30 million. But the company's total assets are only $5 million. That cleanup is obviously a job for Superfund.

The EPA's list of 418 especially hazardous sites represents dumps that will be given priority for Superfund financing or placed on the so-called fast track. But progress has been very slow. "If this is the fast track," says John Schauber of the Michigan Department of Natural Resources, "I hope the ones on the regular track don't hold their breath." Adds Congressman James J. Florio (D., N.J.), an author of the Superfund bill, "The key to the program is not making a list, but cleaning up. And there, the record is abysmal." See ENVIRONMENT, Close-Up.

From 1976, when the Resource Conservation and Recovery Act (RCRA) was passed, to 1981, EPA was concerned less with cleanup than with setting up rules to control future toxic-waste disposal so

Monitored from "cradle to grave," the paths of toxic wastes will vary. Some wastes are treated and recovered for reuse. Some are treated, then solidified for burning and burial in a landfill. Some are burned and then buried directly.

Pesticide barrels, empty but still hazardous, are buried deep inside an abandoned missile silo in Grand View, Ida. Shock-resistant and lined with cement, such sites offer the best guarantee against contamination of ground water or soil.

that no new dangerous sites would be created. The agency adopted seven major sets of regulations and guidelines covering various aspects of disposal. The heart of the program involves what is called "cradle-to-grave" monitoring of the wastes. These rules require companies that produce the wastes to prepare registration papers that must be signed by everyone who handles the wastes, including the company that ultimately disposes of them. At each stage, copies are sent back to the producer of the hazardous wastes and to EPA, allowing both to verify that the wastes have been disposed of in the proper manner.

The EPA system is based on the fact that there are acceptable ways to dispose of the wastes. There are at least half a dozen techniques, each with its own advantages and limits. They include recovery and reuse by the original producers, use by a second industry, chemical or biological treatment, and burning or burial.

An ideal solution, of course, is to put the wastes to work. Before the passage of RCRA, disposal was generally so cheap that it was often more cost-effective to buy new raw materials than to recover them from wastes. But with the increasing costs of raw materials — especially petroleum — and of waste disposal, companies refined their processing techniques to minimize waste and devised new ways to recover raw materials from it.

A good example of such recovery involves polyvinyl alcohol, a chemical agent used in the textile industry for sizing yarns before they are woven into cloth. J. P. Stevens & Company, Incorporated, in Greenville, S.C., developed a special filtration procedure that recovers as much as 96 per cent of the alcohol from the waste stream. This prevents nearly 5 million pounds of nonbiodegradable polyvinyl alcohol from being released into the environment each year.

On the principle that one man's poison is another man's meat, some areas have established waste exchanges to unite companies that produce wastes with those who might be able to use them. For example, waste solvents produced by the electronic industry are often purer than the solvents required for many other manufacturing processes, and could be used in those processes. The materials most commonly listed on exchanges are solvents and oils, paper, wood, scrap metals, and surplus chemicals.

If wastes cannot be recycled, they can often be detoxified, or made nonpoisonous, by relatively simple chemical treatment. The most common treatment is adjustment of acidity. For example, highly acidic pickle liquors — preparations used in electroplating and other metal-finishing industries — can be neutralized with lime to make them harmless. Such treatment also precipitates, or separates out, metals so that they can be removed by settling or filtration. Even if simple chemical treatment does not make a material completely harmless, it can often reduce the volume that must be disposed of. Other, more complex and expensive chemical processes can be used for specific pollutants, but such procedures are generally much more expensive.

Chemical treatment can be both effective and efficient if it is carried out regionally. For example, in West Germany and some other parts of Europe, an acidic waste from one company may be used to neutralize an alkaline waste from a second company nearby. Unfortunately, only a very few waste disposal companies in the United States are using this approach.

Biological treatment can also be useful. The most common type is incorporation of waste into the earth by a method called land farming. Petroleum companies have practiced land farming for nearly 20 years to dispose of sludge from oil refineries. Typically, sludge is spread on the surface of a field in a 3- to 6-inch layer, allowed to dry, and worked into the ground with a disk harrow. Nutrients may also be added to promote the growth of aerobic, or air-loving, bacteria that can decompose the sludge. At an Exxon Corporation oil refinery in Baytown, Tex., sludge is disposed of by land farming at the rate of 400 tons per acre per year.

Land farming obviously cannot be used for materials containing metal or chemicals that would kill the aerobic bacteria, but it has

Do Wastes Poison Us?

The toxic chemicals found in hazardous wastes have two types of effects on human health: *acute* (short-term) and *chronic* (long-term). Some of the most obvious acute effects have been observed in persons who live near a toxic-waste disposal site. But most of the acute and all of the chronic effects have been documented only in laboratory animals or in people who have been exposed to exceptionally high concentrations of certain chemicals.

Some acute effects of chemical wastes are obvious. Many wastes are flammable or explosive. Some are highly acidic, highly alkaline, or otherwise corrosive, and can affect the skin. Others can irritate the linings of the nose, throat, and lungs. Many organic chemicals that are eaten or breathed produce kidney problems as the body tries to eliminate them. Most of these problems end when exposure stops. However, some chemicals containing chlorine produce a severe and long-lasting rash called chloracne.

Other acute effects can be more severe and lasting, but they are much more difficult to document since they mimic disorders that occur naturally. The most important class of these is reproductive disorders. Many chemicals interfere with sexual function by disrupting biological processes. Others are mutagens, or substances that produce changes in the genetic material of both sperm and eggs. The most commonly observed effects in men include sperm that are altered in appearance under the microscope or more subtly altered so that they cause either impotence or reduction in the amount of sperm produced, or result in birth defects. It is exceptionally difficult to attribute such effects to exposure to chemicals, however, unless the exposure has been very high, as was the case with workers in Virginia exposed to Kepone in 1974 and 1975 and men who worked with the pesticide dibromochloropropane in California from 1957 to 1977.

Certain chemicals can produce infertility, spontaneous abortions, and birth defects in women but, again,

these cases are difficult to document. Studies among female anesthesiologists in the United States and England; among the wives of men who work with vinyl chloride; and among women exposed to the herbicide 2,4,5-T — an ingredient in Agent Orange — near Alsea, Ore., and at Love Canal in Niagara Falls, N.Y., have suggested an increased incidence of spontaneous abortion. However, critics say that the studies were not conducted properly.

Birth defects are the most distressing reproductive outcome for families and for society. Birth defects have been associated with certain drugs, such as limb malformations among children of women who used thalidomide when pregnant, but it is difficult to associate them with other chemicals.

One effect that has been demonstrated, however, is low birth weight — less than 5½ pounds — and its related problems of malformation, abnormal development, and infant death. A significant increase in the number of low-birth-weight babies is "the most convincing" reproductive effect reported at Love Canal and in areas near lead smelters.

The primary chronic effect of toxic chemicals is cancer, but the incidence of cancer is also extremely difficult to link to exposure because there is a period of 20 to 30 years or longer between exposure and the onset of disease. Again, the only well-documented links are among persons subjected to exceptionally high exposures. These include the occurrence of acute myelogenous leukemia — a disease of the white blood cells — in workers exposed to benzene, and lung cancer among asbestos workers and cigarette smokers. Other chemicals that have been associated with tumors include diethylstilbestrol (DES), vinyl chloride, and acrylonitrile.

Most problems with hazardous wastes are so recent, however, that the period between exposure and possible onset of cancer has not yet elapsed. It could easily be another 10 or 20 years before the ultimate effects of leaks, spills, and dumping become apparent. [T.H.M. II]

Chloracne, a chronic and disabling skin disease, results from dioxin reaching the skin — either by direct contact or as an airborne vapor.

proved useful for sludge from paper mills and fruit canneries, sewage sludge, pharmaceutical wastes, and some organic chemical wastes. Some of the limitations of land farming can be overcome by composting, a process similar to that practiced by the backyard organic gardener who heaps up garbage, straw, leaves, and manure and allows the mixture to decompose naturally. Decomposition proceeds more rapidly in a compost pile than on a field because the denser mixture reaches a higher temperature. Composting can be carried out in a closed container, keeping any metals present out of the earth. The method is used frequently for sewage sludge.

Perhaps the ideal solution for flammable wastes is incineration. However, EPA requires that a hazardous waste be 99.99 per cent consumed in the burning process and that emissions from the incinerator be very low. Meeting these rules requires high technology instead of the simple boilers that have been used to burn municipal solid waste. Incineration is usually a multistep process. First, solid wastes are placed in a rotating furnace where heat drives gases out of organic solids. Gases from this furnace go to a secondary chamber for more complete combustion. Exhaust gases are then cooled with water, treated to remove acids, and treated again to remove ash before they are finally released to the atmosphere. Ashes in the furnace are periodically removed and buried. For very hazardous wastes, this process can cost as much as $2,000 per ton, compared with a maximum of about $400 per ton for burial without burning in a secure landfill, or specially constructed pit.

Wary of the unknown but suspected dangers posed by industrial wastes, citizens of a town with toxic dump sites clearly display their feelings at a large protest rally. Such demonstrations point up the difficulty of establishing disposal sites approved by both EPA and local residents.

Treating the exhaust gases that result from incineration is one of the most expensive aspects of this method, and scientists are investigating ways to avoid that necessity. One good way might be to burn the materials in cement kilns, lime kilns, or glass-melting furnaces, where pollutants in the exhaust would be harmlessly incorporated into the cement, lime, or glass produced. Pollutants might even be beneficial—for example, chlorides in the wastes might help stabilize concrete. Manufacturers have been reluctant to use this method, however, because EPA has issued no guidelines on who would be responsible if anything went wrong.

Another alternative is to burn flammable wastes at sea in incinerator ships. Backers of this method say that most of the pollutants in exhaust gases occur naturally in the oceans, so the exhaust could be absorbed by seawater and diluted without harm. There are now two U.S. incinerator ships and one West German vessel that burn wastes at sea, and more are planned. The chief criticism of this approach has focused on the need to transport the hazardous materials to docks—risking train derailments along the way—and to store them until they can be loaded onto ships. Also, some

Cask and Carry for Nuclear Waste
A 150-ton railcar cask, *below,* used in transporting nuclear solid waste, consists of a lead inner-containment shell that is surrounded by a stainless steel outer shell. The cask is mounted on a railcar, *bottom,* and the assembly crashed into a wall to test the cask's ability to withstand an accident such as a train crash or fire.

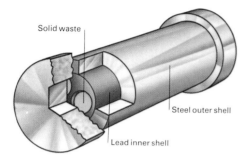

Solid waste

Steel outer shell

Lead inner shell

researchers question whether the ocean can really remain unpolluted. Others warn that working on incinerator ships may be extremely hazardous to the crews' health.

Despite the many choices available for disposal of hazardous wastes, few industries use any of them routinely. Most wastes are too low in value to recycle, too inert for chemical treatment, too difficult to degrade biologically, or too contaminated with heavy metals and other nonflammable materials for incineration. For these materials, the disposal option of last resort is burial in a secure landfill. Indeed, most waste producers consider the first four options merely as ways to reduce volume before burial. Burial is not the ideal solution — and not necessarily even a good solution — but it is the only realistic one we now have for many materials. The problem, then, is to regulate landfills so as to minimize potential problems created by the escape of toxic materials.

In the past, a secure landfill was generally constructed by digging a large hole in compacted clay, a material that water and wastes usually cannot penetrate. Muddy, unsolidified sludge and drums of waste were placed in the hole and covered with earth. Then the site was capped with clay to keep water out. No one gave it any further thought. That solution can work if there are no cracks in the clay lining and if the clay cap is not disturbed. However, serious problems arose at the much-publicized Love Canal landfill near Niagara Falls, N.Y., for example, when the cap was disturbed by construction. Resulting cracks allowed rain water to fill the hole and overflow, carrying hazardous chemicals into the air, water, and soil of the Love Canal area.

New EPA regulations modify the old approach for greater safety. They require a thicker layer of clay as well as plastic pit liners to ensure against leakage. A sump-pump system, similar to those in many cellars, must also be installed so that any water that may enter the hole can be removed and treated. Most important, the rules require that a network of monitoring wells be drilled around the site and periodically checked for 20 years after the site is closed to detect any leakage.

An additional way to ensure that chemicals within a landfill do not leak into the surrounding soil or water is to solidify the wastes before burial. Solidifying processes fall into four general classes. Cementation techniques, as the name suggests, involve the addition of cement or similar materials to the sludge to form a concretelike solid. Pozzolanic techniques are named after the city of Pozzuoli, Italy, where volcanic ash has been mined for thousands of years. They involve the use of lime and ashlike materials to form pozzolanic concrete. The most common source of raw materials for this process is fly ash — itself a waste product of electrical power plants.

Thermoplastic techniques use materials such as bitumen, asphalt, paraffin, and certain plastics that soften when heated, bind to

Rugged grandeur will become a radioactive grave if the Department of Energy proceeds with plans to bury nuclear waste in Davis Canyon, within a mile of Utah's scenic Canyonlands National Park region.

wastes, and solidify when cooled. Organic techniques involve adding materials to the waste to form an inert plastic that binds them tightly so they cannot enter soil or water.

At least 40 companies have developed solidification processes for hazardous wastes. But they have had limited use because of their expense and because people do not want toxic waste, no matter how nicely solidified, buried near their homes.

Radioactive wastes present much the same problems and potential solutions as other hazardous wastes. There are two notable exceptions: the amounts involved are much smaller, and there has never been any appreciable harm discovered from leakage of nuclear wastes at a disposal site. However, people fear these wastes much more, perhaps because radioactivity lasts such a long time and has such dreaded effects.

Since the dawn of the atomic age in 1942, the United States has accumulated some 78 million gallons of extremely contaminated or high-level radioactive waste produced by defense industries and another 25 million gallons produced at nuclear power plants. There are also nearly 90 million cubic feet of slightly contaminated or low-level radioactive solid waste that includes clothing, equipment, tools, laboratory trash, and isotopes used in hospitals or pharmacies. Some of the low-level waste was dumped at sea before 1970 — when questions were raised about safety — and some has been buried. But all the rest is in storage at the various sites where it was produced, awaiting ultimate disposal. At nuclear power plants, the waste is kept in barrels in pools of water. In hospitals, it is usually kept in a lead-lined room.

There are several options available for ultimate disposal of radioactive wastes. Most low-level waste can be incinerated if adequate precautions are taken to remove radioactive ash from the exhaust gases. Several countries routinely dump low-level waste into the ocean. Each year, European countries — particularly Great Britain — dump thousands of barrels of low-level waste into the Atlantic Ocean, an amount equal in radioactivity to the total amount so far dumped by the United States. Japan is planning to dump similar quantities into the Pacific Ocean.

The U.S. Department of Defense would like to resume ocean dumping if EPA can be persuaded to relax its guidelines. In particular, the U.S. Navy will need to dispose of three or four nuclear submarines each year for the next 30 years and would like to scuttle them over deep ocean trenches. The nuclear fuel in four submarines would equal the amount of high-level radioactive waste dumped into the ocean each year by all other countries. There is a vigorous debate among the military, scientists, and environmentalists about the potential effects of such dumping.

High-level waste requires a safer disposal route, and the most likely approach will be solidification, followed by burial in a stable rock formation deep underground. In 1982, the U.S. Department of Energy decided that thermoplastic borosilicate glass would be the best medium for nuclear-waste solidification and authorized construction, starting in 1984, of a facility in Aiken, S.C. In this process, which other countries are already using, powdered borosilicate glass will be combined with the waste in a melting furnace until the two materials are thoroughly mixed. The molten mixture will be poured into stainless steel canisters, each 10 feet high and 2 feet in diameter and virtually impermeable.

The canisters will then be stored at the Aiken plant until the government decides which type of rock formation would make the best burial place. Even when the appropriate type of formation is decided on, selecting a location might be quite difficult because people are even more strongly opposed to nuclear-waste storage sites than to other hazardous-waste disposal sites. It will probably be necessary to choose several sites so that no one state will bear the burden of being America's nuclear dump.

The problems for all types of toxic wastes, then, are similar, and the solutions straightforward; the focus is on costs and public acceptance. The economic problem will undoubtedly be solved in the time-honored fashion of passing the costs on to the consumer. Gaining public acceptance will be more difficult, and will probably require a lot of public education. Meanwhile, if we wish to enjoy the benefits of modern technology, we are going to have to tolerate the nuisances that go with them.

The Afar's Bountiful Legacy

By Jon E. Kalb

**A tumultuous geologic history has left the Afar
Triangle in Ethiopia with a rugged terrain
and a wealth of prehistoric fossils.**

The Afar Triangle in northeastern Ethiopia is a region once considered so desolate and forbidding that early explorers called it a "landscape of horror." Towering plateaus to the west and south and isolated mountains to the east enclose some 60,000 square miles of blistering salt plains, broken and eroded terrain, and one of the world's most active volcanic ranges. The Afar, however, is also a unique geologic laboratory whose ancient deposits hold a scientific wealth of prehistoric fossils.

What makes the Afar a particularly fascinating place for geologists — and what drew me there in early 1971 — is its position at the junction of three rift valleys. A rift is a giant crack in the earth's crust that forms when tensions within the earth cause the crust to separate into huge segments called plates. The long, narrow depressed area created where this occurs is called a rift valley.

Because of this phenomenon and the resulting accumulation of thick deposits in the valleys, the Afar holds one of the most complete geologic records in East Africa, a record stretching back 5 million to 6 million years. In addition, the Afar's deposits have provided an abundance of animal fossils and stone tools, as well as the fossils of some of our earliest ancestors.

The Afar is a region of extremely low elevations — 400 feet below sea level in some areas — and of extremely high temperatures — as hot as 135°F. at times. The Afar nomads who live there have long been recognized as one of the hardiest groups in Africa. Because of its inhospitable climate and terrain, the fiercely independent nature of its people, and the fact that Ethiopia was never colonized by European powers, the Afar was one of the last major areas in East Africa to be explored by scientists.

This harsh land has a dynamic geologic history. By about 100 million years ago, the East African Plate, on which the country of Somalia sits, had begun to separate from the African Plate, on which most of the African continent sits. Further separation of these plates created the East African Rift Valley, which is actually a series of lakes, valleys, and rivers that extend along the eastern side of Africa from the Afar to Mozambique.

By at least 40 million years ago, the Arabian Plate, on which the Arabian Peninsula sits, had begun to separate from both the African and East African plates. This movement contributed to the opening of two more rift valleys, which filled with water and became the Red Sea and the Gulf of Aden. These widening rifts eventually extended into the Afar, where they met the East African rift, forming a triple rift junction. Someday, water from the Red Sea and the Gulf of Aden will break through the mountains that sit as a barrier between the water and the Afar and flood the region.

The Afar is not the only triple rift junction on earth. It is, however, the only such junction on dry land where the rifts are still separating. Furthermore, the separation of the earth's crust is so great in some places in the Afar that geologists can observe types of volcanic rocks that are normally found only at the bottom of oceans.

Even without this attraction, however, the Afar would be a geologist's paradise. For example, in some parts of the Middle Awash Valley, which cuts through the southern part of the Afar, the sedimentary deposits — layers of rock and volcanic ash laid down during a particular period — are among the oldest in East Africa. Furthermore, the fossil record in the deposits is remarkably complete — providing an almost continuous fossil record from 5 million to 6 million years ago to the present. Even more valuable, some deposits in the Afar represent periods only poorly represented in deposits elsewhere in East Africa.

The author:
Jon E. Kalb is a research scientist at the Vertebrate Paleontology Laboratory in the Balcones Research Center at the University of Texas in Austin.

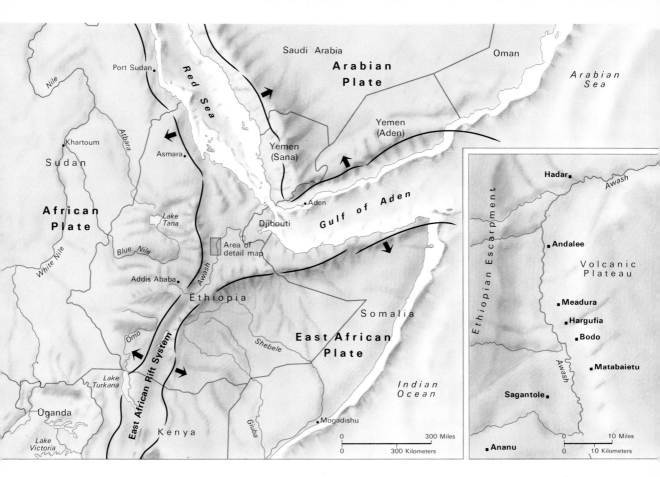

In late 1971, French geologist Maurice Taieb and I formed the International Afar Research Expedition, a multidisciplinary team of scientists, to study areas in the largely unexplored Awash Valley. This group discovered that the ancient deposits in the valley contained even more than an invaluable geologic record. Deep within the heavily eroded recesses of the valley, we mapped vast areas of fossils. The Afar contains a wealth of fossils because for millions of years, it was a hospitable home for many types of animals.

One site — Hadar — discovered by Taieb has proven to be one of the richest fossil sites in Africa. The sedimentary deposits at the site, which are up to 850 feet thick, contain an enormous concentration of excellently preserved animal fossils that date back at least 3 million years. In many places, the fossils simply lay exposed on the ground. And they were often so abundant that the team found many bones from the same animal.

Among the fossils discovered at Hadar were bones from about 70 species of extinct mammals. More interestingly, however, Hadar has produced one of Africa's largest collections of fossils from *hominids* — early human ancestors. Hadar's most famous hominid fossil is a skeleton named Lucy, discovered and named in 1974 by anthropologist Donald C. Johanson of the Institute of Human Origins in

The Afar Triangle, an anthropological gold mine in northeastern Ethiopia, is a triple rift junction — a point where three rift valleys meet. The valleys formed when three lithospheric plates began to separate from each other, creating rifts or cracks in the earth. The most significant fossils have been discovered at sites along the Awash River, which flows through the rift valleys and into the junction.

Berkeley, Calif. Estimated to be about 3 million years old, it is the oldest and most complete hominid skeleton ever found. Lucy was classified by Johanson and his colleagues as a new species of *Australopithecus*, which they called *Australopithecus afarensis*.

Hadar and other sites in the Afar are so rich in fossils because of a rift valley's capacity to serve as a sedimentary trap. For millions of years, rivers flowing into the Afar from the Ethiopian highlands brought sediment — fine-grained particles of decomposed rock — with them. The sediment quickly accumulated into thick deposits on river bottoms, on the flood plains along the rivers, and on the beds of the lakes fed by the rivers. Lava and ash from the region's volcanoes added to the deposits. Buried in the sediment were the bones of animals and hominids that died along, or in, the rivers and lakes.

Some of the bones turned to fossils. Fossils are the hardened remains of plants and animals. Most fossils form when the material in bone or shell is dissolved by water in the ground and replaced by minerals. In addition, minerals fill in the small air spaces in the bone — in effect, turning the bone to rock.

As the ancient rivers helped bury the animal bones, other rivers later uncovered them by eroding the sedimentary beds. Over thou-

The Rift Valley: from Fissure to Fossil
A rift valley forms when tensions in the earth's crust caused by an upwelling of magma cause the crust to crack, separate, and sink, forming a narrow depression. As the rift opens, rock continues to split from the valley walls and sink, causing the valley to grow deeper and wider. Eventually, magma pushes through the floor of the valley and forms volcanoes.

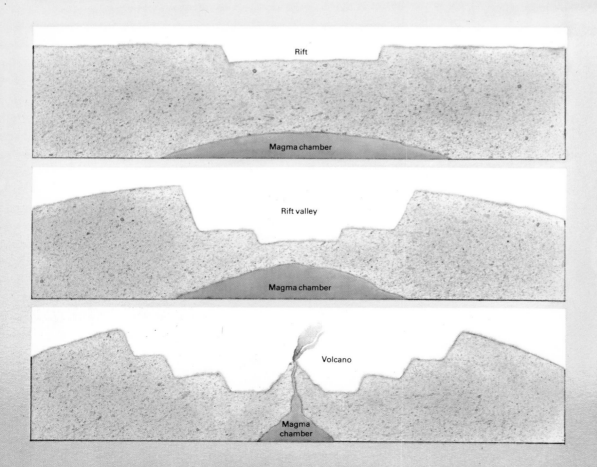

Rift

Magma chamber

Rift valley

Magma chamber

Volcano

Magma chamber

sands of years, the river waters gradually sliced into the valley floor, creating a rugged terrain of eroded hills and stream beds similar to the terrain in the Badlands of South Dakota.

About 175,000 years ago, during a period of major climatic change, such erosion took place on a grand scale. The amount of rainfall decreased and the Afar was struck by a prolonged dry period lasting at least 25,000 years. Apparently, the lakes in the rift valleys dried up. Many of the rivers trickled to streams or disappeared.

Taking their place were fast-flowing seasonal streams that ran briefly during periods of heavy rain. The powerful eroding force of these streams dramatically changed the landscape of the Afar. In addition to sediment, these streams laid down massive deposits of gravel, derived from rocks in the highlands. The gravel, which consisted of pebbles and boulders up to 8 inches in diameter, tore into the older sedimentary deposits like enormous sheets of sandpaper, carving out steep-sided hills and deep ravines. Similar but less severe periods of erosion since then exposed the sedimentary deposits and fossils in them.

The Afar's dry climate helped preserve the fossils once they were exposed. Thus, the great abundance of fossils in the Afar and at

Rivers flowing into the rift valley carry sediment from adjacent highlands. The sediment and the remains of animals that died near the rivers rapidly accumulate into thick deposits. Later, erosion, caused by streams flowing after prolonged dry periods or during seasonal rainy periods, exposes both the sediment and fossils.

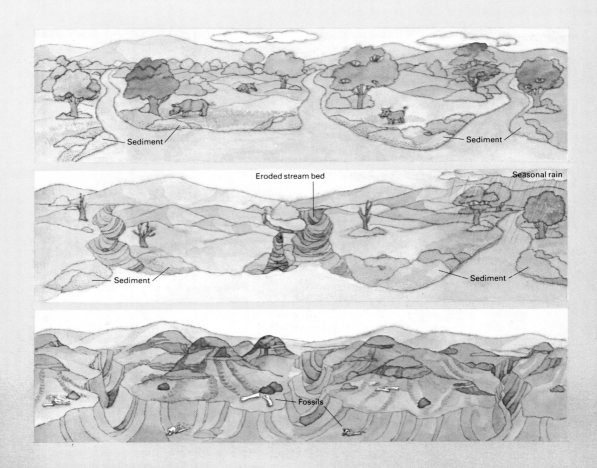

Sediment · Sediment · Eroded stream bed · Seasonal rain · Sediment · Sediment · Fossils

An anthropologist carefully brushes away sediment covering a baboon skull, from 300,000 to 400,000 years old, at Bodo.

other sites in the East African Rift Valley is due chiefly to this process of rapid burial, exposure, and preservation. It is not necessarily proof that the region is the cradle of human origins.

In early 1975, with the encouragement of the Ethiopian Ministry of Culture and Sports Affairs, I established the Rift Valley Research Mission in Ethiopia (RVRME). An Ethiopian-based organization, RVRME had a full-time Ethiopian staff, including students and graduates of Addis Ababa University in the capital.

The primary targets of our field work were in the unexplored parts of the Middle Awash Valley. There, we hoped to find fossil-bearing deposits both older and younger than the 3-million-year-old fossil deposits at Hadar.

Older deposits, we hoped, would produce hominid fossils from the period 4 million to 8 million years ago. This period, during which hominids are believed to have begun to walk fully upright, represents a major gap in the hominid fossil record. In particular, we hoped to find evidence of what anthropologists believe were the ape-like ancestors of *Australopithecus*. Many anthropologists believe *Homo*, the group to which modern human beings belong, developed from *Australopithecus*.

One of the oldest fossils found in the Afar is a molar, *left,* from a very primitive species of African elephant. Found near Sagantole, the fossil is from 4½ million to 5 million years old. A row of molars from an ancient species of rhinoceros, *above,* found at Matabaietu, dates from 2 million to 2½ million years ago.

Younger deposits, we hoped, would contain fossil evidence of early *Homo,* the group to which modern human beings belong. No *Homo* fossils older than about 2 million years have been confirmed.

The key to finding deposits older than those at Hadar lay in the unique aspects of the region's geology. As a rift valley forms, enormous sections of rock split from the central area of the valley and *subside* (sink into the rift). This downward sliding rock then becomes the floor of the valley. Rivers flowing onto the valley floor deposit new sediment on top of the older subsided rock. The new sediment is deposited chiefly in the lower, more central parts of the valley. As the rift continues to widen, this process of splitting and subsidence repeats itself. Thus, as the valley becomes deeper and wider over millions of years, older sedimentary deposits are found progressively higher along the sides of the valley and farther away from the center of the valley.

The center of the triple junction where the three rift valleys meet has also subsided. In fact, the sinking there is greater than anywhere else in the southern Afar. Over millions of years, sediments have tended to become concentrated not only in the central areas of the individual valleys but also toward the central part of the triple junction. This explains why the final drainage point of the Awash River lies nearly at the center of the triple junction. The river, which flows through all three rift valleys, drains into Lake Abbe, along Ethiopia's eastern border with the country of Djibouti. So we reasoned that if we wanted to find fossils older than those at Hadar, we must look upriver — that is, south from Hadar toward the higher elevations and away from the triple junction.

Using Afar nomads as guides, we began our exploration of the Middle Awash Valley in mid-1975 in a badlands area called Ananu about 60 miles southwest of Hadar. By late that year, we had found a small but significant collection of index fossils suggesting that the site was from 5 million to 6 million years old. Index fossils are those found in sediments of a certain type or age and are used to date sediments whose age cannot be established by other means. To date index fossils, geologists date the sediments in which they are found by charting their position in or between layers that include volcanic material whose age can be estimated by measuring the decay of radioactive elements in them. Among the index fossils we found at Ananu were those of *Stegotetrabelodon*, the most primitive form of elephant known in Africa, which became extinct about 5 million years

Thousands of Acheulian hand axes and cleavers, looking like pebbles on a beach, lie scattered over the ground at Meadura. Like the Acheulian hand ax, (inset), found nearby, the Meadura hand axes are tear-shaped tools sharpened on both edges.

ago. We also found primitive fossils of *Anancus*, a mastodonlike creature that became extinct in Africa about 4 million years ago.

Not only were the fossils at Ananu clearly older than those at Hadar, it also appeared that they existed solidly in the Miocene Epoch, a geologic period that lasted from about 5 million years to about 23 million years ago. Fossil deposits from the end of this period — about 5 million to 9 million years ago — have rarely been found elsewhere in Africa. Later, around Ananu, we found many other index fossils — including bones from primitive forms of monkeys, pigs, antelopes, and horses — which confirmed our preliminary estimate of the age of those deposits.

Late that year and in early 1976, we explored areas north of Ananu. In an area named Sagantole, we discovered more fossil deposits about 4 million to 5 million years old. By mid-1976, following the discovery of yet more sites, my colleagues and I were convinced that if fossils from our earliest ancestors were buried in the ancient deposits of the Awash Valley, they would be found not at Hadar, but at sites along the southern stretches of the Awash River.

Our initial surveys of the older deposits completed, we turned north to find younger deposits. At a site called Matabaietu, 45 miles

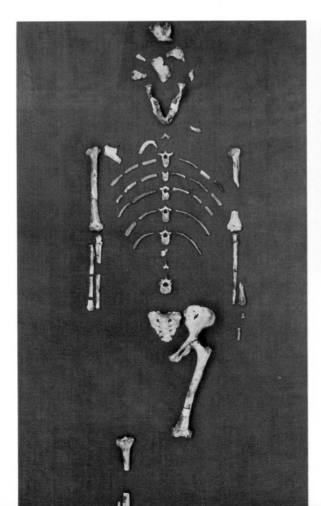

The most important hominid fossils found in the Afar are the Bodo skull, *above,* which is 300,000 to 400,000 years old, and the Lucy skeleton, *left,* dated to about 3 million years ago.

south of Hadar, we found deposits that, according to the index fossils, appeared to be 2 million to 2½ million years old. At the site was evidence of five types of primates, including splendidly preserved fossils from a type of baboon similar to that now found only in the Ethiopian highlands, and another common today throughout East Africa. We also found fossils from two types of monkeys.

Evidence of the fifth primate, however, came not from fossils but from artifacts. At Matabaietu and several sites to the north, we discovered primitive stone tools, which may have been made by a very early form of *Homo*. These tools, which are simply crudely chipped pebbles, are thought to be the first type of stone tools and are believed to have been in use from about 2½ million to about 1½ million years ago.

In 1973, at Hadar, I had found a large, somewhat rectangular stone tool with a cutting edge at one end called a cleaver. It had been crafted according to what archaeologists call the Acheulian pattern of toolmaking. The most common Acheulian tools are oval-shaped hand axes that are pointed at one end and sharpened on both edges. The Acheulian pattern is considered the most successful type of toolmaking because it lasted for more than 1 million years, from about 1 million to 1½ million to less than 100,000 years ago.

That cleaver was the first Acheulian tool found at Hadar. In terms of archaeological significance, however, that single cleaver had little value because its worn and polished surface indicated that it had been carried by streams from its place of origin. Nevertheless, I was fascinated and did not forget about the cleaver.

Then one day in 1975, while my colleagues and I were crashing and digging our way through badlands about 30 miles south of Hadar, we came to a site called Meadura. There, to our delight, we found Acheulian stone tools by the thousands. Hundreds simply lay heaped on the surface. Many others protruded from eroded hillsides.

Because we commonly found these tools with animal fossils, it appeared that Meadura contained a number of butchery sites — places where animals were slaughtered and eaten. Based on an analysis of the site's index fossils, we estimated that Meadura had been inhabited 200,000 to 300,000 years ago. We were also intrigued when some of the fossil bones showed evidence of having been burned. So Meadura may be among the oldest sites known for evidence of fire use by humans.

But Meadura was just part of the story. After setting up a base camp there, we surveyed areas to the north, south, and east. And at all those places, we found Acheulian tools and animal fossils. Later, we moved camp south to a place called Hargufia. There, we found not just thousands of Acheulian tools — but tens of thousands.

We moved camp again, several miles south to a place called Bodo. Once more, we found tools and animal fossils, including bones from perhaps as many as 12 hippopotamuses that appeared to have been

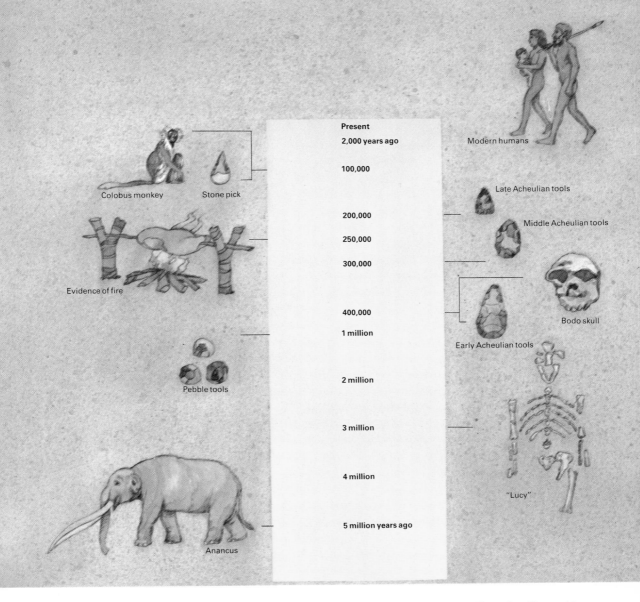

Present
2,000 years ago

100,000

200,000

250,000

300,000

400,000

1 million

2 million

3 million

4 million

5 million years ago

Colobus monkey

Stone pick

Evidence of fire

Pebble tools

Anancus

Modern humans

Late Acheulian tools

Middle Acheulian tools

Bodo skull

Early Acheulian tools

"Lucy"

slaughtered. We also found a pig skull with a round, sunken fracture in the center, which we guessed had been made with a heavy instrument such as a stone hand ax. Nearby we came upon large boulders of dense volcanic rock weighing about 100 to 200 pounds each. We believe the Bodo toolmakers rolled the boulders to the site from a rock-strewn area about a mile away for use as a convenient source of stone.

All in all, we discovered stone tool sites spread almost continuously over an area 15 miles long. The abundance of these tool sites is strong evidence that the Middle Awash Valley probably holds the world's largest single concentration of Acheulian tools. Moreover, we found the tools in possibly as many as 11 different levels within

The scientific wealth in fossils and artifacts found in the eroded terrain of the Afar Triangle records a history of hominid and animal evolution stretching back more than 5 million years.

A student from Addis Ababa University displays a prehistoric stone tool found in the Middle Awash Valley.

deposits more than 300 feet thick. This indicates that hominids lived in the area over a long period of time.

Yet we had not found any trace of the hominids themselves. Then, in October 1976 at Bodo, we found a beautifully preserved hominid skull. We identified it as belonging to a very primitive form of *Homo sapiens* or a late form of *Homo erectus*, the species from which *Homo sapiens* developed. By carefully searching the area surrounding the skull and screening the loose sediment beneath it, we found numerous fragments of the skull and so were able to reconstruct much of the cranium. We estimated it to be about 400,000 years old. The skull alone was a significant discovery. But finding the skull along with a wide assortment of tools at the same level in the deposits enabled us to document a definite relationship between a specific level of physical development in early *Homo* and a specific level of development in toolmaking.

North of Meadura, at a site called Andalee, we found types of tools unlike Acheulian tools. The most typical of these were crude stone picks about 10 to 12 inches long. By identifying index fossils found at the same level in the deposits, we estimated that the tools were about 100,000 years old.

Who made the tools and what were they used for? We were not certain. But animal fossils found at Andalee have provided some clues about the toolmakers and their environment.

Many of the fossil bones we found at the site came from tree-dwelling colobus and vervet monkeys, types of monkeys that still exist today in the Awash Valley. In addition, we found fossils from other forest creatures, such as small antelopes and pigs. Most numerous, however, were fossils from rodents, particularly cane rats, burrowing animals about the size of a small dog. Rodent bones are often found in modern owl pellets, undigested food regurgitated by the owl. We reasoned that since modern owls commonly roost and drop their pellets in wooded areas, ancient owls did also. This may explain in part the accumulation of fossil rodent bones at Andalee.

The tools and fossils we found at the site appear to have been laid down after the prolonged drought that struck the Afar 175,000 years ago. At that time, rivers began coursing their way back into the region. The presence of fossils from forest creatures is evidence that with the rivers came forests. And with the forests came the people we call the Andaleans.

Like the modern Afar nomads, the Andaleans lived along the rivers. But unlike the earlier Acheulian toolmakers, who apparently relied on large animals as the mainstay of their diet, the Andaleans had to be more resourceful. Most of the large game in the area had become extinct or had moved to a more hospitable climate during the drought. So the Andaleans were probably forced to hunt smaller creatures like those whose fossil bones we uncovered. Perhaps, like the owls, the Andaleans considered rodents, particularly the cane rat, a prized meal. And perhaps they used the stone picks to dig out their burrows. Interestingly, today, cane rat is considered a delicacy in parts of Africa. The Andaleans themselves remain a mystery. We guess, however, that they were more like the commonly known Neanderthals, a later form of *Homo sapiens*, than the more primitive form of *Homo* from Bodo.

Future excavations in the Middle Awash Valley will, I believe, uncover not only fossil bones from the Andaleans but other fossils that will fill in more of the gaps in our knowledge of our earliest ancestors. For example, lying within the ancient deposits of the valley may be the fossils that will answer questions raised by the discovery of Lucy. Does she, as Johanson claims, belong to a separate species — *Australopithecis afarensis* — and was that species ancestral to all other hominids? Or, as anthropologist Richard E. Leakey of the National Museums of Kenya contends, was another creature, older than Lucy, the ancestor of later hominids? Or, as anthropologist Phillip Tobias of South Africa believes, should Lucy be considered simply a slightly different and more primitive form of *Australopithecus africanus*, an early hominid first discovered in South Africa, and not a separate species at all?

But the Afar's remarkable fossil and archaeological record does not end in prehistoric times. Near Lake Abbe stand mysterious arrangements of large stones. No one knows for sure who put them there, but they may date to early Afar inhabitants of the region. Perhaps the stonework may be ruins from the fabled land of Ophir mentioned in the Bible (I Kings 9-10). It was to Ophir that King Solomon of Israel sent his ships when he established trade relations with the Queen of Sheba 3,000 years ago. The name *Ophir*, some Ethiopian scholars speculate, may be derived from the word *Afar*.

Thus, the nearer we come to the present, the more closely prehistory in the Afar becomes interwoven with Ethiopia's own ancient past. For this reason, I believe that Ethiopia must protect and preserve its vast prehistoric resources. And, in fact, increasing numbers of Ethiopian scholars and students are becoming more deeply involved in this work.

In order to assist these efforts, the Ethiopian government in October 1982 temporarily halted all prehistory research in that country. The government announced that the action would remain in effect until it had drawn up modern policies guiding future research. Most especially, Ethiopia believes it must develop its own museums, research institutions, and scientists in order to study and preserve its priceless prehistoric sites. It is essential that the international scientific community help Ethiopia achieve its goal.

Meanwhile, the fossils that may provide evidence of our earliest ancestors await discovery. As significant as these fossils may be, I believe they will be only one part of the remarkable story scientists will eventually uncover in the Afar's ancient deposits.

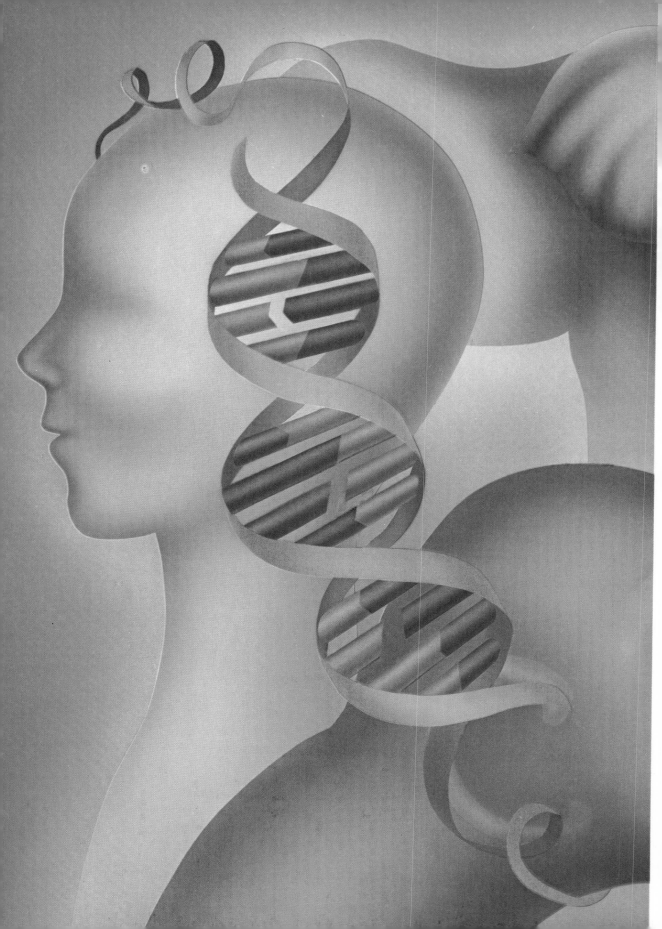

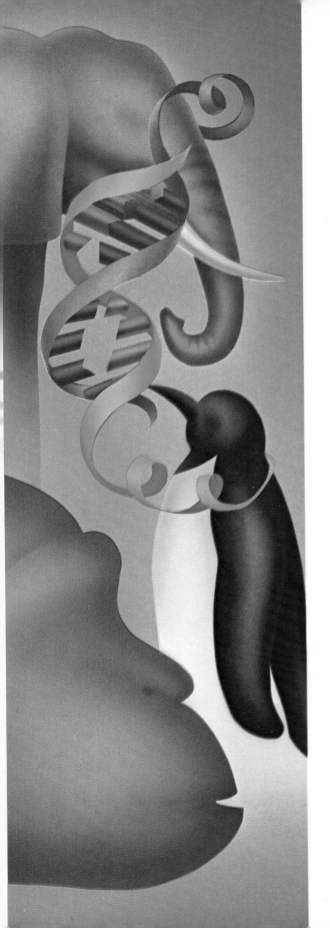

Molecular
Clues to
Our Origins

By George Alexander

**Anthropologists who believe the key to
our past lies in living cells are challenging
theories based on the fossil record.**

For nearly 100 years, scientists studying human origins have scrambled up and down sun-broiled gullies, trekked across barren plains, and delved into caves in their search for fossil bones from our prehistoric ancestors. Using the teeth, skull fragments, and other fossils they have uncovered, these anthropologists have painstakingly tried to construct a clear picture of how, when, and where human beings evolved from more primitive ape-like creatures.

Even as the search for older and more complete fossils goes on, however, some anthropologists have shifted the focus of their investigations. Instead of examining ancient bones, these anthropologists analyze molecules from the cells of living descendants of those fossilized creatures.

Molecular anthropologists are focusing their research on biochemical molecules because they believe that a single human cell — or a cell from any other living creature — is a marvelous library of old as well as current information about life. This is because the genetic material in cells remains relatively unchanged over long periods. As time passes, however, some mutations, or changes, do occur. Molecular anthropologists believe that these mutations reveal a great deal about the evolutionary history of various species — including human beings.

By analyzing molecules from living organisms, molecular anthropologists have come to several astonishing conclusions, some of which challenge the pattern of human evolution based on an interpretation of the fossil record. First, they contend that human beings, chimpanzees, and gorillas — all members of a group of mammals known as primates — are much more closely related than anyone previously suspected. Outwardly, of course, the three species look very different. Inwardly, however, the molecular similarity is remarkable. In fact, molecular anthropologists have discovered that almost 99 per cent of the proteins and genetic material in the cells of humans are identical to the proteins and genetic material in the cells of chimps and gorillas. Second, the molecular anthropologists argue, this close relationship indicates that humans, chimps, and gorillas evolved from a common ancestor about 15 million to 20 million years later than the fossil record says.

Although an increasing number of scientists today are studying evolution from a molecular point of view, the idea is not really new. In 1901, George H. F. Nuttall, a biologist at Cambridge University in England, attempted to determine the relationship between species by measuring immune reactions.

Nuttall knew that when antigens — foreign substances such as viruses and bacteria — invade the body, certain cells in the blood manufacture molecules called antibodies. The antibodies identify antigens so they can be destroyed by the rest of the immune system. Nuttall also knew that antibodies are specific — that is, that they are custom-designed to react with only one type of antigen. That is why antibodies used to immunize us against a polio virus will not protect us against a measles virus. Finally, Nuttall knew that when antigens and antibodies are combined in a solution, a precipitate forms. In this case, the precipitate appears as a milky substance.

In his experiments, Nuttall used as antigens certain proteins found in blood serum, the liquid portion of the blood that remains after a clot forms. He injected serum into animals from a variety of species, thereby stimulating the production of antiserum, serum containing antibodies. Nuttall speculated that if serum from one animal species was mixed with antiserum from a different but closely related species — such as dogs and wolves, or horses and zebras — the reaction would be strong. That is, the precipitate would be thick and cloudy. But if the serum and antiserum came from two distantly related species, such as wolves and zebras, the reaction would be weak, and the precipitate would be thin and almost transparent.

And that is precisely what Nuttall found in some 16,000 experi-

The author:
George Alexander is a science writer for the *Los Angeles Times*.

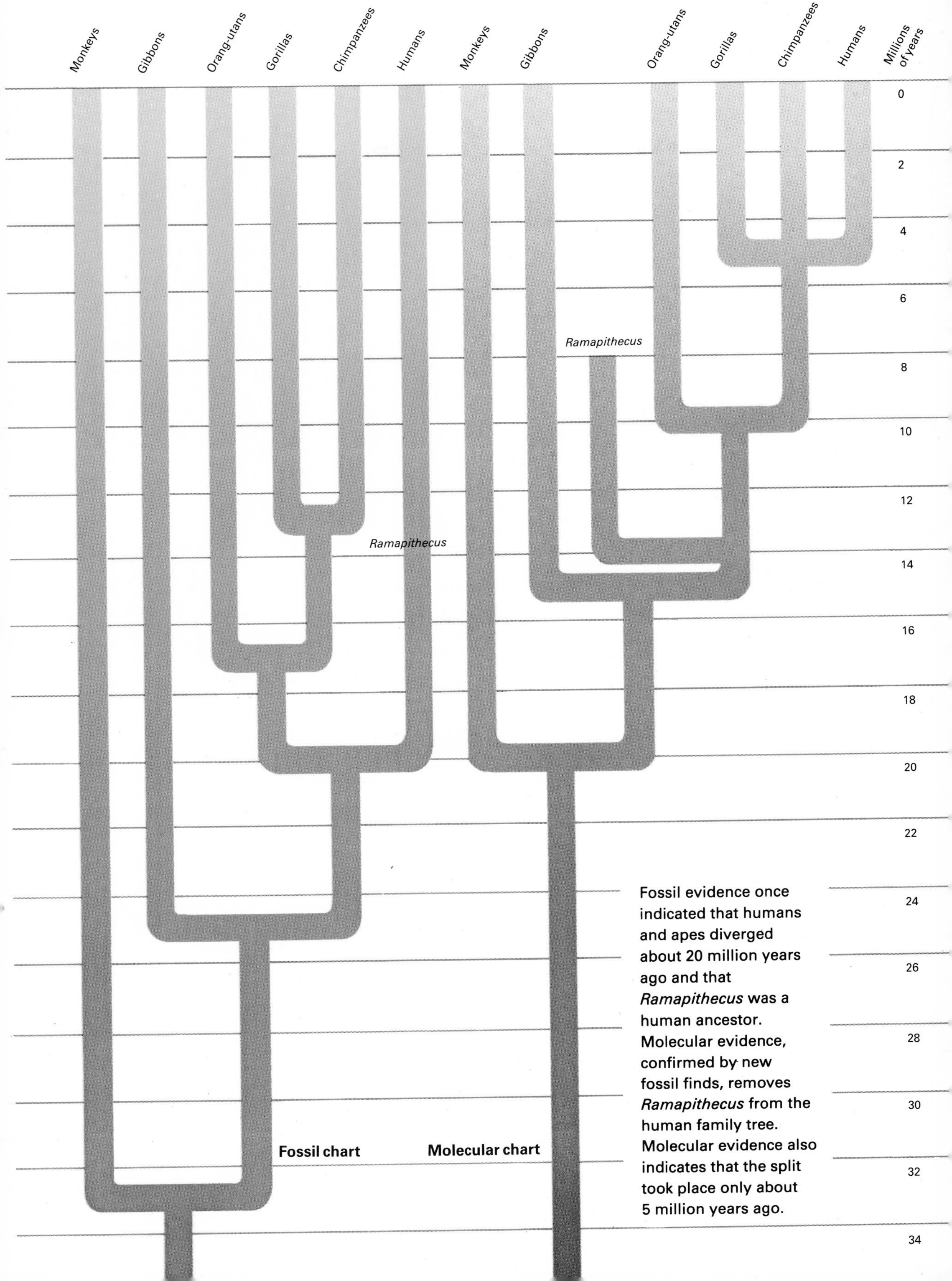

Monkeys Gibbons Orang-utans Gorillas Chimpanzees Humans Monkeys Gibbons Orang-utans Gorillas Chimpanzees Humans

Millions of years

0
2
4
6
8
10
12
14
16
18
20
22
24
26
28
30
32
34

Ramapithecus

Ramapithecus

Fossil chart   **Molecular chart**

Fossil evidence once indicated that humans and apes diverged about 20 million years ago and that *Ramapithecus* was a human ancestor. Molecular evidence, confirmed by new fossil finds, removes *Ramapithecus* from the human family tree. Molecular evidence also indicates that the split took place only about 5 million years ago.

ments he conducted with serum and antiserum from nearly 1,000 different species. Animals that had been classified as related species because of their similar body structure proved in Nuttall's experiments to be those animals whose molecules formed strong biochemical bonds. And the molecules of animals not closely related in body structure formed weak bonds. "The persistence of the chemical blood relationship between the various groups of animals serves to carry us back into geologic time," Nuttall wrote prophetically in 1904, and "will lead to valuable results in the study of various problems of evolution."

So it did — but not in Nuttall's lifetime. His research was ignored for more than 50 years until another scientist, immunologist Morris Goodman of Wayne State University in Detroit, picked up in the late 1950s where Nuttall left off. Like Nuttall, Goodman used serum and antiserum to test immune reponses between species. But while Nuttall simply estimated the cloudiness of the precipitate, Goodman used a technique called immunodiffusion that provided more precise measurements.

Goodman began his experiments by scooping out three small craters in a disk of agar — a jellylike extract made from seaweed — leaving a triangular section of agar in the middle of the disk. He then placed drops of serum from two species in two of the craters and antiserum from one of those species or a third species in the third crater. The droplets spread through the agar like water through a sponge. Where the serums and antiserum met, a reaction occurred and white lines of precipitate formed.

Goodman found that if the two species were distantly related, the drops of serum reacted weakly and so the lines of precipitate were unequal in length. If, however, the serums came from closely related species, they reacted strongly and the lines of precipitate were equal in length.

Goodman's comparisons of serums from various species of primates revealed many evolutionary patterns most scientists would have expected. No one was particularly surprised to learn that, on a molecular level, the least similar primates were humans and lemurs — big-eyed, long-tailed animals with fluffy fur. Slightly more similar were humans and monkeys, then humans and gibbons — the smallest member of the ape family — then humans and orang-utans.

Scientists were surprised, however, at the results of Goodman's comparison of human, chimpanzee, and gorilla serums. He found that all three species were so remarkably similar that he could not say whether human-chimpanzee serums matched more closely than did human-gorilla serums or chimpanzee-gorilla serums. Thus, Goodman provided evidence that humans and apes were more closely related than anyone previously suspected.

Goodman's research, published in 1962 and 1963, caused quite a stir in anthropology circles because it flew squarely in the face of the

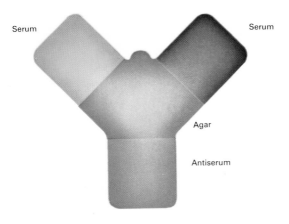

Serum

Serum

Agar

Antiserum

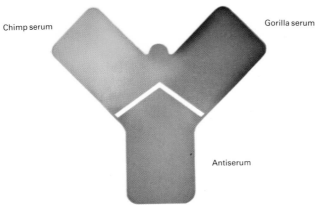

Chimp serum

Gibbon serum

Antiserum

Bloodlines
Blood serums from two species meet antiserum from one of those species or a third species in agar. The lines of precipitate that form reveal how closely related species are. Lines formed from distantly related species, such as chimps and gibbons, are of unequal length. Lines formed from closely related species, such as chimps and gorillas, are nearly identical. Human serum and chimp serum also indicate a close relationship.

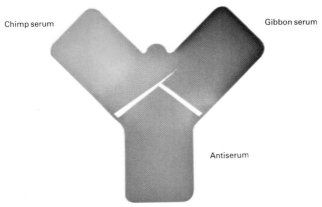

Chimp serum

Gorilla serum

Antiserum

Chimp serum

Human serum

Antiserum

117

then-widely-held belief that chimps and gorillas sat on a completely different branch of the evolutionary tree than did humans. Goodman's conclusions punched a very large hole in this traditional view of evolution. If the molecular evidence was accurate, then humans, gorillas, and chimps belonged on the same branch. It was a difficult hypothesis for many scientists to accept, and, indeed, many did not accept it. At least not then.

In 1967, two other scientists, biochemist Walter M. Fitch of the University of Wisconsin School of Medicine in Madison and molecular biologist Emanuel Margoliash of Northwestern University in Evanston, Ill., disclosed the evolutionary role of another biological molecule, a protein called cytochrome c. Found in all living creatures, it helps cells combine food with oxygen to produce energy.

All proteins are composed of smaller units called amino acids that are linked together in long chains like beads on a string. The sequence or order of amino acids determines the nature of a protein and, thus, its function. Fitch and Margoliash compared the sequence of amino acids in the cytochrome c of 20 different species.

They discovered that some of the amino acid sequences were amazingly similar. For example, they found that all 104 of the amino acids making up cytochrome c in humans and chimps followed exactly the same sequence. On the other hand, when they compared human cytochrome c with cytochrome c from horses, they found only 82 amino acids in the same position.

Fitch and Margoliash theorized that by analyzing the genes coding for the amino acids that did not match, they could determine how closely related the 20 species were and the order in which they diverged — split off — from their common ancestors. Genes are made up of deoxyribonucleic acid (DNA), a molecule that is responsible for the transmission of inherited characteristics and acts as a blueprint for the production of proteins.

Like most scientists, Fitch and Margoliash assumed that all living creatures evolved from a common ancestor. Different species developed as mutations occurred in the DNA of their cells. The scientists speculated that the more closely the DNA matched, the more closely related the species were. On the other hand, the more differences there were in the DNA, the more distant was the relationship. With the data from their analysis of the DNA, Fitch and Margoliash constructed an evolutionary tree that showed the divergence of the 20 species. Significantly, their tree closely resembled the traditional evolutionary tree based on the fossil record. It seemed that as far as the relationship among species was concerned, the molecular evidence generally agreed with the fossil evidence.

The missing factor in the research done by Goodman and Fitch and Margoliash, however, was the question of time. When had the various species, including humans, split from their common ancestor? Goodman, for his part, was comfortable with the traditional

Gorilla

Chimpanzee

Gibbon

Orang-utan

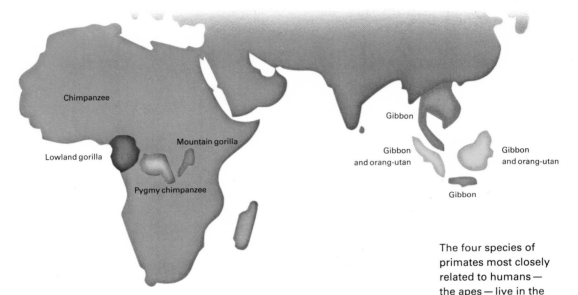

Chimpanzee

Mountain gorilla

Lowland gorilla

Pygmy chimpanzee

Gibbon

Gibbon
and orang-utan

Gibbon

Gibbon
and orang-utan

Gibbon

The four species of
primates most closely
related to humans —
the apes — live in the
tropical regions
of Africa and Asia.

estimate that hominids — early ancestors of human beings — had split from apes 20 million to 25 million years ago. He attributed the similarities in various human, chimpanzee, and gorilla blood proteins to a slowdown in the DNA mutation rate. That is, he believed that after the split, mutations had simply taken longer to occur.

In 1967, however, two scientists at the University of California, Berkeley, found what they believed to be the answer to this question of time in another blood protein — albumin. Allan C. Wilson, a biochemist, and Vincent M. Sarich, a chemist and anthropologist, compared albumin samples from a variety of species, including primates, in much the same way Nuttall had tested blood proteins. Sarich himself contributed the first human albumin sample.

The scientists prepared flasks of solution containing antiserum from various species and added albumin. They then shone a light on the precipitate that formed. The light passed through the precipitate and onto a photoelectric cell, a device that conducts an electrical current when light shines on it. By measuring the strength of the current from the cell, the scientists determined how much light passed through the precipitate. Using this data, the scientists assigned a numerical value to each reaction and charted the values on a scale that they called the index of dissimilarity. They concluded the numbers revealed the relationship between various species.

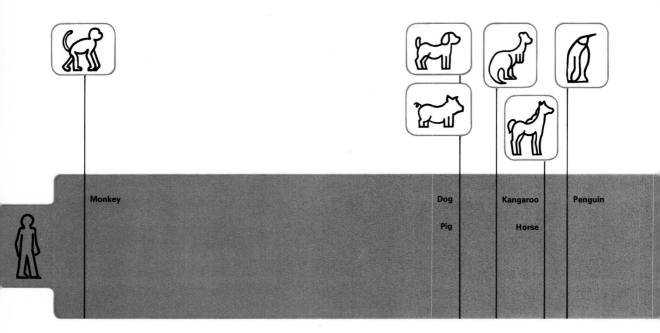

Monkey

Dog

Pig

Kangaroo

Horse

Penguin

The Cytochrome Connection

The evolutionary distance between humans and several other species is revealed by an analysis of the order of amino acids in cytochrome c, a protein found in all living creatures.

The evolutionary distance between members of the same species was established at 1 unit. The distance on the index between human albumin and cow albumin, the scientists found, is 20 units. However, the distance between humans and chimps is only 1.13 units.

The next step was to determine whether the changes in the albumin occurred steadily over time. To do this, the scientists compared the amino acid sequence of the albumin of primates and carnivores — a group of animals, including dogs, lions, and tigers, that feed chiefly on meat. Working from the theory that primates and carnivores evolved from a common ancestor, Sarich and Wilson speculated that the distance between every living primate species and every living carnivore species should be the same. And that is what they found. Their data suggested that, contrary to what Goodman believed about a slowdown in the mutation rate, mutations in the amino acid sequences of the albumin of related species occur at a steady rate.

In order to translate their measurements into estimates of when the various species diverged from a common ancestor, Wilson and Sarich turned to the fossil record. It strongly suggested that the ancestors of modern humans and apes diverged from Old World monkeys — monkeys from Asia and Africa — about 30 million years ago. Wilson and Sarich then developed an equation in which the average distance between the two groups — which turned out to be 2.3 units on the index of dissimilarity — corresponded to 30 million years. At that point, the scientists realized they had developed a molecular clock.

When they applied their molecular clock to the albumin of various primate species, they derived some divergence times that were inter-

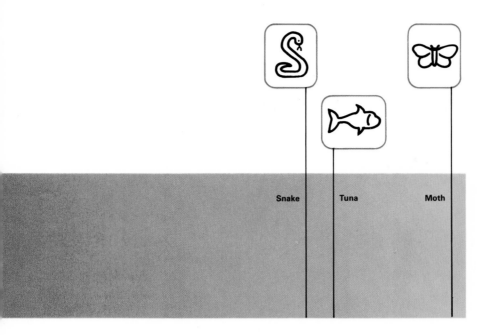

Snake   Tuna   Moth

esting but not necessarily startling. For example, they calculated that gibbons and siamangs — a type of gibbon found in the jungles of Southeast Asia — split from their common ancestor about 10 million years ago. Orang-utans were next, striking out on their own about 8 million years ago.

These conclusions were hardly astonishing because they roughly agreed with the fossil record. But what came next was a real shocker. "It seems likely," Wilson and Sarich declared in a report on their work published in 1967, "that apes and man share a more recent common ancestry than is usually supposed." How recent? By applying their equation to the 1.13-unit difference between humans and chimps, the scientists concluded that the two species had split from a common ancestor somewhere between 4½ million and 5 million years ago.

At first, that estimate had about as much effect on fossil anthropologists as a firecracker might have on a bank vault. At that time, nearly all anthropologists firmly believed that the split had occurred from 20 million to 25 million years ago.

Much of their confidence was based on their knowledge of an ancient primate named *Ramapithecus*, a creature that lived from about 8 million to 14 million years ago. *Ramapithecus* apparently walked semiupright and its teeth and jaw resembled those of later, more humanlike creatures. Although the fossil remains of this creature were scanty, its characteristics made the ancient creature seem more like a human ancestor than an ape forebear. As a result, many scientists believed *Ramapithecus* was one of the first hominids.

Wilson and Sarich and other molecular anthropologists disagreed. How could *Ramapithecus* be a hominid when, according to the molec-

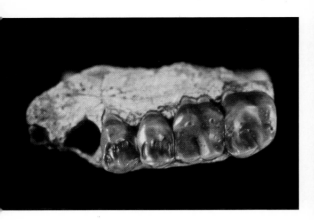

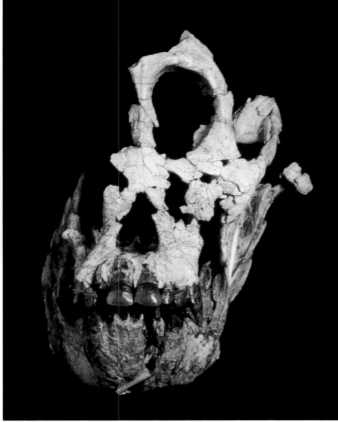

An 8-million-year-old *Ramapithecus* jaw, *above,* discovered in Pakistan in 1932, seemed to suggest that the apelike creature was a direct human ancestor. Better evidence, in the form of a partial skull, *right,* of a nearly identical creature from the same period, was found in Pakistan in 1979. It dispelled the idea that *Ramapithecus* belonged on the human family tree.

ular evidence, the first hominids did not come into existence until 3 million years after *Ramapithecus* became extinct?

By 1982, many fossil anthropologists had begun to agree with the molecular anthropologists' argument that *Ramapithecus* was not a human ancestor. This change in thinking resulted from the discovery in Pakistan in 1979 of an 8-million-year-old skull fragment. The fossil was found by a team co-directed by anthropologist David R. Pilbeam of Harvard University in Cambridge, Mass. Although Pilbeam named the fossil *Sivapithecus,* he believes it is very similar — if not identical — to *Ramapithecus* fossils found earlier.

"I now believe *Ramapithecus* is not in the line of descent for hominids," Pilbeam said of his analysis of *Sivapithecus.* Instead, Pilbeam and many other anthropologists believe that *Ramapithecus* was an ancestor or a close relative of the creature that evolved into the orang-utan.

Additional support for the molecular anthropologists' theory has come as scientists have delved deeper into the structure of DNA itself. The DNA molecule looks like a twisted rope ladder. The rungs on the ladder consist of two matching pairs of chemical compounds called bases. The exact proportion of bases in a DNA molecule and their sequence are unique for every species.

In 1972, molecular biologist David E. Kohne of the Center for Neurological Study in La Jolla, Calif., biophysicist Bill H. Hoyer of the Carnegie Institution of Washington (D.C.), and geneticist J.

Alfred Chiscon of Purdue University in Lafayette, Ind., developed a more precise method of comparing the DNA of various species. Called DNA hybridization, the technique involves splitting strands of DNA lengthwise in order to separate the bases that make up each rung. The scientists then mixed the split strands from two species and allowed them to combine, forming hybrid DNA. The strands joined only at those places where the bases matched.

Next, the scientists heated the hybrid DNA in order to separate the strands again. They discovered that the temperature at which the strands separated depended on the extent to which the bases matched. Strands of hybrid DNA from the same species separated at a temperature of about 85° C. For every 1 in 100 bases in the hybrid DNA that did not match, the temperature at which the strands separated dropped by about 1° C. Thus, the greater the differences in the DNA, the lower the temperature at which the strands of the molecule separated.

The scientists determined that hybrid human-chimp DNA separated at just 1° C below that at which hybrid DNA from two humans or two chimps separated. Therefore, they concluded, the DNA of the two species differed by only 1 per cent, or 1 base in 100. They obtained the same results when comparing human and gorilla DNA. Thus, Kohne, Hoyer, and Chiscon's research comparing DNA confirmed Goodman's serum experiments. In addition, by using the DNA as a molecular clock and comparing the number of mutations with the fossil record, molecular anthropologists again came up with a figure of 4½ million to 5 million years for the split of chimps, gorillas, and humans.

Different tests, different biological molecules, different species, and yet the results seem remarkably consistent. Humans, chimps, and gorillas are so biologically alike, the molecular anthropologists contend, that they must have sprung from a common ancestor as recently as 5 million years ago.

Molecular anthropologists believe their evidence is hard to deny. But if molecules are slow to change, so too can be scientific opinion. Fossil anthropologists have accepted some of the molecular findings, but they do not agree that this new discipline has already answered all the important questions about human evolution or that the answers are more likely to come from biological molecules than from fossil bones.

Only additional fossil finds will confirm the accuracy of the molecular evidence. If someone were to unearth a 6- to 7-million-year-old hominid skeleton, the discovery would badly damage the Wilson-Sarich theory of human origin because, according to the molecular evidence, such a creature did not evolve until 4½ million to 5 million years ago.

At the moment, however, no evidence exists that contradicts the timetable developed by Wilson and Sarich. The oldest unmistakable hominid is Lucy, the 3-million-year-old creature found in the Afar region of Ethiopia in 1974 by anthropologist Donald C. Johanson, now of the Institute of Human Origins in Berkeley, Calif. Roughly 40 per cent of Lucy's skeleton was unearthed. From the fossil bones, Johanson and his colleagues have concluded that she had arms, legs, and a torso similar to those of modern humans, but a brain about the size of a chimpanzee's. That is approximately what scientists would expect of a creature only 1½ million to 2 million years removed from an ape ancestor.

Anthropologist Richard E. Leakey, director of the National Museums of Kenya in Nairobi, who has made a number of significant hominid fossil finds in East Africa, once championed the theory that humans and apes have been walking down different evolutionary paths for more than 20 million years. However, he recently conceded that much of what he once believed is incorrect. And Johanson said, "I always thought 25 million years ago was too old [for the split between hominids and apes], but on the other hand, a split of 5

Touching Bases
Splitting strands of DNA from two species and combining them indicates how closely the species are related. The measure is the match of the bases — compounds that make up the rungs of the DNA ladder.

Human DNA

Gorilla DNA

Human-Gorilla DNA

million years strikes me as a little too recent. I believe we'll find it actually occurred somewhere between 5 million and 10 million years ago." Johanson, like many other scientists, feels that molecular analysis and the fossil record can—and should—complement each other in science's efforts to understand human evolutionary history.

Ironically, many of the scientists who dispute the molecular evidence for a timetable of human evolution accept its results when tracing the history of other species. For molecular anthropologists have also used their skills to solve a number of interesting evolutionary puzzles. They showed, for example, that the giant panda is a member of the bear family and that the extinct Tasmanian wolf was not really a wolf but a carnivorous marsupial. They also discovered that the extinct Siberian mammoth was about as biologically similar to the African and Indian elephants as those two pachyderms are to each other.

The proteins for the experiments with the panda, bear, modern marsupials, and elephants came from living animals. But, interestingly, the protein sample from the mammoth came from the 40,000-year-old frozen carcass of a calf discovered in a Siberian glacier in 1977. The Tasmanian wolf sample was obtained from a bit of dried muscle scraped from a 100-year-old bone.

Meanwhile, the molecular anthropologists continue their investigations into human evolution. One of their newest targets of research is mitochondria—microscopic, sausage-shaped structures found in cells that have their own DNA.

The comparison of mitochondrial DNA from various species has not revealed any startling new information about the molecular kinship of humans and other primate species. It does, however, seem to provide another, independent molecular clock. Because mitochondria contain much less DNA than do the nuclei of cells, they are much easier to study. Moreover, mitochondrial DNA seems to mutate about 10 times faster than does DNA within a cell. This accelerated mutation rate may enable scientists to determine more precisely when mutations occurred as a species evolved. In this way, mitochondrial DNA is like a watch capable of measuring time to the hundredths of a second, whereas cellular DNA is like a watch that can measure time only in full seconds. Finally, unlike cellular DNA, mitochondrial DNA is inherited only from the mother. Cellular DNA, which is inherited from both parents, gets mixed in the reproduction process. By studying mitochondrial DNA, molecular anthropologists also hope to understand some particularly interesting episodes in human history, such as where modern human beings—*Homo sapiens sapiens*—emerged and how various racial groups arose.

It seems nothing less than extraordinary that so much human history could be found in genes and proteins. But these microscopic molecules may indeed be a time machine that will enable us to penetrate the murky past and understand our ancient origins.

The Physics of Color

By Kurt Nassau

Minute changes in energy within the atom provide the pigments for nature's paintbrush.

Our world is awash in color. On a summer day, our eye can delight in butterflies, flowers, shrubs, broad expanses of green grass, blue rivers and ponds, and at day's end — a red sunset. The drabness of a gray winter morning can be relieved by the sight of a cardinal or a blue jay. Color pleases us so much that we have even put nature's paintbrush to work, coloring the visible surfaces of many things that we make and use.

We owe this visual pleasure to cooperation between mechanisms in the atomic world and our visual system. Light emitted from a source — or passing through or reflected from an object — undergoes changes in energy. The energy is carried by tiny particles, called photons. The photons travel to our eyes, which process them in ways that tell us the grass is green or the sky is blue.

Photons have a dual nature. Not only do they behave like particles, they also behave like waves, each vibrating at a certain frequency with a corresponding wavelength, like the water waves created when a stone splashes into a still pool. Wavelength is the distance a photon travels during one complete vibration; its frequency is the number of times it vibrates per second. A photon's energy is measured by its frequency — the higher the

frequency, the greater the energy. The converse is true with wavelength — the shorter the wavelength, the greater the energy.

The range of energy in the band or spectrum of electromagnetic radiation is tremendous. Physicists measure photon energy in units called electron volts (eV). The spectrum extends from less than one hundred-billionth of an electron volt for photons of very long radio waves to more than 100 million eV for photons of very short wavelength, gamma rays. Our eyes sense only a narrow portion of this spectrum — a band from about 1.7 to 3.1 eV, corresponding to wavelengths of about 400- to 700-millionths of a millimeter.

Photons reach our eyes in two ways. They may come directly from sources that convert other types of energy to electromagnetic radiation. Photon sources get this energy in various ways. The sun, for example, obtains energy from nuclear reactions. The chemical energy of burning energizes a candle flame. Electricity supplies energy to the filament of a light bulb and to gases in fluorescent tubes.

Photons also reach our eyes indirectly after transmission through or reflection from objects. The atoms in these objects gain energy by absorbing photons, and they may also give up energy by emitting other photons.

Whether they reach our eyes directly or indirectly, the photons' energy determines an object's color. For example, a light beam that contains only photons within a single, narrow band of energy of about 1.7 eV is red. A beam of slightly higher-energy photons is orange and beams of increasingly higher energy are yellow, green, blue, and — at about 3.1 eV — violet.

Most visible objects do not emit photons of a single, narrow band of energy, and therefore of a single color. Rather, they radiate a mixture of photons whose energies vary widely. The most heavily represented bands of energy determine the colors of these objects. If no band dominates, as in sunlight, the object is white. Sunlight is made up of an almost even mixture of all the colors.

What happens in the atoms that give a substance its color? The action centers on electrons, particles that orbit an atom's nucleus, much as the planets orbit the sun. However, unlike the planets, which stay in their orbits, electrons can jump from one orbit to another. But to change orbits, an electron must take on or give up energy. When given a specific amount of energy, an electron can jump to an orbit farther from the nucleus. When it jumps back, it gives up that energy by emitting a photon or liberating heat.

Electron orbits are somewhat like the rungs of a ladder. Adding energy moves the electron up the energy ladder; emitting energy moves it down. However, the energy ladder differs from an ordinary ladder in that its rungs are unevenly spaced. This means that the energy an electron needs to absorb, or to give up, in order to jump from one orbit to the next may not be the same as the energy change needed for some other step. Furthermore, an electron does not nec-

The author:
Kurt Nassau, a physical chemist, is a member of the technical staff of Bell Telephone Laboratories in Murray Hill, N.J.

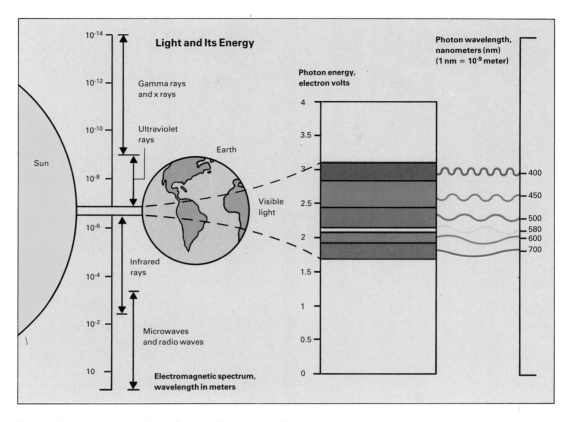

Energy from the sun consists of a broad spectrum of electromagnetic radiation. Visible radiation fills only a narrow band. The color of an individual ray depends upon the wavelength and the energy of its photons — indivisible packets of light.

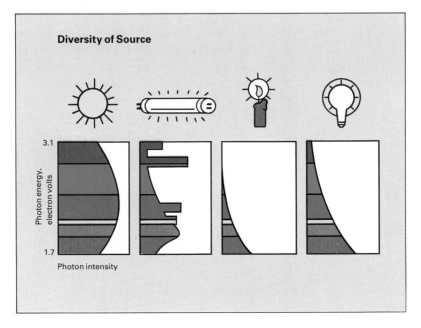

Sunlight is a mixture of nearly equal numbers of photons from throughout the visible band. A fluorescent light's photon distribution is similar to the sun's and so its light is white. A candle and a tungsten light bulb emit mostly low-energy photons, so their light is reddish.

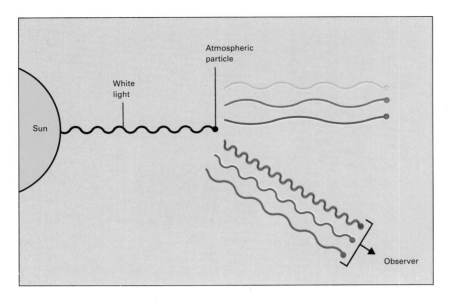

Why the Sky Is Blue
Scattering of sunlight by atmospheric dust and molecules makes the sky appear blue, *right.* A tiny particle, *above,* deflects, or scatters, photons of high-energy violet, blue, and green light to an observer's eye but does not affect other photons, which go on their way unobserved.

essarily use consecutive rungs. Instead, it follows what physicists call selection rules. In many cases, an electron uses one sequence of rungs as it climbs the ladder and another sequence as it descends.

Substances have colors because of differences in their energy ladders and the selection rules. For example, a gas that is suitably excited gives off photons, producing a color that is characteristic of only that gas. Energized sodium vapor, for example, produces the bright yellow light that is used in some street lamps. When a sodium-vapor lamp is turned on, several thousand volts of electricity energize the vapor. The outermost electron in each energized atom of sodium vapor climbs to a high rung on the energy ladder and then returns down the ladder in a certain sequence of rungs, the last two of which are 2.1 eV apart. The energy released in this last step appears as a photon of yellow light.

In a similar manner, a mercury-vapor street lamp produces blue-violet light. The color is different because, in mercury, most of the light is produced by two rungs that are about 2.85 eV apart.

Substances that are not light sources owe their colors to a variety of mechanisms. The colors of one class of materials depend upon the partial transmission of photons through the material. Most gemstones are in this class. When an atom has more than one electron that can be energized, the rungs of the energy ladder correspond to the energy levels of the whole atom. The atom changes its energy level when its electrons, acting together, absorb or emit a photon.

For example, energy changes in three electrons of a chromium atom give rubies their red coloring. Chromium in a ruby is actually part of an impurity, chromium oxide, in which each chromium atom is chemically bound or bonded to six oxygen atoms. When white light from an outside source passes through a ruby, chromium electrons gain energy by absorbing all the violet and green-yellow photons and most of the blue photons. The remaining colors pass through the ruby, giving it the red color. The chromium electrons also give up energy by emitting red photons, which add to the color, and infrared radiation — that is, heat. When these red photons and the other photons that pass through the crystal reach your eyes, you see a red ruby.

Chromium in chromium oxide also gives emeralds their color. However, the bonds between the chromium atoms and the surrounding oxygen atoms are weaker in emerald than in ruby. This difference in bond strength causes a difference in the energy ladder. Therefore the photons absorbed and transmitted have different energies, resulting in the green color of emerald. The chromium also emits a small number of red photons, but they have little effect.

An electron hopping from one atom to another causes the absorption of light that produces the deep blue color of sapphire.

The colors of another large class of substances depend upon the reflection of photons. These substances range from an animal's fur to a plant's leaves to the dyed clothing we wear. In this mechanism,

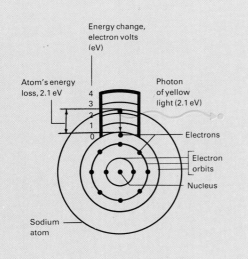

Energy change, electron volts (eV)

Atom's energy loss, 2.1 eV

Photon of yellow light (2.1 eV)

4
3
2
1
0

Electrons

Electron orbits

Nucleus

Sodium atom

Loss Makes Light

Electrically activated sodium-vapor lamps emit yellow light from energized sodium atoms. A sodium atom gives up excess energy when an excited electron falls back to an orbit closer to the nucleus. The energy of the photon of yellow light emitted equals the energy lost by the atom.

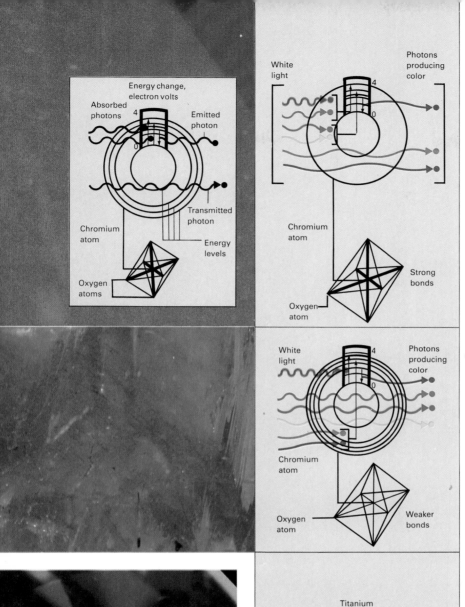

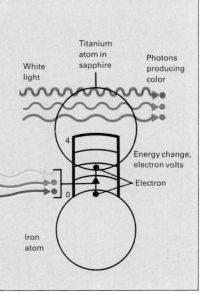

Absorption Causes Color

Photons of violet, blue, green, and yellow light from an external light source are absorbed because they excite a ruby's chromium atom. This atom, in turn, emits a red photon. The remaining colors pass through the ruby, joining the emitted photon to form a combination that gives the ruby its deep red coloring. Similar changes in the energy of chromium atoms also generate color in emerald, but the bonding between atoms is weaker than in ruby. This affects the energy levels of photon absorption, making the resulting color green.

White In, Blue Out

A sapphire gets its blue color when an electron jumps from an iron atom to a titanium atom. Such an electron can absorb a photon of red, orange, or yellow light to make this jump. The remaining photons that pass through the sapphire produce its color.

133

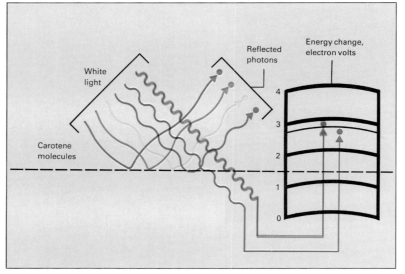

Orange Shade
Carotene molecules, *right,* supply color by absorption and reflection. The molecules increase their energy by absorbing blue and violet photons from white light. The combination of reflected photons gives objects that contain carotene, *above,* their orange and pink coloring.

White light

Reflected photons

Energy change, electron volts

Carotene molecules

4

3

2

1

0

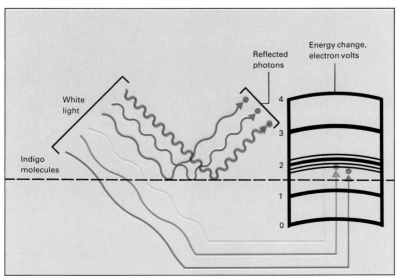

Birth of the Blue
Indigo molecules
also produce color
by absorption and
reflection. The
molecules absorb
yellow, orange, and
red photons from white
light. The combination
of reflected photons
gives indigo and
objects dyed indigo
their blue coloring.

Gold reflects all the colors of white light. However, the colors it reflects most efficiently produce an excess of the light that gives the exquisite coloring.

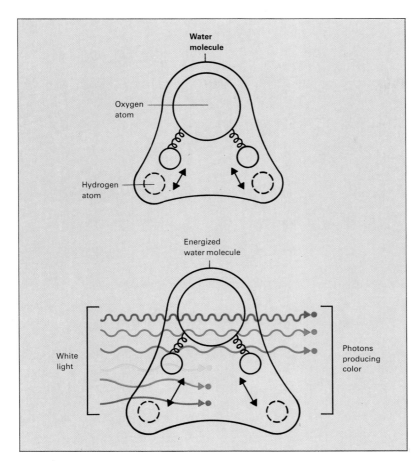

Water
molecule

Oxygen
atom

Hydrogen
atom

Energized
water molecule

White
light

Photons
producing
color

The Ocean Blue
Molecular vibration
colors the sea.
A water molecule, *left,*
boosts its energy by
absorbing photons of
red, orange, and yellow
light, increasing the
vibration of its hydrogen
atoms. Photons
that are not absorbed
pass through such
molecules and give a
body of water, *below
left,* its blue color.

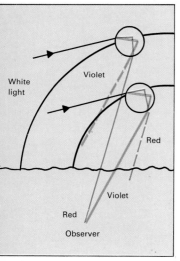

Building a Bow
Acting as a prism, a water droplet at a rainbow's outside edge disperses sunlight so that only a red ray reaches the eye of an observer. Similarly, a droplet at the inside edge sends only a violet ray to the observer. Droplets between the edges fill in the other colors of the visible spectrum.

when photons are absorbed, there is an increase in the energy of electrons shared by many atoms in large organic molecules.

When white light strikes carotene molecules in a carrot, for example, electrons absorb photons at the blue and green end of the spectrum. Photons of the remaining colors are reflected and act on an observer's eyes to produce colors ranging from pink to orange. Carrots, shrimp, and flamingos owe their colors to carotene.

A combination of absorption and reflection accounts for the colors of metals. In some metals, the configuration of energy rungs and the selection rules are such that an object can absorb and emit almost all visible photons. In white light, electrons at these metals' surface constantly absorb and emit tremendous numbers of photons, producing a mirrorlike reflection. Metals such as aluminum and silver emit the same combination of photons as they absorb. This is why they reflect the colors of surrounding objects. If the metal surface is smooth, the outlines of the objects are also reflected. In fact, an ordinary mirror is simply a piece of glass coated with an extremely smooth aluminum or silver backing.

Other metals, such as copper and gold, have selection rules that prohibit them from emitting the same combination of photons as they absorb. When white light strikes such a metal, it emits photons that let us see the metal's own color.

A special kind of absorption and emission called scattering accounts for the blueness of the sky. Atmospheric particles, dust and gas, whose dimensions are about the size of the wavelengths of visible photons, scatter photons of all colors in all directions. The amounts of the various photons scattered depend upon their wavelengths — the shorter the wavelength, the greater the amount scattered. Atmospheric particles therefore scatter more bluish light than reddish light. When you look at a patch of clear sky in the daytime your eyes receive an excess of bluish photons and the sky looks blue.

A large body of water appears blue because of absorption at the red end of the spectrum in the only color mechanism that does not involve changes in electron energy. In this mechanism, entire atoms move within water molecules. A water molecule consists of one oxygen atom bonded to two hydrogen atoms. The molecule can increase its energy by absorbing photons of red, orange, and yellow light. The additional energy makes the hydrogen atoms vibrate toward and away from the oxygen atom, as if the bonds were springs. The remaining photons are transmitted through the molecule, producing a blue color.

Reflection and a geometrical mechanism called wave interference give objects such as soap bubbles their many colors. Wave interference occurs when two waves of the same wavelength, and therefore of the same color, strike a thin film. One wave enters the film, reflects from its inside surface, and re-emerges from the film just as the other one reflects from the outside surface at the point of re-emergence. The wavelengths and the thickness of the film determine the relationship of the two wave shapes at this point. If the two waves are indistinguishable from each other at the point of re-emergence, they reinforce each other, and the point has the color that corresponds to their common wavelength. On the other hand, if the wave shapes are mirror images of each other, the waves cancel each other, and their corresponding color does not appear.

A film's thickness at any point therefore determines its color, so a film whose thickness varies has many colors. Soap bubbles and oil slicks often vary so much in thickness that they appear to display all the colors of the rainbow.

The rainbow itself gets its colors from the reflection and the bending, or refraction, of sunlight passing through water droplets. When a beam of sunlight enters a droplet, the droplet acts as a prism, separating the beam into rays of various colors. Violet light bends the most, followed by blue, green, yellow, orange, and red. The individual rays then reflect from the droplet's back surface and finally re-emerge from the front of the droplet at various angles.

These angles determine the appearance of a rainbow. A person observing a rainbow receives only one color from each droplet in the rainbow. The color depends upon the angle between the sun's rays and the observer's line of sight to the droplet. A droplet at the inside of a rainbow is always at an angle of 40 degrees and produces violet. Droplets at larger angles produce colors in the order of refraction — blue, green, yellow, orange, and — at 42 degrees — red.

Looking at a rainbow, or any other colored object, should stimulate our intellects as well as our eyes. For what comes to us as color is the result of some fundamental principles of the physical world.

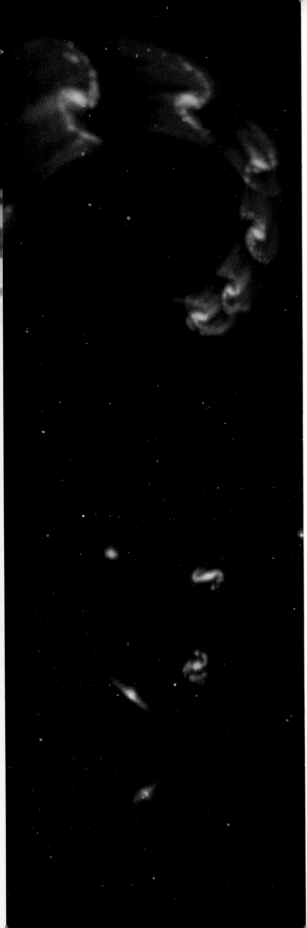

Mapping the Universe

By Margaret J. Geller

Astronomers combine computerized data and observation to determine the size and distribution of objects and voids in space.

Maps are among the earliest written records of civilization. Before the earth could be mapped, it had to be explored. Early maps were thus naturally limited to small portions of the surface of the earth. Although they did not know the shapes of continents and the sizes of oceans, the ancient Greek mapmakers knew that the earth is spherical and they estimated its circumference with remarkable accuracy.

As cartographers of the universe, we are today much as the Greeks were 2,500 years ago. We have a working model, but our detailed knowledge is still limited. We have estimates of the age and size of the visible universe, but we have mapped only about one hundred-thousandth of its volume. The mapped volume is huge in absolute size — about 10,000,000,000,000,000,000,000,000 (or 10^{25}) cubic light-years (one light-year is the distance light travels in one year — 5.88 trillion miles). A map of one hundred-thousandth of the surface of the earth would cover only about 1,800 square miles, or about one and a half times the area of Rhode Island.

We have much information in addition to our detailed maps. We have made detailed observations of some objects in the far reaches of the universe. We have recently learned about very large structures — which may be immense concentrations of matter or vast open spaces — in the universe, and we are just beginning to understand their form and origin.

In order to map the surface of the earth, we travel wherever we can with our measuring apparatus. Inaccessible regions of the earth, such as the ocean floor, require sophisticated, indirect mapping techniques. A map of the universe must be based on still less direct and less detailed information.

Even our own galaxy, the Milky Way, is so vast that we cannot hope to explore it by actually traveling around it. An explorer who started a journey at the dawn of civilization — tens of thousands of years ago — and who traveled at the speed of light would by now have just managed to travel around our galaxy. The Milky Way is a system of 10^{11} to 10^{12} stars. It is a spiral galaxy with a radius of more than 30,000 light-years. The band of stars you see stretching across the sky is the plane of our galaxy.

The portion of the universe that can be explored with large ground-based optical telescopes contains some 10 billion galaxies comparable in mass with the Milky Way. Only one of these galaxies, Andromeda, our nearest neighbor, can be seen with the unaided eye. If the galaxies were uniformly distributed in space, the typical distance between them would be 10 million light-years. This separation is 100 times the size of an average galaxy.

The universe is mostly empty, or at least dark, space. Galaxies could be substantially larger than the images we see on photographic plates. Much of the matter in galaxies may not give out any light. In fact, as much as 90 per cent of the matter in the universe could be dark. According to astronomers' calculations, at least some dark material is needed to explain the motions of galaxies.

Gravity is the physical force that tells matter how to move. Stars are bound by gravity into the systems we call galaxies; galaxies themselves cluster together because of their mutual gravitational attraction. Concentrations of galaxies range from small systems, or groups with a few members, to larger systems called rich clusters, containing thousands of galaxies.

The Milky Way and Andromeda are the two largest galaxies in the Local Group. The Local Group also includes about two dozen tiny neighbor galaxies. About 50 million light-years away from the Local Group lies the nearest rich cluster, the Virgo Cluster. Between the Local Group and the Virgo Cluster lie many groups and chains of galaxies. All of these structures make up the Local Supercluster — consisting of about 100 groups of galaxies. Several more distant rich clusters of galaxies, including Hercules and Coma, are also members of superclusters — clusters of clusters of galaxies. Superclusters may

The author:
Margaret J. Geller is an assistant professor at Harvard University Center for Astrophysics.

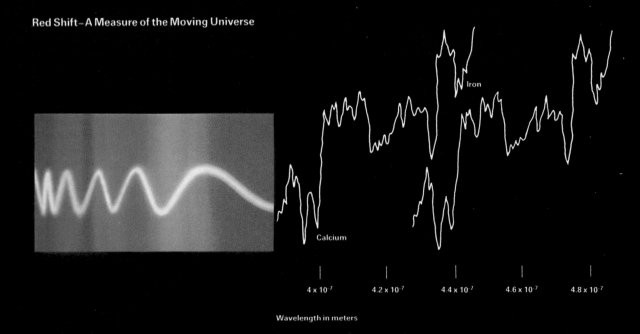

Iron

Calcium

| 4 x 10⁻⁷ | 4.2 x 10⁻⁷ | 4.4 x 10⁻⁷ | 4.6 x 10⁻⁷ | 4.8 x 10⁻⁷ |

Wavelength in meters

be as much as 300 million light-years across. We would like to know how common such structures are and whether others are larger.

How do we learn about the distribution of galaxies in the universe? How do we use the maps we make to discover the structure of the universe? Let's return for a moment to the problem of charting the earth. To describe the earth's surface — particularly mountaintops and ocean floors — we need three numbers: latitude, longitude, and altitude. To locate a galaxy in space we similarly need latitude and longitude — plus the distance of the galaxy from us.

Latitude and longitude are relatively easy to obtain; they simply specify the position of a galaxy on the sky. During the 1940s, astronomers took photographs of the entire northern sky with the 48-inch Schmidt telescope on Palomar Mountain in California. Recent surveys of the southern sky have been made with the 48-inch Schmidt telescope at Siding Spring, Australia, and with the 1-meter telescope at the European Southern Observatory in La Silla, Chile. Millions of galaxies, many as distant as 2 billion light-years, can be found on the photographic plates, but many galaxies are too faint to be seen with a 48-inch Schmidt telescope. Larger telescopes, such as the 4-meter telescope at Kitt Peak National Observatory near Tucson, Ariz., and the 5-meter telescope on Palomar Mountain enable us to probe at least twice as far.

Finding a galaxy's distance from earth is more difficult. We derive all we know about objects outside the solar system from the light they emit. After we have found the position of a galaxy on the sky, we can proceed to measure the spectrum of the light it emits. From the spectrum and our description of the evolving universe, we can

Comparing spectra of iron and calcium observed in a galaxy with spectra of those elements measured on earth reveals a red shift of 10 per cent. This indicates that the galaxy is moving away from us at a velocity of 30,000 kilometers per second.

143

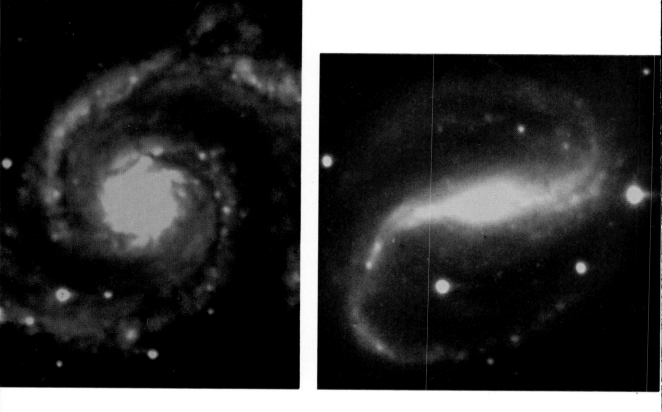

Gravity pulls stars into varied structures, such as galaxies in a typical spiral, *above left,* or barred spiral, *above right.* The dense Coma Cluster, *below,* contains thousands of elliptical galaxies.

find the distance to the galaxy. In order to understand how, we have to learn a bit about spectra.

Atoms and ions of elements emit and absorb light at characteristic wavelengths. For example, if you throw table salt, or sodium chloride, into a gas flame, you see the yellow light emitted by the excited sodium atoms. These are the same spectral lines that make sodium street lights yellow. The same lines identify sodium in a galaxy — with one important difference. The emission or absorption lines in the spectrum of a distant galaxy are shifted toward the red end of the electromagnetic spectrum. The wavelengths are longer and the frequencies are correspondingly lower than the values we measure in a laboratory on earth. The red shift indicates that the galaxies are apparently receding from us. This effect is similar to the change in the frequency of a train whistle as the train moves away from us. The tone of the whistle becomes deeper — the frequency is lower and the wavelength of the sound wave is longer.

However, the comparison of the red shift of a galaxy with the change in frequency of a train whistle is a bit misleading. The galaxies are not really flying apart from one another. Difficult as it may be to imagine, the fabric of space between the galaxies is stretching and with it the wavelength of light is also stretching. It may help to think of the expanding universe as the surface of an expanding balloon. Small paper stickers randomly located on the balloon represent galaxies. The balloon expands, but the "galaxies" do not. Only the separation between neighboring galaxies increases. The galaxies are not racing across the surface of the balloon — the space is expanding. The expanding surface of the balloon — the space — has no center. The expansion looks the same from any point on the surface.

Clearly, then, the universe changes or evolves. It is dynamic, not static. In 1929, astronomer Edwin P. Hubble provided the first observational evidence for an expanding universe. He assumed that galaxies are markers of the expansion. The apparent recession velocity of a galaxy is derived from the red shift of its spectral lines. Hubble showed that the red shift is proportional to the distance of the galaxy from us — that is, the farther away the galaxy, the faster it is moving and the greater its red shift. This relationship gives the third coordinate necessary for a celestial map — distance. Galaxies that are close together on the sky and that have similar red shifts are close together in space.

Before using these tools to examine the galaxy distribution, it is important to understand how the universe evolves. Hubble's expansion law is the same as the one for our balloon model. Imagine that a movie of the expansion has been made. Run it backwards. The galaxies get closer and closer together as we go farther and farther back in time. The universe was more dense at early times than it is today. By running the movie backwards until all the galaxies lie on top of one another in a dense clump, we can measure the age of the

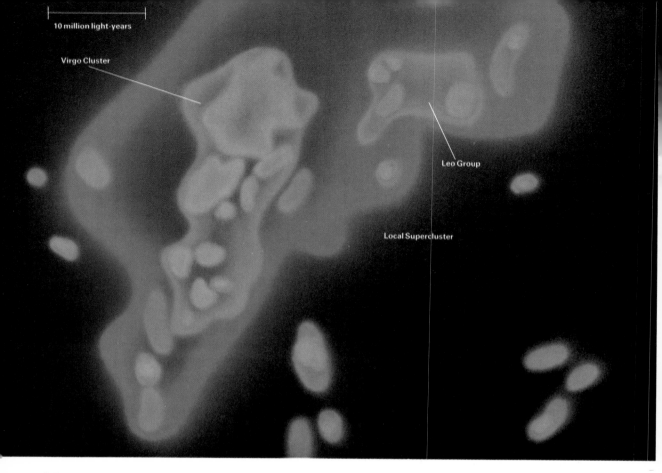

Labels on image: 10 million light-years; Virgo Cluster; Leo Group; Local Supercluster

A Cosmic Archipelago
The uneven distribution of matter in a very small portion of the universe is apparent on a detailed contour map of the Local Supercluster, the giant collection of galaxies closest to us. The loosely organized Leo Group and the more densely packed Virgo Cluster are among about 100 systems combined like islands in a sea of space to form the Local Supercluster.

universe. This dense clump of matter marks the moment of the big bang — the generally accepted beginning of the universe.

We use our measurement of the cosmic expansion rate to tell how long it takes for the movie to run back to the beginning. Thus, the running time of the movie — the age of the universe — is between 10 billion and 20 billion years. The radius of the visible universe is 10 billion to 20 billion light-years, just the distance light has traveled since the initial bang. In other words, looking at distant objects in the universe is equivalent to looking back in time. Light that now reaches us from a galaxy 1 billion light-years away has taken 1 billion years to get here.

The early universe was hot as well as dense. In 1964, Arno Penzias and Robert Wilson of Bell Laboratories in Holmdel, N.J., first detected the radiation from the big bang's "primordial fireball." (In 1978, they won the Nobel Prize in physics for their work.) This radiation is a relic of a time when the universe was 1,000 times hotter than it is now, and only about 1 million years old. The radiation is now red-shifted into the microwave range of the electromagnetic spectrum. In every direction, the amount of this microwave radiation we observe is nearly the same. This remarkable smoothness tells us that the distribution of matter in the early universe was more uniform than it is now. Therefore, the large structures we observe —

galaxies, clusters of galaxies, and superclusters — must develop as the universe evolves.

The development of structure in the universe is closely related to its evolution. Cosmologists have long argued about whether the universe is open or closed. If the universe is closed, its expansion is similar to the expansion in our balloon model. In this model, expansion eventually ceases and the universe contracts to extremely high density. If the universe is open, space is infinite and expansion continues forever. My own work and that of my colleagues indicates that the universe is open.

To understand the relative motion of galaxies separating with the cosmological expansion, we can compare it with the motion of a rocket launched from the surface of the earth. If the velocity of the rocket is too small for it to escape from the gravitational pull of the earth, the rocket falls back to earth. Now think about a galaxy on the edge of an average large region of the universe that contains many galaxies. Whether or not that galaxy can escape from the others depends on its velocity and the total mass in the region. If the mass is large enough, the gravitational attraction of the matter is sufficient to keep the galaxy from escaping and the universe is closed, or bound. The same rocket launched with the same velocity from the moon might escape, because the moon is less massive than the earth. Similarly, if the region of the universe in our example contains less mass, the galaxy will similarly escape, and we say that the universe is open, or unbound.

The concentrations of matter we see in the universe may also be bound or unbound. We know that the planets are bound to the sun. Galaxies are bound systems of stars. The dense inner regions of clusters of galaxies are bound systems of galaxies. Superclusters may or may not be bound systems. If the universe is closed, superclusters would be bound systems. If the universe is open, some may be bound and others may not be. In this case, whether they are bound or not depends on their density — the amount of mass contained in their volume.

As we look at larger and larger structures, the properties of the system become more and more closely linked with the dynamics of the universe. Superclusters, which extend across tens of millions of light-years, are so large that their formation and evolution depend directly on the expansion of the universe.

A supercluster may contain a rich cluster along with several groups of galaxies, or it may contain several rich clusters of galaxies. Superclusters may be anywhere from 10 million to 100 million light-years or more across.

During the 1950s, Gerard de Vaucouleurs of the University of Texas at Austin was the first to define and describe the Local Supercluster. The Local Supercluster has a flattened shape. It is about 80 million light-years long and 30 million light-years across. In 1981,

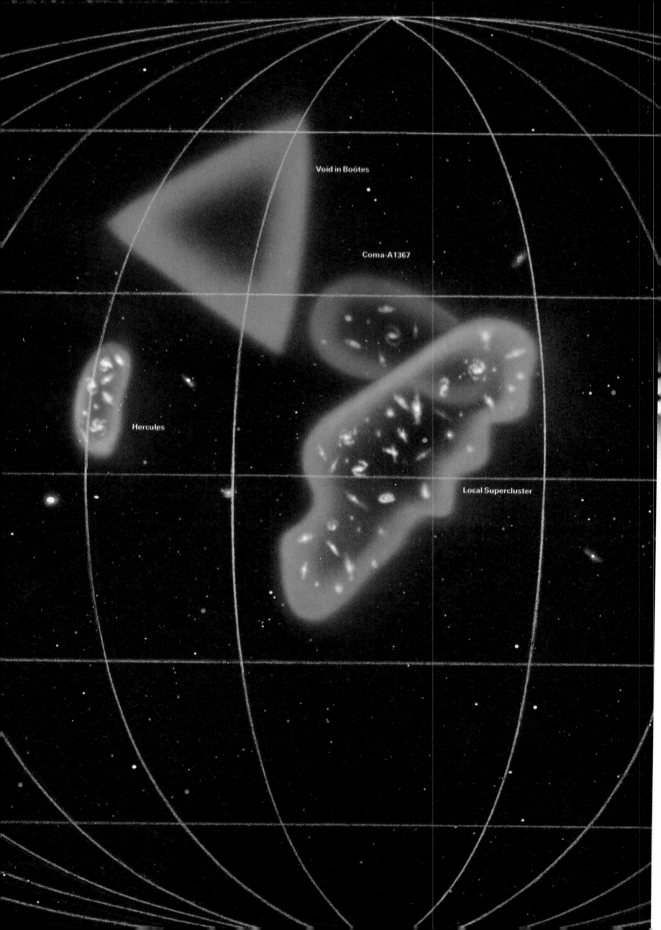

Void in Boötes

Coma-A1367

Hercules

Local Supercluster

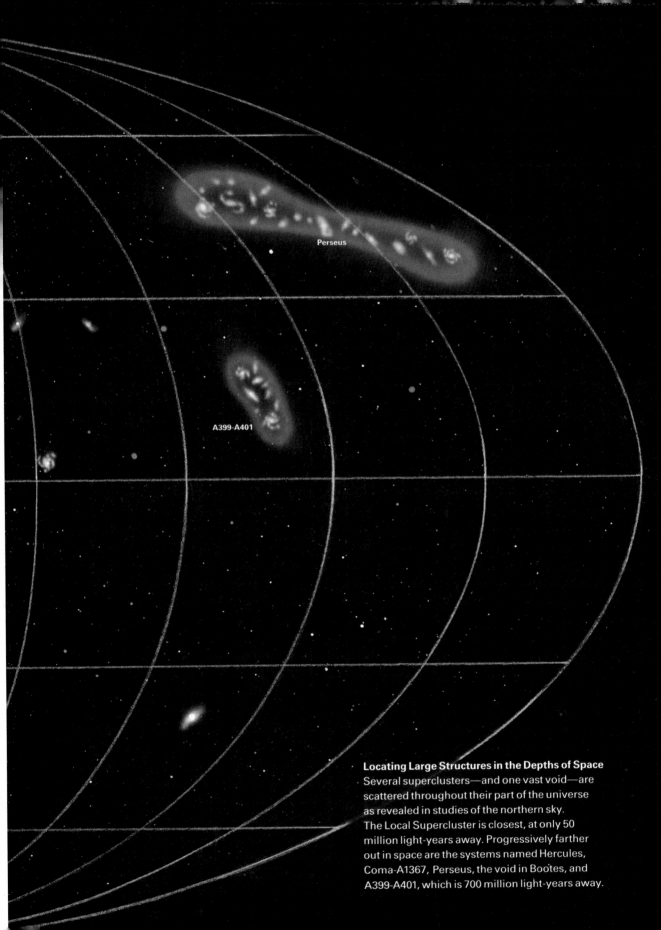

Perseus

A399-A401

Locating Large Structures in the Depths of Space
Several superclusters—and one vast void—are
scattered throughout their part of the universe
as revealed in studies of the northern sky.
The Local Supercluster is closest, at only 50
million light-years away. Progressively farther
out in space are the systems named Hercules,
Coma-A1367, Perseus, the void in Boötes, and
A399-A401, which is 700 million light-years away.

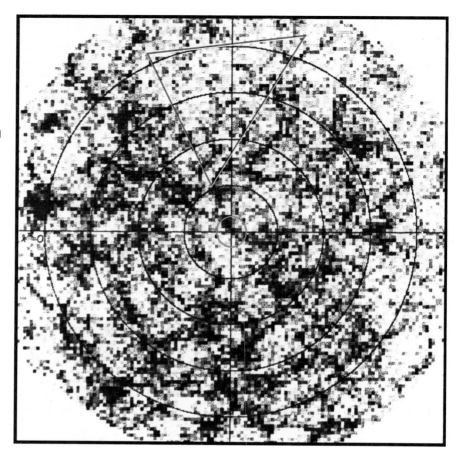

Irregular distribution of matter in the universe is visible on a computerized map of 1 million galaxies spread over the northern sky. The darkest squares hold nearly 40 galaxies apiece; the lightest contain only a few. In the circled area at the map's center lies the densely packed Coma Cluster, and at the top is the vast void in Boötes.

astronomers at the Harvard-Smithsonian Center for Astrophysics in Cambridge, Mass., completed a red-shift survey that provides information about galaxies in this region. Marc Davis, John P. Huchra, David W. Latham, and John Tonry mapped a region about 10^{25} cubic light-years in volume.

Since 1976, the amount of data on the distribution of galaxies has increased dramatically. The measurement of galaxy red shifts has become easier and faster because of the replacement of cameras that require long exposures to make photographic plates by solid-state detectors, which count photons, or particles of light. By 1970, astronomers had measured a few hundred galaxy red shifts; by 1983, they had measured more than 10,000 of them. Among these measurements are some of several superclusters.

The Coma-A1367 supercluster, for example, contains the very dense rich cluster Coma and the cluster A1367. These clusters are neighbors in both position and red shift — that is, they appear to be near each other on the sky and are about equally far from the earth. Coma takes its name from its location in the constellation *Coma Berenices* (Berenice's hair). A1367 refers to the cluster designated "1367" in the catalog of 2,712 rich clusters published in 1953 by astronomer George O. Abell of the University of California, Los Angeles. Coma's number is A1656, but astronomers prefer its name.

The Coma-A1367 supercluster is about 200 million light-years from earth and stretches for at least 40 million light-years across the sky. The nearly 1 million galaxies in the system are contained in a volume of about 10^{23} cubic light-years. In the most dense regions of this system, the galaxies are separated only by distances comparable with their sizes — by about 300,000 light-years.

Among many new studies is one I began in 1982 along with my colleagues at the Harvard-Smithsonian Center for Astrophysics. We are investigating the supercluster called A399-A401, which is so far away that its light takes 700 million years to reach us. The system is easy to study because it consists of only two rich clusters, each containing more than 1,000 galaxies.

Just as there are large concentrations of matter in the universe, there are also large holes — vast empty spaces that could easily house the largest superclusters we know. The 1981 study by Davis and his colleagues revealed a large empty region behind the Virgo Cluster where there are almost no galaxies. But that region and other similar ones found in supercluster surveys pale in comparison with the hole

There is a lack of galaxies measured by a break in red-shift distribution in one recently mapped region of the sky — 400 million to 600 million light-years from the Milky Way in the constellation Boötes. It has been interpreted as a void with a depth of 200 million light-years.

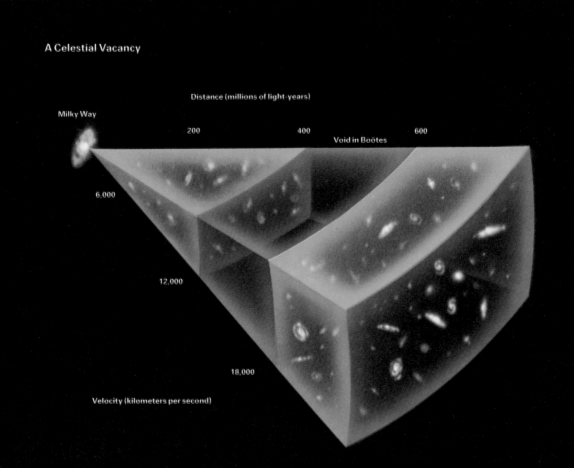

A Celestial Vacancy

Distance (millions of light-years)

Milky Way

200   400   600

Void in Boötes

6,000

12,000

18,000

Velocity (kilometers per second)

found in 1982 in the constellation Boötes. This hole was discovered by Robert P. Kirshner of the University of Michigan in Ann Arbor; Augustus Oemler, Jr., of Yale University in New Haven, Conn.; and Paul L. Schechter and Stephen A. Shectman of Mount Wilson Observatory in Pasadena, Calif.

The four astronomers measured red shifts for a carefully selected sample of galaxies covering a 35-degree, wedge-shaped region across the sky. Surprisingly, they found virtually no galaxies in their sample with red shifts implying recessional velocities between 12,000 kilometers per second (kps) and 18,000 kps. There are many galaxies in the sample that have red shifts less than 12,000 kps and greater than 18,000 kps. From the relationship between the galaxies' apparent recession velocity and distance, we find that the 6,000-kps hole in the red-shift distribution is a hole in space about 200 million light-years deep.

The volume of the void in Boötes is about 10^{25} cubic light-years — an extraordinary amount of nothing. The size of this region is comparable with the entire nearby region of space that astronomers have painstakingly mapped during the last five years. It is larger than most superclusters. It is hard to imagine such a vast emptiness. Some astronomers who find so much nothing difficult to accept suggest that there is dark matter in the void. But no observations require that such dark material be present — the region could very well be almost empty space.

The void in Boötes shows up as an underpopulated region on a map of the northern sky made many years ago by astronomers C. Donald Shane and Carl A. Wirtanen at Lick Observatory on Mount Hamilton in California. These two men spent 12 years, starting in the mid-1950s, counting the nearest 1 million galaxies in the northern sky.

In 1977, astrophysicist P. James E. Peebles and his colleagues at Princeton University in New Jersey used Shane and Wirtanen's data to make a two-dimensional map of the sky. This map shows an unexpected feature — many long filamentary, or threadlike, clusters of galaxies. The longest of these filaments stretches for several hundred million light-years. However, a filament may not be a real three-dimensional structure. One part could be very near us and an apparently linking part could be very distant. We can be sure that the parts are connected physical structures only by measuring the red shifts of the galaxies in them. If the red shifts are similar, the galaxies are in the same place in space and the filaments are real. Because the vast number of galaxies that make up these apparent filaments are quite faint, astronomers will have to spend many nights using large telescopes to solve this enticing problem.

Studies of nearby systems suggest that large filamentary structures do exist. One example is the Perseus supercluster in the region of the sky that contains the constellations Perseus and Pisces, recently studied by Estonian astronomers Jaan Einasto, Mikhel Jôeveer, and Enn Saar. Guido L. Chincarini of the University of Oklahoma in Norman and Riccardo Giovanelli and Martha P. Haynes of the National Astronomy and Ionosphere Center in Arecibo, Puerto Rico, have been using the Arecibo radio telescope to measure red shifts in this system. Red-shift measurements confirm that the Perseus supercluster is a physical system at least 10 times as long as it is wide. It extends for nearly 100 million light-years across the sky.

These very large structures — holes and superclusters — are important for understanding galaxy and cluster formation. We do not yet know whether galaxies or clusters form first. Two of the theories being investigated are the gravitational instability theory and the "pancake" theory. The gravitational instability theory, which Peebles has investigated extensively, says that the galaxies form first. They cluster together because of their mutual gravitational attraction. Computer simulations of such gravitational clustering in an evolving universe match some features of galaxy distribution.

The pancake theory, suggested by Russian astrophysicists Yakov B. Zel'dovich and Rashid Sunyaev of the Institute of Applied Mathematics in Moscow, proposes that large flattened sheets of material the size of clusters or even superclusters form first. They later break up to make galaxies. Some astronomers view the flatness of extended systems like the Local Supercluster as support for this picture.

Although there is debate about the correct model, we can draw a few simple conclusions. We know that matter was more smoothly distributed in the early universe than it is now. In order to make large concentrations of matter in some regions and large voids in others, matter must move from one place to another as the universe evolves. The void in Boötes is so large that galaxies cannot have moved across it in the lifetime of the universe. The void, then, gives us important information about the conditions in the early universe when large structures began to form: in the early universe, matter was clumped into larger concentrations than we had expected. Discovering a great many vast voids and superclusters would convince us that we have to revise our ideas about the origin and growth of structure in the universe.

Along with reassessment of models goes the attempt to acquire more data — to make more extensive and detailed maps. The launch of the Space Telescope in 1986 will enable us to observe still fainter galaxies and so look back far enough to find out whether galaxies or clusters form first. However, fundamental observations of the largest structures in the universe will still be made from the ground because that is the most efficient way to make a large number of spectroscopic observations of the relatively nearby brighter galaxies. From this speck of dust, the earth, astronomer-cartographers will continue to map the vast superclusters and voids — the continents and oceans — of the universe.

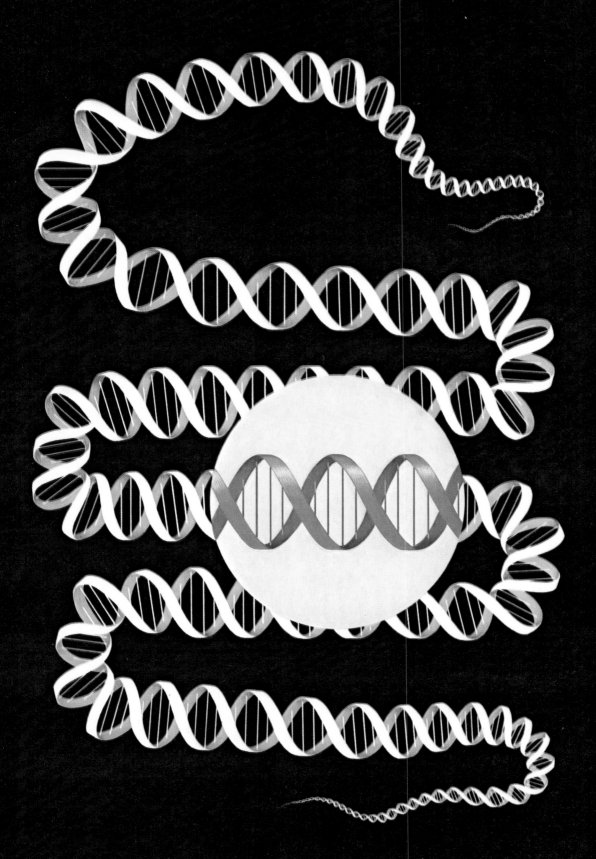

Cancer's Genetic Connection

By Beverly Merz

Scientists probing the mysteries of the cell are finding that we all possess genes that, under certain conditions, can give rise to cancer.

Carol was worried about the raised, mottled mole on her left wrist. Every day she looked at it, it seemed larger than the day before. Was it growing? Could it be cancerous?

Carol had reason to think about cancer. Her 25-year-old cousin had recently completed therapy for Hodgkin's disease, a cancer of the lymphatic system. Her mother had just marked the fifth anniversary of a mastectomy for breast cancer, and her grandmother had died of a malignant tumor of the pancreas. "Cancer seems to run in my family," Carol thought. "Can we inherit genes for cancer?"

The answer is yes. And not just for Carol's family, but for all of us. For some time, medical scientists have been noting that some people seem more likely to develop cancer than others. Then, in the late 1970s and early 1980s, the evidence began to mount that all human beings have genes that can transform normal cells into malignant cells. Scientists have named these genes *oncogenes*, from the Greek prefix *onkos*, meaning *mass*. Hundreds of researchers at institutions in the United States and Europe are now working feverishly to understand how oncogenes may change the cell—and how to prevent or reverse that potential sabotage.

Oncogenes, like all other genes, are segments of deoxyribonucleic acid (DNA), a double-stranded helical molecule that looks like a twisted ladder. The sides of the ladder consist of alternating sugar and phosphate molecules; the rungs are formed from pairs of molecules called bases. There are four base molecules—adenine (A), thymine (T), guanine (G), and cytosine (C)—and they always pair up the same way—A with T and G with C.

All DNA molecules are not the same. The individuality of a given DNA molecule is determined by the relative amount of each base it contains as well as by the order in which these bases appear. Scientists use the bases' initials as a kind of shorthand to describe DNA molecules. "ACTGTC," for example, describes a six-base segment of one DNA strand. The other strand, its complement, must read "TGACCA." In this way, we can get a good idea of how the entire molecule is constructed.

Each gene is a stretch of DNA that is usually thousands of base pairs long. Every human cell has approximately 50,000 such genes, arranged end to end, on strands of DNA. Each of these genes codes for the manufacture of a protein—a complex molecule formed from building blocks called amino acids. However, only the genes coding for proteins needed by a certain type of cell—a red blood cell, for example—are expressed, or switched on, in that cell. The other genes, such as those determining eye color, are present, but remain switched off.

W hen a cell needs to produce a given protein, the segment of DNA with the appropriate gene partially uncoils into separate strands. This gives enzymes—substances that initiate, speed up, or slow down a chemical reaction—access to each strand. The enzymes direct the formation of ribonucleic acid (RNA) on one of the DNA strands. RNA is a single-stranded molecule similar to DNA except for the substitution of the base molecule, uracil (U), for thymine. The RNA strand becomes a complementary copy of the DNA strand on which it is formed.

Once the RNA copy is complete, the DNA strands close and the RNA molecule leaves the nucleus, and travels to a ribosome, a cellular structure responsible for protein assembly. There, the information in the RNA is "translated" three bases at a time. Each of these base triplets, called codons, specifies a particular amino acid. The order in which the codons appear determines the order in which the amino acids must be connected to create the protein. The protein so created may have one of several functions. If it is a structural

The author:
Beverly Merz is an associate editor of the Medical News section of the *Journal of the American Medical Association.*

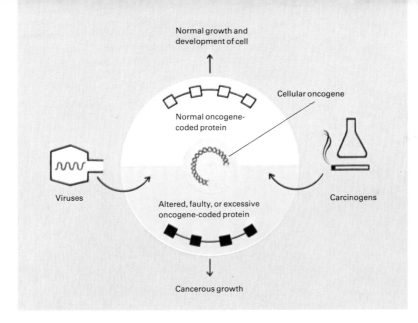

A Gene That Can Cause Cancer
Cancer may be caused when a virus or a carcinogen stimulates
a cellular *oncogene* (cancer gene) to produce an unwanted
protein, a faulty protein, or too much of a needed protein.

protein, it may become part of a muscle or organ. If it is a hormone,
it will regulate bodily processes. If it is an enzyme, it will take part
in some biochemical reaction.

Even a protein produced by an oncogene may perform an essential function in the cell. For example, some oncogene proteins have
been indentified as enzymes that play a role in normal cell growth.
Researchers suspect that, when they have identified the proteins that
each of the approximately 20 oncogenes codes for, they will find that
all are somehow related to cell growth or differentiation — the process that determines that cell's particular role in the body.

Scientists theorize that when an oncogene is functioning normally
in a cell, or when it is "turned off" in a cell that does not need that
oncogene's particular protein, the cell grows and divides normally.
But if the oncogene is switched on at the wrong time or in the wrong
cell, or if it begins producing an improper protein or an excessive
amount of protein, the cell might begin to divide uncontrollably.
And scientists are now collecting evidence that such genetic events
do indeed occur.

The trail leading to such evidence was blazed in the early 1900s
when researchers discovered the first link between genes and cancer.
However, these genes were not discovered in humans or other animals, but in viruses.

The story begins in 1911 with a discovery made by a young physician, F. Peyton Rous. Rous, working at the Rockefeller Institute
for Medical Research in New York City, was trying to trace the
development of *sarcomas* (cancers of the connective tissues) in chickens. He removed tumors from sarcoma-ridden chickens, ground

them up, and forced them through a filter to remove all cells. He then injected the resultant liquid into disease-free chickens. The inoculated chickens subsequently developed sarcomas.

Rous then knew that these new tumors could not have been seeded by transplanted cancer cells. He reasoned that some far smaller agent — perhaps a virus — had passed through the filter to continue its deadly mission. Other scientists, however, dismissed Rous's theory, pointing out that viruses cause contagious diseases. Since cancer is not contagious, they declared, neither chicken sarcomas nor any other type of malignancy could be caused by a virus.

His detractors were eventually proven wrong, and in 1966, Rous received the Nobel Prize for physiology or medicine for his work. In fact, over the years, scientists have learned that many cancers are caused by viruses.

Viruses are the simplest known form of life. They are equipped with only the bare necessities of existence — a relatively small number of genes (ranging from three in the most rudimentary viruses to several hundred in the most complex) encased in a coat of protein molecules. A few viruses also contain some additional proteins and an outer membrane.

Because the meagerly outfitted virus cannot survive on its own, it must live as a parasite inside a cell, using the machinery of its host to make copies of its own genes and to assemble the proteins those genes code for. The genes and proteins are then assembled into multiple copies of the original virus, which are then released from the host cell to spread the infection to its neighbors.

Some viruses — including most cancer viruses — carry their genetic information in RNA molecules, and their genes are copied by inserting them into the cell's DNA. These viruses also carry an enzyme, called reverse transcriptase, that manufactures a complementary DNA strand using the RNA as a pattern. Cellular enzymes construct the remaining DNA strand, and the completed molecule is incorporated into the cell's DNA. Because these viruses carry out transcription in reverse, they were given the Latin prefix *retro* (backward).

Oncogenes were first identified in retroviruses. In fact, the gene carried by the chicken sarcoma virus that Peyton Rous had isolated was the first to be so identified. Decades later, other investigators discovered that the Rous sarcoma virus, as it is now called, contains a specific gene that can cause cancer.

Not all strains of retroviruses cause cancer. In the early 1970s, virologist Peter H. Duesberg of the University of California at Berkeley and researchers at the University of Zurich in Switzerland studied a variant strain of the Rous sarcoma virus that does not produce malignant tumors. They reasoned that the variant strain of the virus probably lacks a gene that is present in the variety that causes cancer. So they decided to match up the segments of the two strains to see which gene the variant was lacking.

Identifying A Cancer Gene

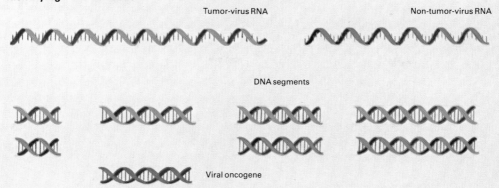

Tumor-virus RNA   Non-tumor-virus RNA

DNA segments

Viral oncogene

Comparison of DNA segments transcribed from the RNA of a chicken-tumor
virus and its nontumor-causing cousin identifies an ocogene.

Finding a Cancer Gene in Normal Cells

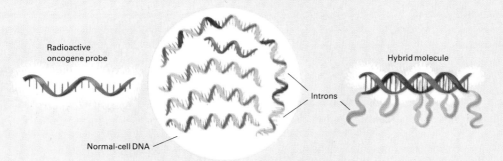

Radioactive
oncogene probe

Introns

Hybrid molecule

Normal-cell DNA

A radioactive viral oncogene probe "fishes out" a cellular oncogene from
the DNA of normal cells by forming a hybrid. Intervening sequences —
introns — in the cellular oncogene do not match and so hang in loops.

Filling Out a Cancer Gene

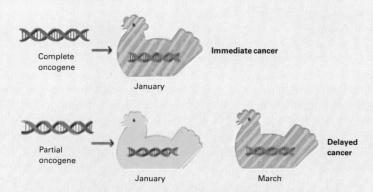

Complete
oncogene

Immediate cancer

January

Partial
oncogene

**Delayed
cancer**

January   March

A retrovirus with just 20 per cent of a chicken-tumor oncogene
can acquire the rest of the oncogene from a chicken cell the virus
has infected and cause the cell to become cancerous.

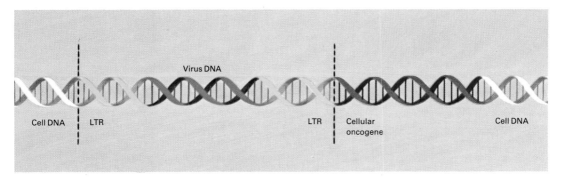

Cell DNA   LTR   Virus DNA   LTR   Cellular oncogene   Cell DNA

Triggering a Tumor
Some viruses without oncogenes contain sequences — called long terminal repeats (LTRs) — that can trigger cellular genes. Such a virus may cause cancer if inserted next to an oncogene in a cell.

To do this, they chopped the RNA of both strains of Rous sarcoma virus into several segments with ribonuclease — a restriction enzyme that cuts RNA molecules at specific sites. By comparing fragments of DNA copied from the virus RNA, the researchers identified a segment from the cancer-causing virus that was absent from the mutants. When they added the DNA fragment to cultures of chicken bladder cells, the cells were transformed into cancer cells. The scientists concluded that this DNA segment — or, more precisely, the RNA sequence from which it was transcribed — contained the oncogene. This oncogene was named the *src* (sarcoma) oncogene.

By the early 1970s, scientists had identified oncogenes among the genes of a variety of cancer-causing retroviruses. All these oncogenes have been given three-letter designations that relate to the names of the viruses that carry them or to the names of the tumors with which they are associated. For example, the *myc* oncogene is associated with the avian myelocytomatosis virus; the *mos* oncogene with the Molony murine sarcoma virus; and the *fes* oncogene with the feline sarcoma virus. These viruses were found to cause cancers in birds, mice, and cats, respectively.

Scientists began to look for explanations of why oncogenes occurred so often in retroviruses, and how these viruses produced cancer in so many vertebrate species. Robert J. Huebner and George F. Todaro of the National Cancer Institute (NCI) in Bethesda, Md., suggested a possible answer. They theorized that vertebrates could have acquired oncogenes from retrovirus infections that occurred millions of years ago. Once the virus oncogene had become incorporated into an animal's DNA, it would be passed from one generation to the next along with other hereditary characteristics. Furthermore, when a species evolved into new species, each of those species would carry the oncogene.

To test this hypothesis, microbiologists J. Michael Bishop, Harold E. Varmus, and Dominique Stehelin of the University of California Medical School in San Francisco in 1972 embarked upon what might be considered a genetic fishing trip. They hoped to pull the *src* oncogene from the DNA of about a dozen kinds of vertebrates, ranging from fish to birds to human beings. To do this, they collected pools of tens of thousands of animal genes, each mass of genes taken from healthy cells of a different vertebrate species.

The researchers used a special lure, or probe, to find the oncogene — a radioactive single-stranded DNA copy of the *src* oncogene. This worked on the principle of molecular hybridization, in which single strands of DNA are made into new double strands, or hybrids. The process involves putting DNA into a solution that separates the double-stranded molecules. One of these strands will combine with a complementary strand of DNA, if there is one in the solution. Thus, if the *src* oncogene was present in the vertebrate DNA, it would pair with the *src* probe, and the radioactivity given off by the resulting hybrid would enable the scientists to locate it.

The scientists had several successful expeditions. They first found the *src* gene in the DNA of normal chicken cells and then went on to discover it in the normal cells of several species of fish and mammals. They finally found it in human cells. The researchers had discovered an oncogene that was common to many vertebrates.

They also found evidence that the *src* gene must have originated in the animal cells, not in the retrovirus. When they studied the hybrids formed by the *src* oncogene probe and the oncogenes extracted from vertebrate cells, they found stretches of DNA in the cellular oncogene that were unpaired in the hybrid. They recognized these unattached segments as introns, or intervening sequences — sections of DNA that do not code for proteins. Introns are found only in cells with nuclei and thus are not in viruses. Since the virus probe contained no introns, the introns in the DNA from the animal cells had nothing to pair with and thus formed single-stranded loops along the length of the hybrid.

The scientists hypothesized that the virus's original set of genes had been inserted next to the oncogene in an early cell — perhaps 500 million years ago. When a cellular enzyme copied the virus genes back into RNA to re-create the retrovirus, it also by chance transcribed the oncogene, at which time the introns were snipped out. The streamlined RNA version of the *src* gene was then packaged into a newly assembled retrovirus and transported out of the cell.

In 1977, biochemist Hidesaburo Hanafusa of Rockefeller University in New York City reinforced this hypothesis. He showed that a strain of the Rous sarcoma virus can capture the *src* oncogene from a cell and then somehow use the oncogene to convert normal cells into malignant ones.

Hanafusa inoculated healthy chickens with a defective strain of the retrovirus that carries only 20 per cent of the *src* oncogene. He found that the chickens did not begin to develop tumors within a few days, as they do when infected with a virus carrying the full *src* gene. However, cancers began to appear after about two months. Hanafusa extracted cells from the tumors, isolated copies of the virus, and added a radioactive probe for the *src* oncogene to the viral

Isolating a tumor-cell oncogene

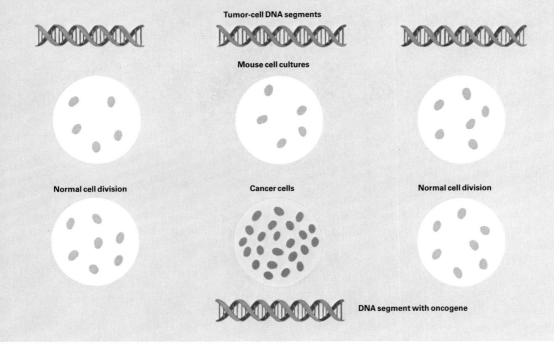

DNA from human bladder-cancer cells is cut into segments and added to mouse cell cultures. A culture in which the cells are transformed into cancer cells, *bottom row, center,* indicates that its DNA segment contains the oncogene. When a radioactive virus oncogene probe, *left,* is added to a strand of the separated DNA, it hybridizes with the cellular oncogene.

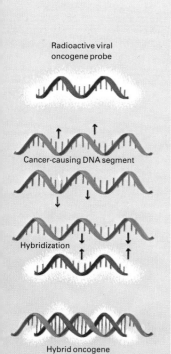

RNA. The probe hybridized completely with the viral RNA, indicating that the full *src* oncogene was now present. Somehow the virus had acquired the missing portion of the *src* gene from the chicken's cellular DNA and, with it, the ability to cause cancer.

Further research determined that a retrovirus can enable a cellular oncogene to cause cancer, even if the retrovirus itself has no oncogene. Colleagues of Hanafusa's at Rockefeller University — William S. Hayward and Benjamin G. Neel — along with Susan M. Astrin of the Institute for Cancer Research in Fox Chase, Pa., provided evidence of this in 1981.

The team was studying the avian lymphoma virus, a retrovirus without an oncogene that may induce tumors in chickens several months after infection. The virus contains sequences called long terminal repeats (LTRs) on both ends of its RNA. These sequences can sometimes act as a triggering device that can cause a gene to produce excessive, and perhaps abnormal, protein. The researchers tracked the avian lymphoma virus DNA (after reverse transcription from RNA) in tumor cells of chickens and found that it nearly always took up residence next to the same cellular gene. They concluded that this cellular gene is an oncogene because it is virtually identical to the *myc* viral oncogene. The investigators suggested that one of the virus's LTRs stimulates the cellular *myc* oncogene to over-produce its protein, which in turn may contribute to the malignant transformation of the cell.

Although the role of viruses in animal cancers has been established beyond doubt, their involvement in human cancers is still unproved — with one exception. The only human cancer that is known to be produced by a virus is leukemia of the T lymphocytes — a type of white blood cell — which is caused by a retrovirus that does not have an oncogene. However, a few other viruses are associated with human cancers. A person who has been infected by such viruses has a higher risk of developing cancer later in life. For example, a person who has had hepatitis B has a relatively high risk of contracting liver cancer. Obviously, it is not ethical to inject humans with viruses suspected of causing cancer, so it is difficult to determine to what extent viruses are implicated. Many scientists think that their involvement is quite limited. Others, noting how many animal cancers are caused by viruses, are not so sure.

What does seem certain is that the oncogenes we have in our cells are involved in the cancer process. But how do these oncogenes cause normal cells to become malignant? Some researchers have proposed that an oncogene in a cell undergoes a mutation caused by any one of the many known *carcinogens* (cancer-causing agents), such as radiation or toxic chemicals. The oncogene would then produce an altered protein.

Other researchers think an oncogene becomes dangerous only when a foreign DNA sequence is placed next to it. This would most likely be a sequence which — like an LTR — acts as a trigger to ac-

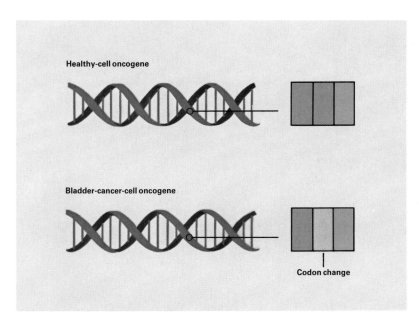

Healthy-cell oncogene

Bladder-cancer-cell oncogene

Codon change

A Lethal Change?
Comparison of a bladder-cancer oncogene with an apparently identical gene from the cell of a healthy person reveals a change of just one codon in the oncogene. The change may confer a susceptibility to bladder cancer.

The Chromosome Connection

When a human cell is ready to divide, its 23 pairs of chromosomes replicate and contract into rodlike structures. At this stage, some chromosomes may exchange groups of genes, an occurrence that can sometimes give rise to cancer. The switch of genes between chromosomes 8 and 14, *below,* is seen in cells from Burkitt's lymphoma. This cancer may occur when an oncogene is placed next to a DNA sequence that normally controls the production of antibody molecules.

tivate the adjacent gene. The foreign DNA would cause the onco-gene to manufacture too much of its protein.

The mutation theory gained prominence in June 1982 when molecular biologist Robert A. Weinberg of the Massachusetts Institute of Technology announced that he had found an oncogene in human bladder cancer cells that is closely related to the *ras* oncogene. That oncogene is found in the Harvey murine sarcoma virus, which causes cancer in rats.

Weinberg had been looking for oncogenes in human cancer cells by adding DNA from those cells to mouse cell cultures. He found several DNA segments that can turn mouse cells malignant. When he added radioactive strands from several known virus oncogenes to the human DNA, only the strand from the *ras* oncogene hybridized, meaning that the DNA contained an identical — or at least a very similar — gene.

Weinberg and other researchers also found a gene in normal human bladder cells that looked like the *ras* oncogene. The scientists wondered whether a gene that supposedly causes cancer in some cells could exist harmlessly in others. Or was there some difference between the *ras* oncogene in normal cells and its counterpart in can-

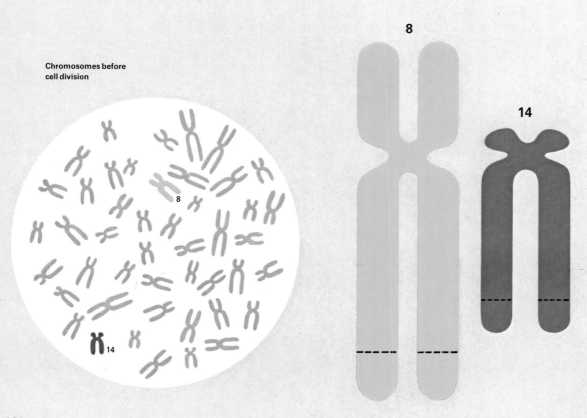

Chromosomes before cell division

8

14

cer cells? To answer that question, investigators in Weinberg's laboratory, in collaboration with other researchers, set about the tedious task of analyzing the *ras* oncogene from both normal cells and cancer cells, nucleotide by nucleotide. Their painstaking analysis revealed just one small difference between the two genes. Where a codon in the segment from normal cells read GGC, they found the codon GTC in the cancer-cell gene. That single nucleotide change would result in the substitution of the amino acid valine for glycine near one end of the gene's protein. This seemed to support the idea that certain genes in our body become oncogenes only when they mutate and produce an altered protein.

However, not all scientists accept this evidence. They speculate that the mouse cell lines used for these studies are already in a precancerous state, a state reached by normal cells only after many genetic and biochemical changes have taken place. They also note that most bladder-cancer cells studied do not have the oncogene with the GTC codon. Instead, the DNA from most such cells contains the much more common gene with the GGC codon. Furthermore, the *ras* gene without the GTC mutation—if it is indeed a mutation and not a relatively rare, naturally occurring form of the

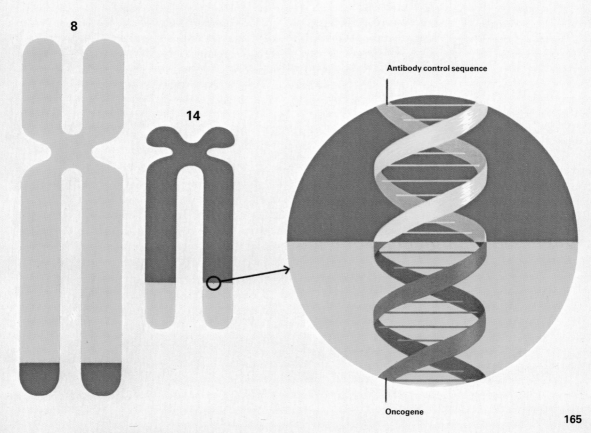

8

14

Antibody control sequence

Oncogene

Exchanged chromosome segments

gene — does not induce cancer in mouse cell cultures. Some scientists believe that another oncogene, or another mechanism altogether, may be involved in most bladder cancers.

Another line of investigation created considerable excitement among cancer researchers in late 1982. This research pointed to yet another oncogene — the *myc* gene — as an alleged culprit in malignancy. In this case, scientists found that the oncogene moved from one chromosome to another during cell division.

Chromosomes consist of long threads of DNA and proteins. A human cell contains 46 chromosomes (23 pairs), numbered 1 through 22, plus the pair of sex chromosomes. When a cell is preparing to divide, each chromosome contracts into a thick, rod-shaped structure and splits into two new chromosomes. At that stage, scientists can see evidence that parts of two chromosomes may have broken off and traded places. They do not know why this occurs, but they have learned that several forms of cancer involve such exchanges.

One of those diseases is Burkitt's lymphoma, a cancer of the B lymphocytes. These are white blood cells that produce antibodies, proteins that alert the rest of the immune system that it is being invaded. They do this by searching out and attaching to invading molecules. In the cells of about 90 per cent of Burkitt's lymphomas, the ends of one chromosome 8 and the ends of one chromosome 14 switch places.

Molecular biologist Carlo M. Croce of the Wistar Institute in Philadelphia set himself the task of determining exactly which genes are located on the chromosome segments that are exchanged. He and other investigators had previously located the genes for producing antibodies on the normal chromosome 14. In research with cell cultures, Croce discovered that copies of the normal human chromosome 14 were able to manufacture the proper antibody molecule, whereas an altered chromosome 14 — one that had traded genes with chromosome 8 — could not. He concluded, therefore, that the antibody-producing genes from the abnormal chromosome 14 had been inactivated when they moved to chromosome 8. He confirmed that conclusion with further experiments.

Croce, in collaboration with cell biologist Robert C. Gallo at NCI, then sought to learn which genes migrate from chromosome 8 to chromosome 14. Other scientists had previously found the *myc* oncogene on chromosome 8 in normal cells. Is it possible, Croce and Gallo wondered, that the oncogene moves from chromosome 8 to chromosome 14? When they used a *myc* oncogene probe to test the segment that moved to chromosome 14, they came up with a hybrid: The oncogene had indeed moved from 8 to 14. This lent strong support to the view that the movement of the *myc* oncogene is involved in Burkitt's lymphoma.

Meanwhile, investigators at Harvard University in Cambridge, Mass., under the direction of geneticist Philip Leder, were mapping a particular set of antibody genes. These genes program a change in the antibody molecule that enables it to leave the B lymphocyte and track down invaders in various parts of the body. When Leder and his colleagues located these antibody genes on chromosome 14, they made a surprising discovery. There was an unidentified piece of DNA in the midst of the genes. Like Croce and Gallo, they had theorized that the *myc* gene had moved from chromosome 8 to chromosome 14. Could this unidentified DNA segment be the migratory *myc*? Using a *myc* oncogene probe, they soon determined that it was.

The Harvard group's discovery implies that the relocation of the *myc* gene near the antibody genes on altered chromosome 14 may play an important role in the development of Burkitt's lymphoma. Perhaps when the B lymphocyte answers the body's demand for a new form of antibody molecule, certain control genes are switched on. However, instead of activating the antibody genes, which normally lie nearby, they activate their new neighbor, the *myc* gene.

At this point, it is difficult to map all the avenues in the oncogene quest, let alone predict where they will lead. Many scientists refrain from making rosy predictions about the possible applications of oncogene research. Malignancy, they point out, is a complex, multistep process. Twenty or more years can elapse from the time a person is exposed to a carcinogen to the day when he or she is diagnosed as having cancer. Even though some cancers — mainly a few kinds of leukemia — show up in children, most malignancies occur in the middle and later years of life.

Investigators therefore believe the activation of an oncogene alone does not necessarily lead to the cancerous transformation of a human cell. Some researchers theorize that several oncogenes in a cell may be necessary for the development of a tumor.

Peter J. Fischinger, associate director of the NCI, agrees that the cancer process is a knotty puzzle, but he thinks it can be solved. For one thing, he says, evidence is accumulating that the inappropriate activation of an oncogene, or oncogenes, is one of the first of many steps that lead to malignancy.

If that is true, then the creation of a diagnostic procedure to spot abnormal or excessive oncogene proteins would enable physicians to identify persons who are in the initial stages of developing cancer. The next step in protecting those patients would be to turn off their oncogenes or to interfere with the manufacture of the oncogene proteins. Fischinger thinks both courses of treatment — either of which would stabilize the cell — may prove to be possible.

"By the end of the 1980s," Fischinger predicts, "I think we will have a much clearer idea of how oncogenes cause cancer. What we've learned already has outstripped our expectations. The knowledge we gain will play an important role in the treatment and prevention of malignancies. The cancer process is very complex, but I believe a great deal of optimism is justified."

New Missions
for Magnetism

By James Trefil

**A force that has been with us since the world
began is used in countless devices that help make
our lives more productive and more enjoyable.**

It is still dark when the alarm goes off in Bill's apartment on the California coast. Like any other commuter, Bill shaves and dresses quickly, picks up his briefcase, and hurries to his car. A short drive on the freeway brings him to a sign that reads "Los Angeles Maglev Terminal — Next Exit."

The terminal looks like an ordinary subway station. At first glance, the train also looks ordinary. But there is only one rail under the train and the cars have rubber tires that run on smooth surfaces on both sides of the rail. As Bill settles back in his seat, the train moves forward on the tires. Gathering speed quickly, it moves into a narrow tunnel from which vacuum pumps have removed most of the air so that air friction does not retard the train's motion. As the train's speed increases, powerful magnets in the bodies of the train cars lift the cars off the ground, so that the train floats a few inches above the rail. Surging forward in the tunnel, suspended in midair, the train now shows its true nature. Another system of magnets in the tunnel walls supplies energy to the train, gradually accelerating it to its top speed of well above 3,100 miles per hour (mph). The train arrives in New York City in about one hour.

Science fiction? For now, yes. But ultrafast ground transportation is just one exciting possibility that modern research has opened up in one of the oldest branches of science — the study of magnetism.

Magnets come in many sizes and strengths, and we put them to use in many common devices. Are you going for a drive this evening? Stored magnetic energy in your car's ignition coil will ignite the gasoline in the engine. Cooking? The motor that runs your blender depends on magnetism to operate. The same is true of the motors in your family's vacuum cleaner, electrical drill, and hairdrier. When you turn on a light, the generator that produces the electricity needs a powerful magnet to work. When you turn on your television set, magnetic forces in the TV tube guide electrons to certain spots on the inside of the screen, where they create the series of colored dots that your eyes and brain perceive as a picture. Even your doorbell has a magnet, a device less than one inch long that exerts a force of less than one pound. By contrast, magnets at junkyards range up to 5 feet in diameter and lift several tons of metal.

Magnetism is everywhere in nature. The earth itself is like a gigantic bar magnet — a long, thin magnet with a magnetic north pole at one end and a magnetic south pole at the other. The "bar" is located beneath the earth's surface, close to the axis of rotation. One magnetic pole is under Ellef Ringnes Island in northern Canada and the other is off the coast of Wilkes Land, Antarctica. The earth's magnetic field — the zone in which its magnetism is effective — ranges from deep inside the earth to a vast region of space.

Scientists have understood magnetic fields well only since the early 1800s. However, people have known for centuries about one of the effects of the earth's field: A sliver of magnetic material, when allowed to pivot freely, will swing around and align itself on a north-south axis. Medieval Europeans and Chinese used this knowledge to develop compasses to help them navigate. Descendants of these devices range from today's Boy Scout compass to the most advanced guidance systems for aircraft.

These instruments work according to a principle that anyone who has played with toy bar magnets understands: Like poles repel and opposite poles attract. Thus, the south pole of a bar magnet repels the south pole of another bar magnet, but attracts that magnet's north pole. The pointer end of a compass needle therefore swings north because the pointer is opposite in polarity to the "end of the bar" in Canada.

The strength of any magnet is greatest at its poles. Furthermore, the earth's magnetic field at a point on the earth's surface is much stronger than the field at a location in outer space above the point.

The author:
James Trefil is a professor of physics at the University of Virginia in Charlottesville.

Birds, butterflies, and bacteria navigate with built-in "compasses."
The same force of magnetism that guides these creatures also moves an
actual compass needle, lifts tremendous weights in a junkyard, focuses
beams to create television images, and drives motors in appliances.

Yet the earth's field is strong enough to hold Van Allen belts—large concentrations of electrically charged particles—600 to 15,500 miles above the earth.

Human beings use compasses and other instruments to detect and measure this vast field because we cannot sense magnetism directly. However, some other creatures have this capability. A species of one-celled bacteria known as *Aquaspirillum magnetitacticum* contains tiny bits of magnetic material arranged like beads on a string. The bacteria use the magnets to orient themselves as they travel toward the mud at the bottom of pools where they live. Bees and pigeons have similar bits of magnetic material in their bodies that may help them navigate by the earth's magnetic field. See THE ANIMAL NAVIGATORS, *Science Year*, 1981.

Other bodies in the universe also are magnetic. The sun, for example, has a magnetic field. Other stars have fields, too, but these stars are so far away that we know less about their fields than we do about the sun's. The Milky Way galaxy has a weak magnetic field that is about one-millionth as strong as the earth's.

At the other end of the scale, the atom possesses a magnetic field. So do particles within atoms.

All these fields—from the galactic to the subatomic—seem to stem from a phenomenon that Danish physicist Hans Christian Oersted discovered in 1820 at the University of Copenhagen. Oersted was performing experiments for a few of his students. In one experiment, he ran an electrical current from a battery through wires. A compass happened to be lying on a table near the wires. Whenever Oersted closed a switch to let current run, a strange thing happened. The needle of the compass moved. Thus, Oersted accidentally made one of the most important discoveries in scientific history: All magnetic fields result from electrical currents—that is, from the motion of electrical charges.

The most common type of magnetic field in nature and in manufactured devices results from a current loop, or the flow of electrical charge around a circle. Physicists describe magnetic fields by means of imaginary lines called lines of force. Arrowheads on these lines indicate the directions in which compass needles placed at various locations in a field would point. Every line of force caused by moving charges is closed—that is, it has no beginning or end point.

A current loop's lines of force encircle the loop like rings on a finger. The direction of lines' arrowheads and the location of the loop's magnetic poles depend upon whether the charge flowing in the loop is negative or positive and upon the direction of flow. Think of a current loop laid flat on the page you are reading with its electrons flowing clockwise around the loop. Lines of force inside the loop would point up and the arrowheads outside the loop would point down. The loop's north pole would be above the loop's center and the south pole below it.

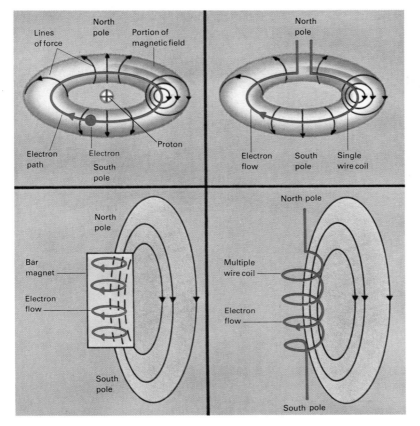

Lines of force

North pole

Portion of magnetic field

Electron path

Electron

South pole

Proton

North pole

Electron flow

South pole

Single wire coil

Bar magnet

North pole

Electron flow

South pole

Multiple wire coil

Electron flow

North pole

South pole

Motion and Magnetism

Moving charges establish magnetic fields whose shapes and polarities depend upon the paths of the charges. An atom's electron orbiting a proton clockwise, *top, far left,* sets up a field in the surrounding region. The lines of force outside the orbit point downward; inside, they point upward. Electrons flowing in a wire coil, *top left,* establish the same kind of field. Electrons circulating in parallel paths in a bar magnet, *bottom, far left,* and in a multiple-turn coil, *bottom left,* set up larger, stronger fields.

The magnetism of an atom results from the circular motion of its charged particles. An atom consists of a spinning, positively charged nucleus around which one or more electrons move in orbits. The nucleus gets its positive charge from its proton or protons. All nuclei except that of the lightest form of hydrogen also contain one or more neutrons, which are electrically neutral. The nucleus as a whole can be thought of as a ball, with its electrical charge spread uniformly throughout. As the nucleus rotates, its bits of charge form current loops that set up a small magnetic field. An electron orbit also fits the definition of a current loop, so the orbiting electrons set up magnetic fields.

In most manufactured devices such as electric motors that use magnetism, electrons flow through wire that has been wound to form a series of superimposed loops. The fields of the loops reinforce one another, so these magnets establish strong fields. A motor's wire loops and an atom's orbital loop set up their fields in the same way. However, in some atoms, only one electron moves around a loop, while a billion electrons may pass through the motor loops.

The magnetism of a bar magnet does not depend upon a current flowing through wires. Instead, the magnetism stems from the combined action of the electron loops in the atoms that make up the bar. In a permanent magnet such as a toy bar magnet or an ordinary compass needle, the atoms — each a tiny magnet — are aligned so that most of their north poles point in the same direction.

Geologists are still trying to determine how moving charges shape the earth's magnetic field. They know that the field stems from the motion of a region called the outer core, which extends from 1,800 to 3,200 miles beneath the earth's surface. This core is made of molten iron and nickel. As the earth rotates, the core swirls in a circular direction. The interaction between charges in the rotating core and the earth's field serves to keep that field in existence.

Meanwhile, other scientists continue to look for new ways to apply magnetism to human needs. One of the most promising practical applications is a nuclear magnetic resonance (NMR) imaging instru-

Two sections of a magnet at Brookhaven National Laboratory, *below,* are wound with a tape of wires that conduct electrical current without resistance at extremely low temperatures. Researchers prepare to lower an assembled magnet, *right,* into a refrigeration chamber for electrical tests.

ment. It helps physicians diagnose illnesses by forming images of internal organs without subjecting a patient to X rays, which damage tissue. NMR depends on the fact that the magnetic strength of each kind of nucleus differs from the strength of all other types.

A patient is positioned in a large circular magnet that produces magnetic fields about 6,000 times as strong as the earth's field. The strong field causes certain nuclear magnets in the patient's body to line up in the direction of the field. The NMR machine beams a radio wave of a chosen frequency through the patient. Some of the nuclei that were lined up by the field absorb energy from the beam and turn over, so that their nuclear magnets change direction. When the radio transmitter is turned off, the realigned nuclei flip back to their original orientation, emitting characteristic and detectable radio signals as they do so. Neither the transmission of magnetic fields and radio waves through the body nor the flipping of nuclei damages tissue. The radio signals from the nuclei indicate how many atoms of a certain kind are at a particular point in the sample.

The machine gathers its information as the magnet rotates slowly around the patient. A computer then combines the signals to construct an image of the interior of the patient's body. Finally, the computer displays the image on a video screen or prints it so that physicians can study it. A physician may look at details of body structure such as the location of small bones in the spine, or may examine the image for tissue that looks unusually light or dark, an indication of possible disease. Hospitals have already begun to experiment with NMR units.

NMR machines use special magnets that avoid problems associated with ordinary high-strength magnets. Any high-strength magnet requires high, steady electrical current in the loops that create the magnetic field. However, such currents in ordinary magnets re-

A worker at Fermi National Accelerator Laboratory in Batavia, Ill., *above,* winds a flat coil of superconducting tape that can conduct electrical current without resistance, creating powerful magnetic fields in a small area. The coil fits inside a yellow housing, *top,* on the floor of the accelerator ring, where it acts as an electromagnet, guiding subatomic particles around the ring.

quire large amounts of power, which is expensive. Furthermore, when currents run through the coils of an ordinary magnet, flowing electrons collide with nuclei of atoms in the wire, generating heat. Unless this heat is removed, it will build up, eventually destroying the magnet. Consequently, ordinary large magnets have cooling systems like those in an automobile. But not even the most efficient cooling system can solve the heating problem. The need to remove excess heat puts severe limits on the current flow — and therefore on the field strength — of ordinary magnets.

The special magnets used in NMR reduce the power requirement drastically, and eliminate the heating. These magnets are based on superconductivity, a phenomenon discovered by Dutch physicist Heike Kamerlingh Onnes in 1911. Onnes was investigating the electrical properties of mercury at temperatures near absolute zero ($-459.67°F.$), the temperature that scientists believe is the lowest attainable. Onnes found that when the temperature falls below a certain level, electrical current flowing in mercury no longer generates heat — that is, mercury becomes a superconductor. Other researchers discovered later that certain other metals also become su-

A crew at Oak Ridge National Laboratory (ORNL) in Tennessee prepares to install a 45-ton superconducting magnet at the lab's Large Coil Test Facility. The magnet, built by Hitachi Limited of Japan, is the first of six that ORNL will test in an international program to develop such magnets for use in controlling nuclear fusion reactions as an energy source.

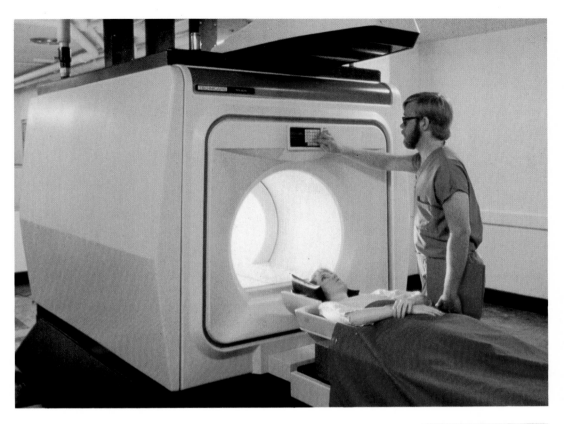

percorducting at extremely low temperatures. However, the mechanism of superconductivity remained a mystery until the 1950s, when physicists John Bardeen, Leon N. Cooper, and J. Robert Schrieffer of the University of Illinois in Urbana-Champaign explained it. The three received the 1972 Nobel Prize in physics for their work with superconductivity. They found that when certain materials become extremely cold, the way that electrons move through the material changes drastically. Once current begins to flow, it will run forever, without losing energy or generating heat. During the 1970s, scientists and engineers worked out the details of producing large numbers of superconducting magnets. Today, dozens of corporations throughout the world manufacture them. Besides NMR instruments, superconducting magnets are used in experimental maglev (*mag*netically *lev*itated) trains and gigantic particle accelerators that probe fundamental secrets of matter and energy.

Magnet manufacturers cannot build superconducting magnets out of copper and iron, the major materials of most ordinary magnets, because these metals do not superconduct. Instead, they use less familiar substances such as niobium and titanium.

The magnetic field of a superconducting loop made of these two materials persists as long as the magnet's temperature remains low

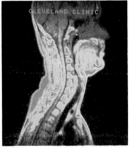

A technician guides a patient into the magnetic chamber of a nuclear magnetic resonance scanner, *top*. This machine examines bone and internal tissue magnetically and without the use of X rays, producing a cross-sectional image of the inside of the body, *above*.

enough. Liquid helium at 7.2°F. above absolute zero keeps today's superconducting magnets cold.

An important milestone in the history of superconducting technology was marked in July 1983. At that time, the Fermi National Accelerator Laboratory (Fermilab) near Chicago turned on its Energy Saver, a system of more than 1,000 superconducting magnets arranged around the circular track of its particle accelerator. The Energy Saver became the world's largest installation of operating superconductors. The circular track is 1⅓ miles in diameter. These magnets are extremely strong. Each can exert more than 15 times as much force as a typical junkyard magnet.

Scientists are using the magnets to experiment on protons. Electrical devices transfer tremendous amounts of energy to the protons, propelling them around the ring. The superconducting magnets, together with an older system of ordinary magnets, keep the particles from flying off the track. When the particles have absorbed enough energy, magnets will steer them off the track into experimental areas, where they will collide with stationary targets. Physicists will then examine these collisions in an attempt to learn more about subatomic particles and the forces that govern them. All of this is being done with less energy than required before.

Fermilab built its own magnet factory and has been a leader in the mass production of superconducting magnets. Mass-produced superconducting magnets will lead to major improvements in the development of the next generation of fast ground transportation in

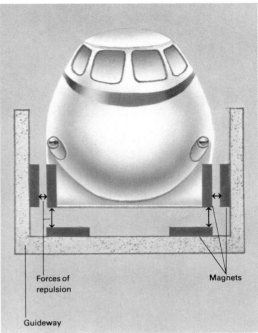

Forces of repulsion

Guideway

Magnets

the form of maglev trains. Each car in these trains will have super-conducting magnets that exert forces of repulsion on a metal sheet or rail beneath the train. This magnetic force will lift the train so that the wheels do not touch the track. The train will not need a power supply to keep it levitated. Magnets mounted in low walls next to the train will alternately attract and repel magnets in the cars to propel the train.

Maglev trains will operate at tremendous speeds because they do not have to overcome the friction between the wheels and the track that an ordinary train does. The maglev would confront only air friction. And some researchers, such as physicist Robert Salter of Rand Corporation, a nonprofit research organization in Santa Monica, Calif., have suggested overcoming this last obstacle by running the train through tunnels or a tube above the ground from which the air has been removed. In either case, the speed-limiting factors would be the quality of the vacuum and the amount of energy the train used to accelerate and decelerate.

Los Angeles to New York City in one hour would be a reasonable expectation for such a maglev train. However, a coast-to-coast tunnel or tube built with today's equipment and techniques would be very expensive. Salter estimates that a tunnel would cost $250 billion. Furthermore, the public might feel that the structure would harm the environment so much that it should not be built.

Prototype maglev trains that operate in the open air are already swifter than the world's fastest ordinary train — the 200-mph French

Support Without Contact
Magnets in the walls and floor of a guideway repel magnets in an experimental train, *above and above left,* with such force that they suspend the train in midair. Since the train does not have to overcome the friction of a track, it can travel at great speed, *opposite page.*

TGV. In December 1979, Japanese National Railways tested a full-scale prototype of a maglev train at 321 mph.

The possibility that superconducting technology may have widespread uses has stimulated the search for new materials that do not require as much cooling as today's superconductors. The Fermilab magnets and the magnets in NMR instruments are made of a niobium-titanium alloy that stops superconducting if its temperature rises to about 32°F. above absolute zero. Liquid helium is the only substance that can efficiently keep this alloy cold enough. However, helium is rare on earth and, therefore, expensive. If researchers could find a material that was a stable superconductor at temperatures up to about 54°F. above absolute zero, then they could cool magnets with liquid hydrogen, which is much cheaper than liquid helium. Another milestone would be 144°F. above absolute zero, in which case they could use nitrogen, which costs even less.

Other scientists are using superconductivity in an attempt to complete a picture of the subatomic structure of the universe. This picture shows a close parallel between electricity and magnetism. For example, the basic equation for the electrical force between two electrically charged bodies has the same general form as the equation for the magnetic force between two magnetized bodies. Furthermore, there are two kinds of electrical charge, positive and negative; and two types of magnetic polarity, north and south. In addition, the motion of electrical charges generates magnetic forces, and changing a magnetic field generates electrical forces.

But here the parallel between electricity and magnetism seems to break down. Moving electrical charges generate every magnetic force ever investigated. However, not all electrical forces are the result of the motion of magnets. For example, a single electron produces an electrical force independent of magnetic activity. However, there is no known particle that produces a magnetic force independent of electrical activity. Furthermore, no one has ever observed a north pole that does not have a south pole associated with it, and vice versa. Thus, if you try to isolate a north or a south pole by cutting a bar magnet in two, you get two complete magnets, each with a north and a south pole.

Scientists have searched for the missing part of the picture for more than 50 years. The magnetic particle they seek would not have closed lines of force. All the lines would point away from the particle or all would point toward it. In other words, the particle would appear to be an isolated north or south pole of a magnet. Physicists have therefore named it a magnetic monopole.

In one of the most exciting experiments in many years, physicist Blas Cabrera of Stanford University in California may have discovered a magnetic monopole. To search for the monopole, Cabrera used a loop of superconducting material and a device that monitored the current in the loop. According to present theories, a monopole

Poles Without Partners
A magnetic monopole is a hypothetical particle. It could appear as an isolated north magnetic pole, with all lines of magnetic force directed outward, or as an isolated south pole, with the lines pointing inward.

that passes through such a loop will change the current by a certain amount. Furthermore, no known event other than an experimental accident will affect the loop in this way.

Cabrera's loop was part of an experiment on the relationship of electrical charge to the energy and vibrational frequency of light waves and similar radiation. He simply left the loop running when it was not being used in this experiment. The loop ran for six months with no sign of success as a monopole detector and then, at 1:45 P.M. on Feb. 14, 1982, the expected jump in current occurred.

Cabrera and other physicists are not absolutely certain that a monopole caused the jump. So, since the summer of 1982, Cabrera and other experimenters throughout the world have been trying to record another jump, which would confirm Cabrera's experiment. By the summer of 1983, no second monopole had appeared.

Meanwhile, theorists have been trying to determine how monopoles might have been created in the earliest moments of the universe. Grand Unified Theories — new ideas about the origins of the universe — state that monopoles exist. These theories define relationships among the forces that govern the motion of matter, except for the force of gravity. These forces include the magnetic force, the electrical force, the so-called strong force that holds atomic nuclei together, and the weak force, which is responsible for certain kinds of radioactivity. According to the theories, all these forces are different aspects of a unified force that controlled matter in the early universe. See CATCHING NATURE'S VANISHING ACT, *Science Year*, 1983.

The theories explain the role of the unified force and the other forces in the creation and control of particles of matter, including monopoles; and they predict how many monopoles experimenters should find and where they should find them. Theorists have pointed out a problem with the fact that Cabrera's apparatus took only six months to record the jump. Some theories imply that equipment such as Cabrera's should take much longer to detect a monopole. If monopoles were as common as the experiment suggests, they would have drained energy from our galaxy's magnetic field. Thus, theorists say, measurements of the present energy level of the galactic field prove that monopoles could not be so common.

Other physicists have theorized that monopoles collected in places, such as the solar system, where there are large accumulations of mass. If these theories are true, then monopoles would be common on earth but rare in the galaxy as a whole. Cabrera's experiment, in other words, touched off just the kind of free-flowing debate that makes science so much fun to do. That debate would end if experimenters detected more monopoles.

The phenomenon of magnetism, which guided early explorers around the globe, may make another exciting journey possible — a mental voyage backward in time, to almost the very moment of the creation of the universe.

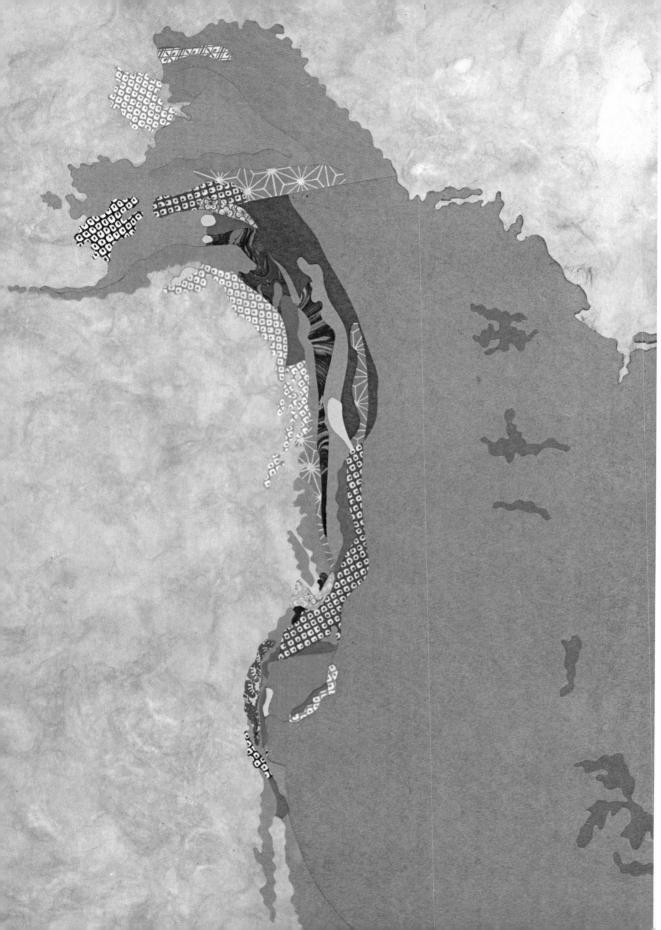

The Patchwork Earth

By Allan Cox and David C. Engebretson

Pieces of land in western North America traveled across the ocean for thousands of miles and millions of years before becoming a part of the continent.

Nestled among the peaks of the Alaska Range, which arcs across southern Alaska, is a mountain that is out of place. Windswept and rugged like its neighbors, it is nonetheless so different that to a geologist it seems as strange as a jungle in the middle of a desert. The mountain is out of place because about 290 million years ago it was an island in the Pacific Ocean.

This tropical island-turned-Alaskan mountain is part of a terrane, a block of the earth's crust whose geologic history is significantly different from that of neighboring blocks. And although this terrane, called the Chulitna Terrane, is unique, it is hardly alone. Nearly all of Alaska and the Pacific Coast of the United States and Canada is a geologic jigsaw puzzle made up of more than 150 pieces of varying sizes that are as different from one another as they are from land farther inland.

The presence of these odd blocks perplexed geologists for decades. Only recently have they discovered that the blocks are foreign imports, some of which formed thousands of miles away in the Pacific Ocean. Their sometimes violent collisions with North America, beginning about 150 million years ago, radically changed the shape of the continent. New discoveries about where terranes came from and how they traveled across the ocean and became part of North Amer-

The western edge of North America, including nearly all of Alaska, is a mosaic of blocks of land whose rocks differ dramatically from those found on the rest of the continent.

ica have also changed geologists' ideas about how continents grow and increased their understanding of the theory of plate tectonics.

According to this theory, the earth's rigid outer shell, called the lithosphere, consists of about 20 huge plates that glide over a layer of partially molten rock called the asthenosphere. Like conveyor belts, the plates carry the continents and oceans with them.

When two plates collide, their edges may telescope together and pile up, forming mountains. For example, the Himalayan mountain ranges in southern Asia grew as the Indian Plate crashed into the Eurasian Plate. When the two plates collide, a process called subduction occurs. One plate bends and plunges under another, much as the steps of an escalator slip beneath the floor at the top of a landing. The heavier lower layer of the plunging plate sinks into the asthenosphere and melts. However, the lighter upper crust peels off and is added to the continent.

For years, geologists believed that continents grew in only two ways, both due to subduction. As a subducting plate melts, it produces globs of molten rock. Because it is less dense than the rocks above it, the molten rock wells up through cracks in the crust and forms volcanoes. And, in fact, many of the world's active volcanoes are found near subduction zones. Lava spewed from a volcano eventually cools and solidifies, forming new rock and adding crust to the edge of the continent.

Continents also grow with the accumulation of sediment — fine-grained particles of rock eroded from the continent. Rivers flowing into the ocean deposit this sediment onto the ocean floor along the edge of the continent. Plant and animal remains may also accumulate. As an oceanic plate subducts beneath a continental plate, the sediment is scraped off the ocean bottom and pushed against the edge of the continent, where it builds up, forming new land.

In addition to thinking that these two processes accounted for all continental growth, geologists believed that the growth occurred slowly and steadily, the way a tree trunk gradually becomes thicker during its lifetime. However, blocks of land along the western coast of North America stubbornly refused to fit the theories. Many geologists doubted that volcanic activity and the accumulation of sediment could account for the large amount of crust added to the continent's western edge during the past 150 million years. Nor could they explain the great diversity of rocks along the coast or the presence of rock so radically different from rock found on continents.

Some geologists began to suspect that continents grow in a third way — by the addition of terranes. The key to their discovery lay not only in new data but also in a new way of thinking about old data.

Geologists began to suspect that some of the blocks formed elsewhere when they observed that in western North America, adjacent blocks of land had vastly different geologic histories. For example, rocks in one mountain might have formed at the bottom of the ocean

The authors:
Allan Cox is dean of the School of Earth Sciences and professor of geophysics at Stanford University. David C. Engebretson is an assistant professor of geology at Western Washington University in Bellingham.

The earth's surface consists of about 20 moving plates — huge segments of rigid crust on which the continents and oceans ride.

220 million years ago, while rocks of the same age in an adjacent mountain formed in a desert on a continent. Some geologists believed that such abrupt and obvious differences proved that the two blocks could not have formed in the same place.

To get a better picture of how and where the blocks did form, geologists began to "read" rock in a different way. Instead of examining individual layers of rock in a cliff or hillside, they began to look at the entire sequence of rock layers in order to re-create the geologic history of a block of land.

Geologists read rock in much the same way that archaeologists read hieroglyphics. Once archaeologists have learned to decipher the curious marks on a clay tablet, the tablet becomes a window on the rich history of such places as ancient Egypt. In the same way, rocks can open windows on the earth's 4.5-billion-year history. Geologists can tell whether a layer of sediment in a rock was deposited on the floor of a deep ocean or a shallow sea, or whether volcanic rock cooled at the bottom of an ocean or on land.

Reading a rock also enables geologists to reconstruct a remarkably detailed picture of the landscape that existed when the rock formed. If a rock has many layers, as terranes often do, the reconstruction becomes even more exciting. Then, geologists can imagine a sequence of landscapes, along with their environments, as things changed over millions — even hundreds of millions — of years. In effect, geologists can create an imaginary movie of geologic evolution in an area. That is what geologists working in western North America began to do with those out-of-place blocks of land.

To understand how geologists read a sequence of rock layers, let us follow one who is examining a particularly interesting cliff in the

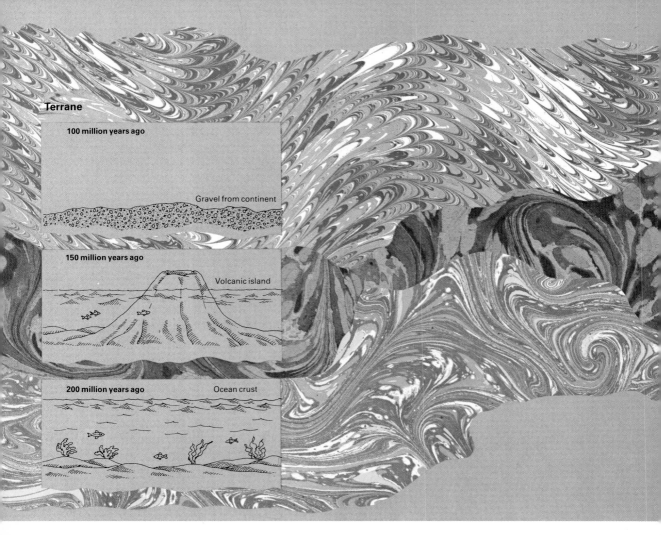

Terrane

100 million years ago

Gravel from continent

150 million years ago

Volcanic island

200 million years ago

Ocean crust

Continent

100 million years ago — Canyon with gravel beds

150 million years ago — Freshwater lake

200 million years ago — Sand dunes

The History in the Stone

Continental rock layers generated 200 million and
150 million years ago are different from those of the same
age in the adjacent terrane because the terrane layers
formed thousands of miles away in a different geologic
environment. The 100-million-year-old layers are the same
because by then the terrane had docked against the continent.

Rock layers in the Chulitna
Terrane, *far left,* pushed upward
when the terrane collided with
North America, are unlike those
found in land formed on the
continent. Pillow lava, *center,*
is typical of rock in terranes
that forms at underwater
volcanoes. In contrast,
sandstone, *left,* a sedimentary
rock, forms only on land.

187

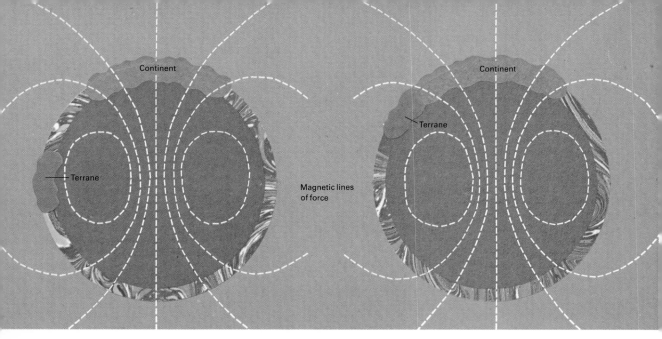

Continent

Terrane

Terrane

Continent

Magnetic lines
of force

Rocks become magnetized in a direction parallel to the lines of force in the earth's magnetic field at the point where the rocks form. A magnetic orientation different from that of nearby rocks of the same age that formed on the continent indicates that the rocks in a terrane formed elsewhere.

Wrangell Mountains in southeastern Alaska. Exposed on the face of the cliff are distinct layers of different kinds of rock. The geologist breaks off a piece of rock from the bottom layer and examines it with a magnifying lens. The crystalline structure of the rock tells the geologist that this layer consists of igneous rock — rock formed from molten lava. Because this particular type of igneous rock forms today on the ocean bottom near subduction zones, the geologist concludes that this ancient layer formed in the same way and that the Alaskan mountain originally was a volcanic island. The appearance of the rock indicates that at first the volcanic rock lay beneath the ocean, but eventually, as the lava built up, an island was formed.

Moving up the cliff, the geologist sees a layer of limestone — rock composed of the shells of microscopic marine organisms. When the organisms died, their shells settled to the ocean bottom, gradually accumulating into layers of rock. Because these organisms lived in shallow water, the geologist knows that, at that point, the volcanic island had begun to sink into the ocean as the crust beneath it cooled and contracted.

Above this layer is another layer of limestone. However, this limestone is composed of sediment from tiny organisms that lived deeper in the ocean. By reading this layer of rock, the geologist determines that the island sank even farther below the ocean surface.

Climbing higher up the cliff, the geologist finds another layer of igneous rock, indicating that a crack opened up in the ocean floor and molten lava erupted from deep within the asthenosphere. Once again, the flow of lava was so great that an island rose above the water. However, more limestone layers farther up the cliff tell the geologist that the island sank again and was covered, first by the skeletons of shallow water organisms, then by those of organisms that lived far below the surface.

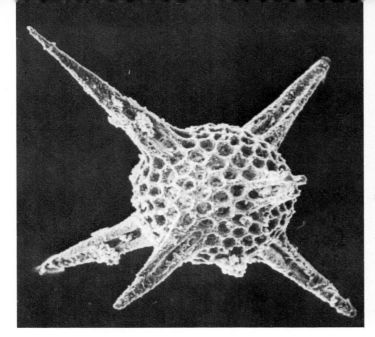

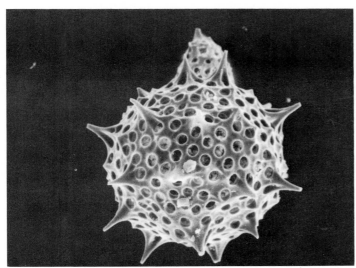

Delicate and ornate, microscopic radiolarian fossils, such as the 370-million-year-old starburst radiolarian, *above left,* reveal the age of rocks in which they are found. Spiked-ball radiolarian, *left,* is 180 million years old. Cone-shaped radiolarian, *above,* is 110 million years old.

Up to this level in the cliff, the geologist has not found one grain of sand from the type of rock that forms on a continent. All the rock studied so far formed in the ocean. Farther up the cliff, however, the picture changes abruptly. For the first time, the geologist sees layers of sediment from continental rock.

To the geologist, the record in the rock is clear evidence that the mountain formed in the ocean, away from North America or any other continent. Only much later — as indicated by layers of continental rock — did the mountain become part of North America.

Additional evidence that such strange blocks of land were foreign rock came when geologists began to date the rock. Geologists determine a rock's age through either radiometric dating methods or by

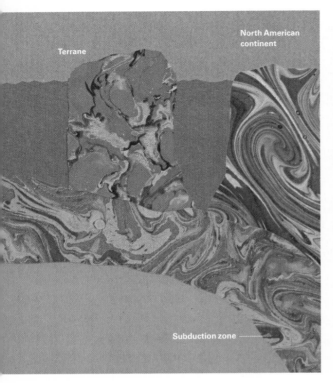

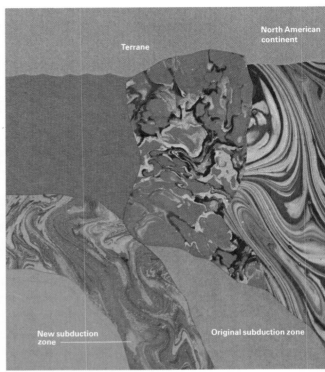

Joining Forces
A terrane becomes attached to a continent when the oceanic plate on which it is riding plunges at a steep angle under a continental plate and into the earth's hot mantle at a subduction zone. The terrane clogs the subduction zone, welding itself to the continent and forcing the zone farther away from the continental plate.

examining fossils in the rock. In radiometric dating, an element that decays into another element at a known rate is used to determine the age of an object. For example, one form of the element uranium decays into lead, and one form of the element potassium decays into argon. By comparing the amount of each element in a particular rock, scientists can determine how much time has passed since the rock was formed. Radiometric dating works best with igneous rock.

To date sedimentary rock — rock composed of layers of sediment — geologists use fossils. In particular, they use certain types of fossils called index fossils, which are found only in rock of a certain age. To establish the age of this type of rock, scientists look for a cliff or other exposure with more than one layer. Some rock layers must contain fossils. Other layers must be igneous rock whose age can be established by radiometric dating. From the positions of the sedimentary and igneous rock layers, scientists can determine the age of the fossil-bearing layers. Once scientists know the age of the rock in which a particular index fossil is found, they know the age of any rock that contains the same fossil. Using index fossils, geologists worked out dates for more layers of rock in the foreign blocks.

In the 1950s, geologists M. L. Thompson and Harry E. Wheeler of the University of Washington in Seattle and Wilbert R. Danner of the University of British Columbia in Vancouver, Canada,

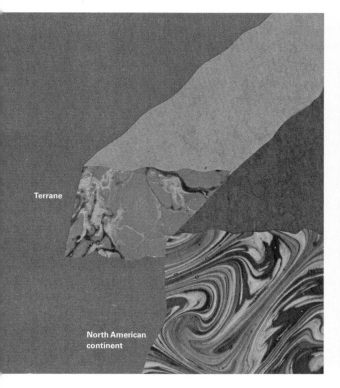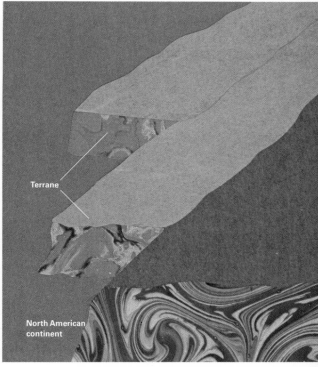

Side Steps
A terrane may become attached to a continent in another way if the oceanic plate collides with the continental plate at an angle or if the two plates are traveling alongside each other. Pieces of the terrane may shear off and adhere in several places as it moves along the coast.

pointed out that certain microscopic marine fossils from the Permian Period, which lasted from 290 million to 250 million years ago, had been found throughout western North America. Significantly, these fossils did not appear anywhere else on the continent. However, they were common in rock from the Permian Period in Japan, China, Indonesia, and other areas in the Far East. Some geologists explained the strange distribution of these fossils by theorizing that the microorganisms had traveled across the Pacific Ocean in currents that flowed along narrow seaways. These geologists compared the seaways to land bridges that allowed animals to cross from continent to continent.

Then in 1971, James W. H. Monger of the Canadian Geologic Survey and geologist Charles A. Ross of Western Washington University in Bellingham discovered that a thin band of rock about 300 miles inland from Canada's western coast contained 250-million-year-old fossils from organisms that had lived near the equator in the Tethys Sea, an ancient sea located in what is now the southwest Pacific and Indian oceans. Monger and Ross saw this as evidence that both the fossils and the rock had formed in the Tethys Sea. They also reasoned that if this rock was a foreign import, then the land west of it — that is, between the rock and the coast — also had to be foreign.

However, geologists were still unable to establish a complete chronology for the out-of-place blocks because they could not date chert—a sedimentary rock plentiful in terranes but one that geologists thought did not contain datable fossils. Then, in 1975, geologist Emile A. Pessagno, Jr., of the University of Texas at Dallas discovered that dissolving chert in hydrofluoric acid freed microscopic skeletons called radiolaria. The skeletons of these minute marine organisms resemble ornate glass Christmas tree ornaments. Because radiolaria are found in chert of many different ages, they can be used as index fossils to date the chert.

Once geologists can date nearly all the layers in a block of land, they can construct its chronological history. And that is what geologists began to do with the out-of-place blocks of land. For example, they now know that the interesting cliff in the Wrangell Mountains formed as a volcanic island about 330 million years ago, began to sink for the first time about 290 million years ago, and slid far below the ocean surface about 240 million years ago. Sediment from continental rock did not appear in the block until about 140 million years ago, indicating that by that time, the terrane had docked against North America.

By the mid-1970s, however, geologists had not determined where terranes originated nor the paths they had taken as they moved across the ocean. Then data from an entirely different line of research provided answers to these questions and at the same time convinced many geologists that advocates of the terrane theory were on the right track. That line of research is paleomagnetism—the record of magnetism in ancient rocks.

The magnetic field surrounding the earth can be thought of as an imaginary series of lines, called lines of force, that curve from pole to pole. When rocks form, they become magnetized in a direction parallel to the lines of force at that location. For example, since the lines of force at the earth's equator are nearly horizontal, a rock formed there becomes magnetized in a horizontal direction—that is, its magnetization is like that of a bar magnet aligned in a direction parallel to the earth's surface. At the North Pole, the lines of force are nearly vertical. Thus, a rock formed there has an almost vertical magnetic orientation—that is, one aligned in an almost perpendicular direction to the surface.

Once a rock forms, its magnetic orientation does not change, even if the rock is transported thousands of miles away. Moreover, rocks retain their magnetic orientation for hundreds of millions of years. Thus, by determining a rock's magnetic orientation, geologists can determine the latitude at which it formed.

When geologists began to examine the magnetic orientation of rock in Alaska, they discovered a curious thing. In 1977, geologists David L. Jones, Norman J. Silberling, and John Hillhouse of the United States Geological Survey discovered that the magnetic ori-

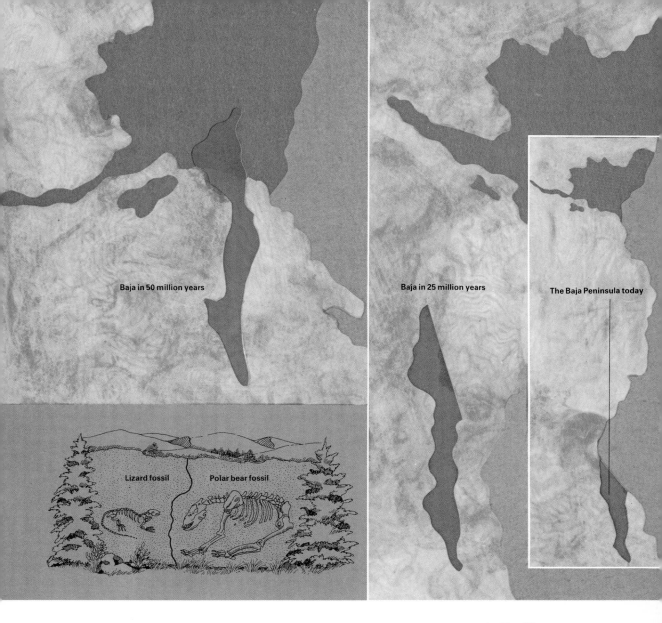

Baja in 50 million years

Baja in 25 million years

The Baja Peninsula today

Lizard fossil   Polar bear fossil

entation of rocks in the Wrangell Mountains was nearly horizontal. Rocks formed at that far northern latitude have a more vertical orientation. Jones and his colleagues concluded that the Wrangell Mountains had actually formed far to the south near the equator. Their discovery of other blocks of land in Canada and the northwestern United States with a similar geologic history convinced them that the mountains were only part of a larger foreign land mass, which they called the Wrangellia Terrane.

Since then, geologists have discovered and mapped more than 150 terranes in North America. These terranes vary in length from about 15 miles to more than 1,500 miles and, in some places, they extend inland more than 300 miles.

In 50 million years, the Baja peninsula terrane, now off the northwest coast of Mexico, will have traveled up the North American coast to southern Alaska. Where the terrane meets the continent, the fossil bones of a polar bear and a lizard might appear side by side.

By calculating the paleomagnetic orientation of each rock layer in the terranes, geologists can determine their route as they were carried across the Pacific Ocean. Geologists can also work out terrane tracks by calculating the path of the plate on which the terrane rode.

Today, most of the Pacific Ocean sits on the Pacific Plate, whose eastern edge abuts the western edge of the North American Plate. Hundreds of millions of years ago, however, the Pacific Plate was much smaller and two other oceanic plates, the Kula and the Farallon plates, lay between the Pacific and North American plates. Many geologists believe most of the North American terranes that originated in the mid-Pacific rode piggyback on these two plates.

The Kula Plate has completely disappeared, subducted beneath the North American Plate millions of years ago. Remnants of the Farallon Plate, however, still exist today. One section, which lies off the coast of Oregon and Washington, is currently sinking beneath the North American Plate and feeding Mount St. Helens and other volcanoes in the Cascade Range.

To track the movement of plates, geologists often use hot spots — nearly stationary plumes of molten rock that rise from deep in the asthenosphere. A plate moving over a hot spot is pierced by the molten plume and a volcano forms. As the plate passes over the hot spot, the plume produces one volcano after another in that part of the plate passing above it. Eventually, long volcanic mountain ranges form on the plate. Because a hot spot remains stationary, it can be used to determine the path of the plate.

If the plate on which the terrane rode has disappeared, as the Kula Plate has, geologists can determine its movements indirectly by calculating the movement of still-existing plates that once bordered it, such as the Pacific Plate.

By calculating the paleomagnetic orientations in terranes' rocks and the movement of the plates they rode on, geologists can determine how fast the terranes traveled. At their speediest, they moved only about 6 inches per year, about as fast as fingernails grow. For example, at this rate the Wrangell Mountains' 6,000-mile journey across the Pacific would have lasted as long as 63 million years.

Despite the terranes' leisurely pace, however, their docking against the North American coast was anything but gentle. In many cases, the collisions were extremely violent.

When a terrane-bearing plate collided head-on with the continent, the terrane began to slide with the plate into the subduction zone. However, because the terrane was lighter than the oceanic plate, it clogged the zone. Eventually, a new subduction zone formed on the ocean side of the terrane, which was now attached to the continent.

When an oceanic plate crashed into the continental plate at an angle, pieces of the terrane sheared off and became attached to the continent in long narrow strips as the plate moved along the coast. For example, sections of the Wrangellia Terrane are strewn along the Pacific coast from Oregon to Alaska. This seems also to have happened when the two plates moved alongside each other, as the Pacific and North American plates are doing today.

New terranes crashing into North America also jostled terranes already attached, slicing off sections, even turning and twisting them, before jamming them against the continent thousands of miles north. Many terranes were pushed and shoved along the coast for millions of years before they finally became attached to the continent. Sometimes, the force of the collision bent the layers of rock in the attached terrane, producing folds like those in a crumpled rug. Sometimes, large horizontal slices of the terrane were pushed miles inland over the continental rock.

Terranes appear to have become affixed to North America in a piecemeal fashion. Geologists believe that for short periods — lasting only tens of millions of years — terranes arrived in a fairly rapid succession, adding large chunks to the coastline. Longer intervals followed during which no terranes arrived and continental growth continued in a slow, steady way only through volcanic activity and the accumulation of sediment.

Like terranes, terrane theory has come a long way. Yet geologists still have much to learn about these foreign imports. For example, some geologists are beginning to believe that terranes may be responsible for the formation of many of the world's mountain ranges. They theorize that coastal mountains, such as the older parts of the Andes in western South America, formed as terranes piled up along the coast. Other geologists contend that terranes could have even caused mountains to form farther inland. For instance, they suggest that the force of the terranes' collisions with North America triggered waves of motion in the continent's crust that caused the crust to buckle and created the Rockies.

Geologists are also discovering that terranes may be very widespread, especially in areas ringing the Pacific Ocean. In 1979, geophysicists Wulf A. Gose of the University of Texas in Austin and Gary R. Scott, formerly of the same school, found paleomagnetic evidence indicating that Central America consists of at least four large terranes. In 1981, a team of Australian and Chinese scientists led by geophysicist M. W. McElhinney of the Australian National University in Canberra, using the same techniques, discovered a number of terranes in China, Siberia, and parts of Southeast Asia. Geologists from Japan and New Zealand have recently proposed that their countries are a mosaic of terranes.

Because of terranes, geologists may now have to significantly revise not only their theories of how continents and mountains grow, but also the history of the Pacific Ocean Basin and the land masses bordering it as well. The secrets in these out-of-place blocks of land may also give them a deeper understanding of the powerful forces that have shaped — and continue to shape — the earth.

New Light
on Photosynthesis

By Joseph J. Katz

**If scientists can learn to duplicate the process
by which plants convert sunlight to chemical
energy, humanity will enter a new era of plenty.**

Life in all its many forms depends entirely on sunlight. Green plants and certain bacteria use the sun's energy directly. But all other living organisms, from amebas to human beings, rely for their continued existence on the organic matter produced by green plants. The energy stored in plants—rooted plants on land, algae in the oceans and lakes—either passes up the food chain from one animal to another, or comes directly to your dinner plate.

Plants use sunlight to create energy-rich organic compounds from carbon dioxide, water, and minerals. The process is called *photosynthesis*, which means *putting together with light*. Organic compounds are complex carbon-containing molecules that all living things on earth are made from.

Green plants make up the world's largest chemical "factory." Scientists estimate that terrestrial and ocean plants manufacture almost 200 billion tons of organic matter every year. Most of it is produced by microscopic plant life, primarily algae, in the oceans. In addition,

all of the vast oil and coal deposits that provide the bulk of the energy needed by modern industrial society are the product of photosynthesis in bygone geologic eras. The oxygen in our atmosphere, which today makes respiration and combustion possible, is a byproduct of photosynthesis.

Because of its crucial role in sustaining the cycle of life on earth, photosynthesis has been studied intensely by scientists for the past two centuries. Their interest in photosynthesis has increased since the early 1970s, stimulated by the prospect of using sunlight, a virtually inexhaustible resource, to satisfy the energy requirements of the world's rapidly growing population. Research into the ways that plants use sunlight may lead to processes that artificially duplicate natural photosynthesis. At Argonne National Laboratory in Illinois, my colleagues and I have long been involved in experiments that may help achieve that goal.

Scientists currently are limited in the ways they can apply the energy in sunlight. They can either extract it as heat or convert it directly into electricity with solar cells. Plants use sunlight in a completely different way. Many hundreds of millions of years ago, they evolved the ability to convert solar energy to electron energy. This energy drives a multitude of chemical reactions to produce carbohydrates, proteins, and fats — the foodstuffs on which all animal life depends — as well as many other substances made of organic compounds, such as rubber and cotton.

Much current research on photosynthesis is focused on understanding the initial conversion of light energy to electron energy in a plant leaf. Understanding that conversion process would enable us to mimic photosynthesis in the laboratory — and eventually on a large industrial scale.

Photosynthesis in plants is carried out in specialized structures called chloroplasts. In land plants, chloroplasts are located in leaf cells. They are one-tenth to one-fifth the size of the cell. The electron microscope reveals that chloroplasts have a complex structure, with a system of internal membranes folded into a series of thin, interconnected disks called *thylakoids* (from the Greek, meaning *sacklike*). The thylakoids are arranged in closely packed stacks resembling piles of coins.

Scientists have put together a picture of these structures from electron micrographs of portions of leaves from which the water was removed. (Specimens to be examined by an electron microscope cannot contain water.) But scientists do not know for certain what these structures look like in the living plant.

All plants synthesize their organic compounds in the same way. They use the energy in light to convert carbon dioxide and water into organic matter and oxygen gas.

The conversion of carbon dioxide to more complicated carbon compounds requires an input of electrons — known to the chemist as

The author:
Joseph J. Katz is a distinguished senior scientist emeritus at Argonne National Laboratory in Illinois.

reduction. A plant gets the electrons it needs by removing them from water, releasing oxygen into the air as a by-product. The process of removing electrons from water, or from any other kind of molecule, is called oxidation.

Some photosynthetic bacteria, although they are able to make their own food from sunlight, have not evolved the ability to oxidize water. Instead, they must obtain electrons from other sources, such as hydrogen sulfide or organic acids. Consequently, these photosynthetic bacteria do not produce oxygen.

The ease with which green plants use low-energy red photons to split water molecules is one of the central mysteries of photosynthesis. Water is a very stable substance and strongly resists having its electrons removed. It is doubtful that artificial photosynthesis can become commercial until scientists have learned how to duplicate this basic ability of plants.

Light travels in waves. But it also consists of small packets of energy, called photons. Photons in visible light come in every color of the rainbow, ranging from blue light — the most energetic — to red light — the least energetic.

Chemical reactions initiated by light are common. In fact, organic chemists routinely use light energy to synthesize a number of highly complex molecules, including many not found in nature. There are major differences, however, in the way chemists use light in the laboratory and the way it is used by plants.

Chemists usually must use blue light, and sometimes the even more energetic ultraviolet light, to provide power for their reactions. But green plants carry out photosynthesis primarily with very low-energy red photons (although they also use blue light). This talent for using the lowest energy photons in light to carry out chemical reactions — and to do it with high efficiency — is one of the key secrets of photosynthesis that scientists are trying to penetrate.

Most of a plant's chemical reactions consist of either "light reactions" or "dark reactions." The conversion of light energy to chemical energy is a process that is driven by a steady stream of photons. These light reactions appear to take place entirely within the thylakoids. Here the photons are gathered and their energy locked into chemical compounds by subsequent chemical reactions which store the trapped energy.

The dark reactions, so called because they can take place in the absence of light, produce the many organic compounds that result in growth of the plant. Scientists understand these reactions quite well. However, they still have much to learn about the initial light-energy conversion, and that is where they are focusing most of their research on photosynthesis.

The light reactions use a special group of substances, the photosynthetic pigments. Of these, the most important — indeed, one of the most vital molecules in all of nature — is chlorophyll. Chloro-

Sunlight Goes to Work

Photosynthesis begins when photons of energy from the sun strike a leaf. The light is absorbed by chloroplasts, whose internal membranes contain the plant's chlorophyll. The membranes are folded into a series of flat disks, which are arranged into stacks, containing groups of chlorophyll molecules. Each group, a photosynthetic unit, consists of many antenna chlorophyll molecules and one reaction center molecule. When a photon strikes an antenna molecule, its energy is passed from one antenna chlorophyll to another and is finally trapped by the reaction center chlorophyll.

phyll gives plants their green color. There are about a dozen closely related forms of chlorophyll, but all green plants that produce oxygen contain a molecule called chlorophyll a, and many of them contain lesser amounts of a nearly identical molecule, chlorophyll b. Chlorophyll a is the most important chlorophyll and consequently has been the most intensively studied.

Plants also contain another group of pigments called carotenes, which are yellow or red. The brilliant colors of autumn leaves are created by carotenes. Carotenes probably act to protect chlorophyll from deteriorating during the growing season.

Chlorophyll has a very complicated molecular structure. Some of the world's outstanding organic chemists spent more than 50 years working out the details of that structure. Yet it is uncertain that our picture of the molecule is complete. Nor are we sure that we have detected all of the chlorophylls in nature.

The chlorophyll molecule looks somewhat like a ping-pong paddle. It has two parts: a head, which is the working part of the molecule; and a tail, which anchors the molecule in the thylakoid membrane. The head consists of 12 carbon atoms and 4 nitrogen atoms linked into a giant ring. At the center of the ring is a magnesium

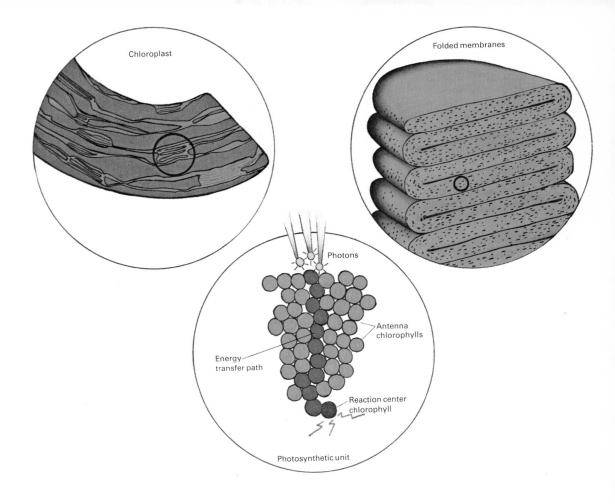

Chloroplast

Folded membranes

Photons

Antenna
chlorophylls

Energy
transfer path

Reaction center
chlorophyll

Photosynthetic unit

atom. The arrangement of the atoms in the ring is what makes chlorophyll green (see THE PHYSICS OF COLOR).

Chlorophyll serves several functions in the conversion of light energy to chemical energy. First, because it is highly colored, chlorophyll strongly absorbs the photons of visible light. Although it absorbs blue and red light most easily, chlorophyll collects light over the entire visible spectrum.

Having absorbed photons, the chlorophyll puts their energy to work. When a photon strikes a chlorophyll molecule, it gives up its energy to an electron in one of the molecule's atoms. This electronic excitation provides the energy for the light reactions. The conversion takes less than a billionth of a second.

Scientists had assumed that any excited chlorophyll molecule could make direct use of a photon's energy. However, they now know that the capture and conversion of a single photon require the cooperation of a large number of chlorophyll molecules. This stems from research conducted in the 1930s. By exposing chlorophyll to flashes of light and measuring the oxygen produced, scientists determined that some 300 chlorophyll molecules are involved in the capture and conversion to chemical energy of a single photon. This

The Energy Conveyor Belt
Energy from sunlight drives two series of photosynthetic reactions. The first begins when a photon hits an antenna chlorophyll molecule, *left*. The energy is passed from one antenna molecule to another and finally to a still-unidentified reaction center chlorophyll (dark glasses). Here the energy is transferred to an electron, taken from the breakdown of a water molecule. The electron enters a series of chemical reactions (gears), one of whose products is ATP, an energy-rich compound that the plant uses to power other reactions.

Photon

Electrons

ATP

Reaction center

Reaction center

Water

Oxygen

Antenna chlorophyll molecules

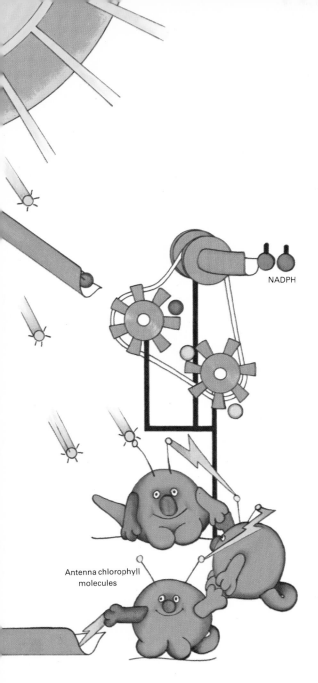

NADPH

Antenna chlorophyll
molecules

Each de-energized electron then
passes into the second reaction
center (paired chlorophylls).
The reaction center molecule
uses photon energy collected by
its own team of antenna
molecules to send electrons
along two alternate pathways.
Some electrons return to the
first system to make more ATP.
Others enter into a second
set of chemical reactions (gears
on right) that produce NADPH,
another high-energy compound
used later by the plant.

team of molecules — plus other molecules that act
as electron transfer agents — is called a photosynthetic unit (PSU).

All but one of the chlorophyll molecules in the
PSU act as light collectors. They are called antenna chlorophyll. The excitation energy resulting
from the capture of a photon is transferred from
one antenna chlorophyll to another until it is
finally trapped by a specialized pair of molecules
called reaction center chlorophyll. The reaction
center molecules then transfer that energy to an
electron, extracted earlier from water, which takes
part in the light reactions.

Most scientists accept the idea that in most
green plants there are two kinds of reaction centers that operate at two different wavelengths. Scientists have exposed plants to red and blue light,
separately and together, and measured the
amount of oxygen the plants produce. They found
that the yield of oxygen is significantly larger
when the two colors of light are used at the same
time than when they are used separately. This
suggests that two photosynthesis systems, or photosystems, each with its own reaction center, are
working cooperatively.

The two photosystems must be connected by an
electron pathway. The reaction center of one photosystem presumably extracts electrons from water and gives them an initial energy boost. This
generates oxygen as a by-product. The other reaction center raises those electrons to even higher
energy levels, creating significant chemical reducing power. That reducing power is used to produce an energy-rich molecule called NADPH.
Along the way, the two photosystems also create
another important high-energy molecule, adenosine triphosphate (ATP). The energy stored in the
chemical bonds of those two compounds provides
the power for the dark reactions.

Although the theory of the two photosystems is
widely accepted by scientists, many questions
about the photosystems are still unanswered.
Among the biggest uncertainties is the nature of
the oxygen-generating photosystem. This photosystem's reaction center, if it in fact exists, may be
constructed differently from the other photosystem's reaction center.

There is evidence that the photosynthetic reaction center that produces reducing power consists of a pair of chlorophyll molecules. Chlorophyll, like most organic compounds, contains an even number of electrons because the electrons that create chemical bonds come in pairs. Thus, when a reaction center molecule emits an electron, it is left with a single, unpaired electron. The data from various laboratory experiments suggest that the unpaired electron is not confined to a single chlorophyll molecule but rather is shared equally by two molecules of chlorophyll.

This is the essential difference between antenna molecules and reaction center molecules. Antenna molecules, which may be either chlorophyll a or b, are in close contact with their neighboring antenna molecules but are not chemically joined to them. While this arrangement enables them to pass energy along, it does not permit them to hold onto it. In contrast, a reaction center molecule, formed by two molecules of chlorophyll a acting as a unit, can somehow trap and use the excitation energy to extract electrons from water and give them an energy boost.

Researchers have proposed various models for the exact way the molecules are linked. Experiments with laser light have indicated that the two chlorophyll molecules must be arranged in parallel, with their heads overlapping, before they can absorb light energy and eject electrons.

In the formation of a chlorophyll reaction center, the central magnesium atom of one chlorophyll molecule and one of the five oxygen atoms attached to the ring of the other chlorophyll molecule play the most important parts. The magnesium atom is electron deficient. Therefore it has a strong tendency to share electrons with another atom or molecule.

Water molecules are ideally suited to this purpose. A pair of water molecules can link two chlorophyll molecules. The oxygen atom in a water molecule shares electrons with the magnesium atom of one chlorophyll, while the water molecule's two hydrogen atoms form weak bonds (hydrogen bonds) with an oxygen atom of the second chlorophyll. This locks the two chlorophyll molecules into a parallel configuration with their rings in close contact.

If this model for the reaction center is correct, it provides us with an important step toward developing artificial photosynthesis. Obviously, we must thoroughly understand the structures and processes of the natural leaf before we can duplicate them.

Scientists have, in fact, already learned how to create artificial reaction center molecules. So far, they have developed two methods for synthesizing the centers. In one of these procedures, chlorophyll is dissolved in a solvent that does not contain any atoms that can share electrons with magnesium. Water is then added, and each chlorophyll molecule attracts a molecule of water to its magnesium atom. In a warm solution at room temperature, the chlorophyll mol-

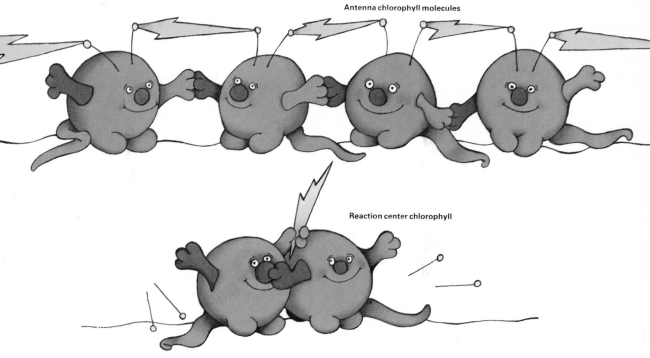

Antenna chlorophyll molecules

Reaction center chlorophyll

Energy Grabbers
Antenna chlorophyll
molecules transmit
electron energy but
cannot hold it. A
reaction center molecule
can trap the energy
because of its dual
structure: two linked
chlorophylls, with an
oxygen atom (arm) on
one attached to the
magnesium atom (nose)
of the other.

ecules tend to float about singly rather than organize themselves into pairs. However, if the temperature of the mixture is lowered, the molecules' tendency to form hydrogen bonds increases. At sufficiently low temperatures, $-30°F$. to $-150°F$., the reaction center pairs begin to form of their own accord.

The other method of creating artificial reaction centers is done at room temperature through a process of molecular "surgery." Using chemicals that act as a sort of molecular scalpel, researchers have learned how to amputate the tails of chlorophyll molecules. They replace the tails with a molecule that forms a bridge between the two. The result is two chlorophyll rings tethered to each other by a chemical link, much like the heads of two tennis rackets connected by a chain. If these molecules are put into a solution containing water or alcohol, they obligingly fold themselves into the desired parallel configuration.

Chlorophyll molecules probably never link up this way in plants. Nevertheless, the procedure is very useful because the artificially joined pairs, in their folded arrangement, have many of the properties of the natural reaction center chlorophylls. Artificial reaction centers thus make it possible to study the phenomenon of electron ejection in the laboratory.

Having created a reasonably satisfactory synthetic reaction center, scientists have begun, in a very preliminary way, to construct an artificial thylakoid. At Argonne, we have been experimenting with metal foils coated with synthetic reaction centers. These centers transfer an electron from an electron donor — a substance with extra electrons — to an electron acceptor — one with a deficiency of elec-

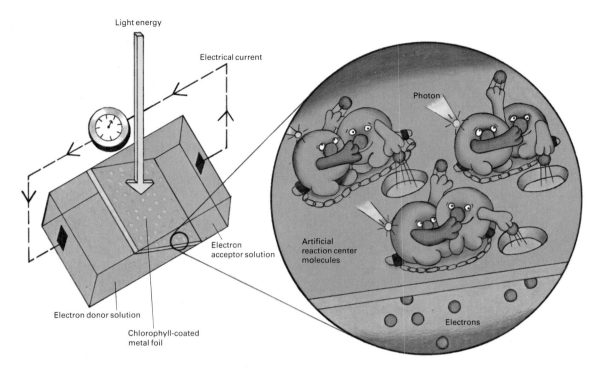

Light energy

Electrical current

Electron
acceptor solution

Artificial
reaction center
molecules

Photon

Electrons

Electron donor solution

Chlorophyll-coated
metal foil

A current model of a synthetic leaf is similar to a real leaf but has no antenna molecules and cannot extract electrons from water. It contains a metal foil coated on one side with artificial reaction center chlorophylls. Photons cause the chlorophylls to emit electrons, which are absorbed by an electron-acceptor solution. A donor solution provides new electrons. The electron flow creates an electric current.

trons. We insert a coated piece of foil into a two-compartment cell constructed in such a way that the chlorophyll is immersed in a water solution of an organic electron acceptor. The other compartment of the cell contains a solution of an electron donor, which is in contact with the uncoated side of the metal foil.

When we shine a strong light on the coated side of the foil, the artificial chlorophyll reaction center molecules eject electrons, which are readily taken up by the acceptor solution. The chlorophyll pairs then replenish themselves by drawing electrons through the foil from the donor. If an electrode is attached to each end of the device and the electrodes are connected with a wire, an electric current flows through the wire.

We have not been able to achieve very high efficiencies with this system so far. Still, there is little doubt that it demonstrates the feasibility of using artificial reaction center chlorophyll to imitate the energy-conversion process used by living plants. This model puts us firmly on the road toward artificial photosynthesis.

That road, however, will be a long one. Scientists must solve many major problems before artificial photosynthesis will be possible on a large industrial scale. The most important problem is how to use water as a source of electrons, as plants do.

We must also learn how plants transport electrons so efficiently. Natural photosynthesis consists, in essence, of the transfer of electrons from water to carbon dioxide. Plant thylakoid membranes must therefore contain some sort of transmission network for electrons. Technology uses copper or aluminum wire to transport electrons. Plants transfer electrons through chemical compounds that can easily accept or donate electrons. Most of these compounds have been identified, but how they are arranged within the leaf, and how the electron transfer system functions as a whole, are still very much a mystery.

Plants use photosynthesis to survive and reproduce, but to what ends would we use artificial photosynthesis? The possible uses of solar energy obtained this way are nearly endless. For example, by breaking water apart to obtain electrons, we would also be obtaining hydrogen gas for fuel. We could produce huge amounts of carbohydrates and proteins to feed the world's population. We could use the energized electrons to provide power for reactions to synthesize an enormous range of chemical compounds. All these things would be made, quite literally, "out of thin air," using carbon dioxide and sunlight as the basic raw materials.

The production of food — artificial farming — would perhaps be the most important use of commercial photosynthesis. Many regions of the earth receive abundant sunshine but lack the proper soil, water, or climate to make agriculture feasible. Artificial farming would enable us to synthesize food in automated factories, freeing humanity at last from having to contend with plant diseases, insect pests, drought, fertilizer requirements, and soil depletion. The energy in sunlight, much of which is used by plants for their own growth, would be directed entirely to chemical synthesis. Thus, it is conceivable that artificial farms would be more efficient than green plants in using solar energy.

A synthetic farm would probably consist of many large tanks — transparent to admit sunlight — each divided into two compartments. These chambers would be separated by a membrane coated on one side with artificial chlorophyll reaction center molecules. One compartment of a container would hold water, from which the reaction centers would extract electrons. The other compartment would contain any one of a great variety of chemical solutions. When struck by sunlight, the chlorophyll reaction center molecules on the membrane would pump energized electrons into the solution to drive reactions. A system of pipes would connect all the tanks in the farm. The pipes would circulate chemicals to the proper cell compartments and collect the reaction products. The output of an artificial farm would probably include edible carbohydrates and proteins; fibers, such as cotton, flax, and linen; and various *polymers* (long-chain molecules), like rubber.

Needless to say, this technology will not come to pass overnight. Many years of sustained effort by thousands of scientists and engineers throughout the world will be required to attain the goal of practical artificial photosynthesis. If and when they succeed, however, humanity will enter a new era, in which it will have an inexhaustible supply of the necessities of life.

For Further Reading

Additional information on some of the subjects covered in the Special Reports may be found in these books and magazine articles.

Staying Around the Nest
Barash, David P. *Sociobiology and Behavior*. Elsevier Press, 1982.
Goodwin, Derek. *Crows of the World*. Cornell University Press, 1976.
"Why You Do What You Do," *Time*, Aug. 1, 1977.
Wilson, Edward O. *Sociobiology: The New Synthesis*. Belknap Press, Harvard University, 1975.
Woolfenden, Glen E., and Fitzpatrick, John W. *The Florida Scrub Jay: Demography of a Cooperative-Breeding Bird*. Princeton University Press, in press.

Rebuilding Bodies
Kucherov, Alex. "More Spare Parts for the Human Body," *U.S. News and World Report*, Dec. 28, 1981/Jan. 4, 1982.
Skurzynski, Gloria. *Bionic Parts for People: The Real Story of Artificial Organs and Replacement Parts*. School Book Service, 1978.
White, S. L. "The Real Science of Body Building," *Mechanics Illustrated*, July 1981.

Acid from the Sky
Howard, Ross, and Perley, Michael. *Acid Rain: The Devastating Impact on North America*. McGraw-Hill, 1982.
Likens, Gene E.; Wright, Richard F.; Galloway, James N.; and Butler, Thomas J. "Acid Rain," *Scientific American*, October 1979.
Ostmann, Robert, Jr. *Acid Rain: A Plague upon the Waters*. Dillon, 1982.

The Secrets of Living Lights
Fichter, George S. "Bizarre World of Undersea Lights," *International Wildlife*, January/February 1978.
Horsburgh, Peg. *Living Light: Exploring Bioluminescence*. Julian Messner, 1978.
Jacobs, Francine. *Nature's Light: The Story of Bioluminescence*. William Morrow and Company, 1974.
Lloyd, James E. "Mimicry in the Sexual Signals of Fireflies," *Scientific American*, July 1981.

Herpes Is Forever
Langston, Deborah P. *Living with Herpes: The Comprehensive and Authoritative Guide to the Causes, Symptoms, and Treatment of Herpes Virus Illnesses*. Doubleday, 1983.
The Helper. The Herpes Resources Center, P.O. Box 100, Palo Alto, CA. 94302.

Laying Waste in America
Brown, Michael. *Laying Waste: The Poisoning of America by Toxic Chemicals*. Pantheon, 1980.
Epstein, Samuel S.; Brown, Lester O.; and Pope, Carl. *Hazardous Waste in America*. Sierra Club Books, 1982.
Maugh, Thomas H., II. "Toxic Waste Disposal a Growing Problem," *Science*, May 25, 1979.
Maugh, Thomas H., II. "Biological Markers for Chemical Exposure," *Science*, Feb. 5, 1982.
"The Poisoning of America," *Time*, Sept. 22, 1980.

Molecular Clues to Our Origins
Gribbin, John, and Cherfas, Jeremy. *The Monkey Puzzle*. Pantheon Books, 1982.
Lewin, Roger. *Thread of Life: The Smithsonian Looks at Evolution*. Smithsonian Books, 1982.

The Physics of Color
Nassau, Kurt. *The Physics and Chemistry of Color*. John Wiley and Sons, 1983.
Overheim, R. D., and Wagner, D. L. *Light and Color*. John Wiley and Sons, 1982.

Mapping the Universe
Ferris, Timothy. *Galaxies*. Sierra Club Books, 1980.
Gregory, Stephen A., and Thompson, Laird A. "Superclusters and Voids in the Distribution of Galaxies," *Scientific American*, March 1982.
Waldrop, M. Mitchell. "The Large-Scale Structure of the Universe," *Science*, March 4, 1983.
Waldrop, M. Mitchell. "The New Inflationary Universe," *Science*, January 28, 1983.
Weinberg, Steven. *The First Three Minutes: A Modern View of the Origin of the Universe*. Basic Books, 1976.

Cancer's Genetic Connection
Bishop, J. Michael. "Oncogenes," *Scientific American*, March 1982.
Miller, Julie Ann. "Spelling Out a Cancer Gene," *Science News*, Nov. 13, 1982.

New Missions for Magnetism
Pykett, Ian L. "NMR Imaging in Medicine," *Scientific American*, May 1982.
Trefil, James. *The Unexpected Vista*. Scribner's, 1983.

The Patchwork Earth
Jones, David L.; Cox, Allan; Coney, Peter; and Beck, Myrl. "The Growth of Western North America," *Scientific American*, November 1982.
Overbye, Dennis. "The Jigsaw Earth," *Discover*, April 1983.

New Light on Photosynthesis
Baker, Jeffrey J. W., and Allan, Garland E. "The Uphill Energy Pathway — Photosynthesis," *The Study of Biology*, Addison-Wesley, 1982.
Govindjee and Govindjee, Rajni. "The Absorption of Light in Photosynthesis," *Scientific American*, December 1974.
Miller, Kenneth R. "The Photosynthetic Membrane," *Scientific American*, October 1979.

Science File

Science Year contributors report on the year's major
developments in their respective fields. The articles in this
section are arranged alphabetically by subject matter.

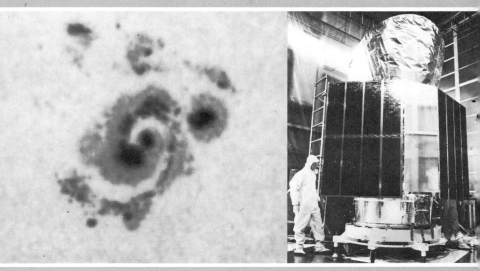

Agriculture

Several improved crop plants were developed by agricultural scientists in 1982 and 1983. Scientists at Kansas State University of Agriculture and Applied Science in Manhattan reported in February 1983 that they had crossbred a potato with two varieties of tomato to create a "pomato." The researchers, led by plant pathologist James F. Shepard, fused leaf cells of Russet Burbank potatoes and Nova and Rutgers tomatoes. The hybrid potatoes acquired the tomatoes' natural resistance to blight disease and can also tolerate drought.

In January, researchers at Colorado State University in Fort Collins, under the direction of plant physiologist Murray W. Nabors, reported that they had used genetic engineering techniques to produce a new variety of oats. The genetically modified oat plants can grow in soil twice as salty as that tolerated by ordinary oat plants. This was the first use of laboratory methods for altering plant genes to increase a food plant's tolerance to environmental stress.

Plant scientist James Quick, also of Colorado State University, announced in November 1982 that his research team had developed a variety of winter wheat that resists damage from hail. The new wheat plant, named Hail, also produces 15 per cent more grain than other high-yield varieties of wheat.

In May 1982, scientists at the Ohio Agricultural Research and Development Center in Wooster reported that a rare perennial variety of corn discovered in Mexico can be harvested for several years without replanting. The perennial corn would also greatly reduce soil erosion. The investigators speculated that the corn might be hardy enough to grow in the mild winters of the Southern United States.

The Weyerhaeuser Company of Tacoma, Wash., reported in February 1983 that it has used genetic engineering to produce "supertrees" that grow much faster than ordinary trees. Weyerhaeuser officials said they have increased their production of Douglas firs and loblolly pines by 70 and 300 per cent, respectively.

Students at Michigan State University in East Lansing collect cereal leaf beetles, *below,* as part of a study on using wasps for controlling these pests. A *Lemophagus curtus* wasp, *below right,* injects its eggs into the larva of a cereal leaf beetle, thus dooming the beetle to be eaten by baby wasps.

Agriculture

Continued

Scientists at the Corn Insects Research Unit in Ankeny, Iowa, place larvae of the black cutworm on test plots of corn seedlings, *above left,* to assess the damage caused by the caterpillars at different stages of plant growth. An entomologist at the research unit examines moths caught by a sticky trap, *above right.* The traps help to predict when farmers will find cutworm eggs in their fields.

Growth regulators. Plant physiologists C. Dean Dybing of the U.S. Department of Agriculture and Charles L. Lay of South Dakota State University in Brookings reported in July 1982 that chlorflurenol, a chemical that stimulates plant growth, significantly increases the oil in flaxseeds. The researchers discovered that applying just 25 to 50 grams of chlorflurenol per hectare of flax (⅔ to 1½ ounces per acre) boosts the oil content of the seeds by 10 to 20 per cent. The chemical can also increase the oil content of soybeans, wheat, and oats, according to the researchers. Their report was one of the first to show that a plant-growth regulator can improve the food value of a crop.

In March 1983, researchers at Michigan State University in East Lansing and the Procter & Gamble Company in Cincinnati, Ohio, reported that spraying with triacontonal, another growth regulator, enhances the growth of corn plants. The chemical, which stimulates plant growth even when used at extremely low concentrations, is one of the most effective regulators so far developed.

Root-colonizing bacteria. Plant pathologists Milton N. Schroth and Joseph G. Hancock of the University of California in Berkeley reported in June 1982 that root-colonizing bacteria of the genus *Pseudomonas* may suppress many plant diseases caused by other bacteria. The *Pseudomonas* successfully competes against the other bacteria and prevents them from colonizing plant roots. The *Pseudomonas* produces compounds called siderophores, which combine with iron in the soil, thereby making it unavailable to the disease-causing bacteria, which need a supply of iron to survive. In effect, *Pseudomonas* causes the harmful bacteria to starve to death. This protection from damaging bacteria allows the plants to grow larger and increase their yield.

Embryo splitting. Colorado scientists reported in May 1983 that they had produced about 100 calves by splitting cattle embryos and reimplanting the two halves of each embryo into other cows. Researchers R. Peter Elsden,

Entomologists at the ARS Bioenvironmental Bee Laboratory in Beltsville, Md., inspect an empty tray that had been brimming with a special bee diet. Honeybees ate every bit of the food, while consuming only part of a pollen-based diet and almost none of a soybean diet. The so-called Beltsville Bee Diet – a mixture of whey, yeast, and sugars – is inexpensive and keeps for months.

George E. Seidel, and Timothy J. Williams of the Animal Reproduction Laboratory at Colorado State University used microsurgical instruments to divide the embryos when they were 6 or 7 days old. At that point, an embryo consists of just 40 to 70 cells, which have not begun to differentiate into specialized tissues. After splitting an embryo, the scientists put the halves into the uteri of foster mother cows. About 50 per cent of the divided embryos died, but those that survived developed into normal calves.

British scientists at the Institute of Animal Physiology in Cambridge, England, took embryo-splitting technology one step further, producing four lambs from a single sheep embryo. Four appears to be the largest number of animals that can currently be produced from a single sheep or cattle embryo. All the offspring from a single embryo, like natural twins or quadruplets, are genetically identical.

Embryo splitting will give scientists a new experimental tool for studying animal genetics. It also offers promise for increasing livestock production.

Role of small farms. Politicians and economists have long debated the importance of small family farms in the United States. Many analysts insist that American agriculture would suffer if large corporate farms took over the growing of most of our food. However, agricultural economist Luther G. Tweeten of Oklahoma State University in Stillwater reported in March 1983 that many assertions about small farms are incorrect.

In a study comparing small farms and large farms throughout the United States, Tweeten found that the operators of small farms do not have a higher standard of living, nor are they better custodians of soil and energy resources. According to Tweeten, federal government programs have not hastened the demise of small farms. His report also indicated that family farms do not contribute significantly to the economic and social well-being of nearby towns and cities. Tweeten further concluded that small farms are not essential for economic competition in the agricultural industry.

Biological controls. Soil scientists and microbiologists at Michigan State

Agriculture

Continued

University in East Lansing reported in December 1982 that bacteria in lake sediments and sewage can break down poisonous chemical pollutants called halogenated aromatic compounds. These compounds include certain powerful chlorine-containing weedkillers. Through a process not fully understood, anaerobic bacteria—bacteria that live in the absence of oxygen—remove atoms of chlorine or other so-called halogens from these compounds, which then break down into methane and carbon dioxide. Anaerobic bacteria might help in removing toxic substances from the environment.

Yellow nut sedge is one of the most persistent weeds in the world and a serious nuisance to agriculture. In March 1983, a team of plant scientists with the U.S. Department of Agriculture and the University of Georgia's Coastal Plain Experiment Station in Tifton reported that yellow nut sedge can be controlled by exposing it to a rust fungus called *Puccinia canaliculata*. The scientists said the fungus dehydrates and kills nut sedge plants.

Rising carbon dioxide levels in the atmosphere may be having a profound—and beneficial—effect on the production of food crops and other renewable resources. The amount of carbon dioxide (CO_2) in the earth's atmosphere is increasing by 2 parts per million every year due to the massive burning of fossil fuels in the industrialized countries of the world. During photosynthesis, green plants take in CO_2 and give off oxygen. A higher concentration of atmospheric CO_2 improves crop yields and increases photosynthesis by green plants. It also provides more plant nutrients by stepping up nitrogen fixation in the soil. Increased CO_2 levels give crops greater resistance to stress and air pollutants.

These positive effects, which have been confirmed by recent studies, should help to offset the negative effects of increased CO_2—notably a rise in the temperature of the atmosphere. Many scientists are predicting that worldwide warming will cause the polar icecaps to melt, raising the level of the oceans.   [Sylvan H. Wittwer]

Anthropology

The discovery of the oldest fossil bones from a hominid—a human ancestor—was announced in June 1982 by anthropologists J. Desmond Clark and Timothy D. White of the University of California, Berkeley. The fossils, which have been dated to about 4 million years ago, were found in the Middle Awash Valley in the Afar Triangle of Ethiopia, one of the richest sources of prehistoric fossils in the world. See THE AFAR'S BOUNTIFUL LEGACY.

The fossils consist of a thighbone and parts of the front portion of a skull. Measurements of the skull fragments indicated that the creature's brain was about the size of that of a modern chimpanzee. The thighbone showed that the creature was fully adapted to upright walking.

Clark and White theorized that the creature belonged to the species *Australopithecus afarensis*, the same species as "Lucy," the 3-million-year-old fossil skeleton found at Hadar in Ethiopia in 1974. However, the new fossils cannot definitely be assigned to that species because the scientists did not find the creature's jaws and teeth, among the most important bones used in classifying hominids.

Walking papers. Did Lucy, the oldest known hominid, walk upright on the ground all the time or did she still spend much of her time in the trees? Studies published in 1983 raised new questions about the walking ability of Lucy, discovered by anthropologist Donald C. Johanson of the Institute of Human Origins in Berkeley, Calif.

In March 1983, anthropologist Randall L. Susman and anatomist Jack Stern of the State University of New York at Stony Brook contended that Lucy's shoulder blade and her hand and foot bones show anatomical features similar to those of primates that climb trees. The two scientists agreed that Lucy's knee, leg, and hip indicate that she walked upright, an interpretation first presented in 1979 by anatomist C. Owen Lovejoy of Kent State University in Ohio. However, Susman and Stern pointed out that Lucy's toes, which they see as long and curved like an ape's, indicate that she had not

Anthropology

Continued

Skull fragments and parts of a thighbone found in Ethiopia and dated to about 4 million years ago are the oldest known fossil bones of a human ancestor.

completely abandoned life in the trees. They also suggested that her thumb was more apelike than humanlike.

Susman and Stern theorized that Lucy may be what scientists used to call the "missing link," an intermediate form of hominid between apes and humans. Thus, Lucy may represent a hominid species that, while almost completely adapted to full-time upright walking, may also have retained features enabling it to remain in the trees to eat, sleep, and escape from predators.

In January 1983, three anthropologists argued that the issue of Lucy's walking ability may be complicated by disease. Della Collins Cook of Indiana University at Bloomington; Jane E. Buikstra of Northwestern University in Evanston, Ill.; and Jean C. De-Rousseau of New York University in New York City reported that Lucy suffered from Scheuermann's disease.

Characterized by a prominent curvature of the spine in the middle of the back and an enlargement of the vertebrae, Scheuermann's disease is a rela-

tively common, but largely harmless, condition in modern human beings. It usually begins in adolescence and heals by age 20. Although the exact cause of the disease is unknown, it is also often found in people who regularly lift heavy objects. Cook and her colleagues suggested that in Lucy's case, the heavy object she lifted might have been her own body as she climbed about in the trees.

Neanderthal error explained. Anthropologists long believed that Neanderthals, an early subspecies of *Homo sapiens*, walked in a slouching posture with bent knees. This belief was based chiefly on an inaccurate reconstruction by paleontologist Marcellin Boule in 1911 of a male Neanderthal skeleton found in La Chapelle-aux-Saints, France. Since then, scientists examining other Neanderthal skeletons have discovered that these early human beings stood and walked fully erect. Most scientists believed Boule erred because he failed to recognize bone deformities in the skeleton that had caused its slouching posture.

Margaret Mead Under Attack

Margaret Mead and
Samoan girl in 1925

In 1928, a book about adolescence in Samoa by a young anthropologist from Barnard College in New York City helped change American attitudes about child-rearing and the role culture plays in forming character. Margaret Mead, the author of the book *Coming of Age in Samoa*, later became one of the United States most respected anthropologists.

In early 1983, however, another book about Samoa accused Mead, who died in 1978, of totally misrepresenting culture in that South Pacific society. *Margaret Mead and Samoa: The Making and Unmaking of an Anthropological Myth* quickly attracted international attention. The author of the book, Derek Freeman, professor emeritus of anthropology at the Australian National University in Canberra, in turn drew heated criticism from many other anthropologists. Mead's defenders maintain that by attempting to discredit her most famous work, Freeman has questioned her competence as a commentator on human nature and culture.

In her book, Mead, who spent nine months in Samoa in 1925 and 1926, portrayed Samoan society as peaceful and generally free of passion and conflict. She reported that because of relaxed child-rearing practices, Samoan adolescents experienced few of the sexual or identity crises that affect American teen-agers.

Freeman, who spent six years in Samoa between 1940 and 1981, presents a very different view. He found the Samoans to be highly competitive, aggressive, sexually repressed, and prone to such violent crimes as assault and rape. He reported that Samoan children are harshly disciplined and frequently beaten. And that instead of encouraging sexual freedom, the Samoans highly prize the virginity of adolescent girls.

According to Freeman, Mead went to Samoa not to observe and report on Samoan culture but to find support for the theory of cultural determinism. This theory contends that an individual's personality is influenced chiefly by social and other cultural factors. Freeman charges that Mead and other American anthropologists of the 1920s were eager to counter the then widely accepted theory of biological determinism, which states that human character is determined by heredity and other biological factors. This theory was used by some people to justify racism. Thus, evidence that Samoan adolescents did not suffer from the biologically motivated stresses all adolescents were supposed to experience would demonstrate the importance of cultural influences. Freeman argues that because Mead ignored biological factors, she missed the realities of Samoan life.

Many anthropologists believe Freeman's book correctly points out some flaws in Mead's methods and insights. For example, she simplified the contradictions in Samoan society and her knowledge of the Samoan language was imperfect.

However, Mead's defenders have attacked Freeman's contention that Mead's conclusions were totally in error. They contend that while Mead may have been simplistic in her insights about Samoa and that some of her data may have been wrong, her conclusions were right.

Freeman's critics have been most vehement about his position on the question of cultural determinism. They say that Freeman misstates Mead's position when he claims that she believed biology plays no part in the formation of character. Mead and other cultural determinists never claimed that behavior was determined solely by cultural influences. They used cultural factors to explain significant behavioral differences between groups, such as Samoans and Americans.

Furthermore, despite Freeman's claim that Mead overemphasized cultural factors, his own work on Samoa focuses on child-rearing and political authority — both cultural factors — as fundamental influences on Samoan personality. Finally, they point out, Mead's conclusions about cultural influences on character have been confirmed by other anthropologists.

Although Freeman's criticism of Mead seems not to have seriously damaged her reputation, it has made other anthropologists even more aware of one of the greatest hazards in social science research: the data may often be interpreted in more than one way, depending on the particular views of the researcher.   [Bradd Shore]

Anthropology

Continued

In April 1983, however, anthropologist Erik Trinkaus of the University of New Mexico in Albuquerque, who examined Boule's writings, revealed that Boule was aware of the deformities in the skeleton. He attributed Boule's error to misconceptions about human anatomy widely held by scientists of that time and to Boule's own ideas about what primitive human beings looked like.

Headstands. In November 1982, anthropologists Lyle B. Steadman and Charles F. Merbs of Arizona State University in Tempe challenged a Nobel laureate's research indicating that a disease among the Fore people of New Guinea was transmitted by cannibalism. In 1976, anthropologist-pediatrician D. Carleton Gajdusek of the National Institute of Neurological and Communicative Diseases and Stroke in Bethesda, Md., was awarded the Nobel Prize in medicine or physiology for his work on the origin and spread of infectious diseases. This included a mysterious neurological disease, which the Fore called kuru. Gajdusek traced the source of the infection to brain tissue, which, he said, the natives ate during cannibalistic ceremonies.

After studying the Fore, however, the Arizona scientists found no evidence that the natives ever practiced cannibalism. According to Steadman, New Guinea natives often accuse one another of cannibalism. But this refers to a spiritual eating of the soul and not the actual consumption of human flesh. However, New Guinea natives do clean the skulls of the dead and exhibit them as memorials. The scientists concluded that the disease was transmitted by contact with brain tissue through this activity.

First scalping. In June 1982, Berkeley's Timothy White reported that jagged cuts on a 300,000-year-old *Homo erectus* skull discovered in Ethiopia in 1976 are the first evidence of the scalping of one hominid by another. The cuts on the skull, called Bodo after the site where it was discovered, were apparently made by a stone knife, rather than the teeth or claws of a carnivore.   [Charles F. Merbs]

Archaeology

Old World. For many years, archaeologists believed that few significant cultural or economic advances occurred during the Mesolithic Period, or Middle Stone Age, which lasted in western Europe from about 10,000 years ago until 7,000 to 4,000 years ago. However, archaeologists are now beginning to re-evaluate the importance of this period. The Mesolithic was preceded by the Paleolithic Period, or Old Stone Age, and followed by the Neolithic, or New Stone Age, during which agriculture and animal husbandry began.

In the summer of 1982, prehistorian J. Grahame D. Clark of Cambridge University in England published an article contending that many advances associated with the Neolithic Period actually had their roots in the Mesolithic Period. In early 1983, archaeologist T. Douglas Price of the University of Wisconsin in Madison suggested that many advances in such areas as technology, food-gathering, and social organization in western Europe can be traced to the period between 12,000 and 5,000 years ago, which includes the Mesolithic.

For example, Mesolithic people developed more efficient methods of transportation, such as boats and sledges, than had been used in Paleolithic times. They also made more efficient and specialized tools, especially those used to obtain food. In northwestern Europe, archaeologists have found a wide array of fishing gear, including harpoons, nets, and rods with prongs for spearing fish. In addition, the tips and edges of weapons and tools made from bone, wood, and antlers were fitted with small chips of stone to give them a sharper edge.

Archaeologists have also found evidence suggesting that Mesolithic settlements were often more numerous, larger, and occupied for longer periods than were Paleolithic communities. Mesolithic settlements were also more often located near rivers or other bodies of water.

In addition, Mesolithic people began to eat a wider variety of plants and animals. For example, they added

Victims of Vesuvius

Skeletons unearthed at Herculaneum tell a story of desperation and sudden death. The remains of a woman, *below,* her finger bones still decorated with gem-studded rings, lie in an archway. A soldier, *below right,* sword at his side, lies sprawled on the beach.

Scholars have long known that the powerful eruption of Italy's Mount Vesuvius on Aug. 24, A.D. 79, buried the city of Pompeii in a searing storm of hot ash. They also believed that the nearby town of Herculaneum had been destroyed by a massive slow-moving wall of mud that flowed down the sides of the exploding volcano, but that most of the residents had escaped.

In November 1982, that long-held theory unraveled when Italian archaeologists announced the discovery of some 80 skeletons along the ancient seashore at Herculaneum. Death at Herculaneum came suddenly. The skeleton of a soldier lay sprawled facedown on the sand, a sword at his side. The remains of other residents lay mangled on the beach.

Many skeletons were found huddled together, clutching moneybags and lanterns in chambers in Herculaneum's sea wall. In one chamber, six adults, four children, and two infants clustered together.

Perhaps the greatest find was an intact but badly charred Roman boat with the skeleton of its helmsman nearby. The vessel lay turned up as if flipped over by a raging sea.

Armed with observations of the recent eruptions of Mount St. Helens in Washington and El Chichón in Mexico, volcanologists quickly explained the victims' sudden death. Herculaneum was hit by at least one suffocating blast of hot wind and volcanic ash and gases, released when a column of ash blowing out of the erupting volcano collapsed. Hot debris in the column crashed back to earth and raced down the volcano's flanks at speeds as high as 96 kilometers (60 miles) per hour. Temperatures may have risen hundreds of degrees.

Responding to a plea by Italian archaeologists, physical anthropologist and bone preservationist Sara Bisel of the Smithsonian Institution rushed to Herculaneum to chemically treat and reassemble the bones of the volcano's victims. In May 1983, Bisel reported that an analysis of 55 victims indicated that many of them may have suffered from lead poisoning.   [Rick Gore]

Borobudur, *top,* a 1,200-year-old Buddhist temple on the Indonesian island of Java, stands restored in February 1983 after an eight-year, $20-million effort. A statue of Buddha, *above,* is one of hundreds lining the stone balustrades of the temple's five square terraces.

more fish to their diet, especially shell-fish. However, these new foods, coming from small animals, were more time-consuming and difficult to obtain than large animals such as deer.

Anthropologist Mark N. Cohen of the State University of New York at Plattsburgh has theorized that dietary changes may have occurred because population increases made traditional food sources inadequate. Although the new food sources were more difficult to obtain, Mesolithic people may have had no other choice. Some archaeologists believe the pressure of increased population may also have led to the development of agriculture.

Tudor treasures. After spending 437 years in the mud off Portsmouth, England, the *Mary Rose,* a Tudor warship, was raised to the surface in October 1982. The flagship of King Henry VIII, the ship capsized and sank in 1545 with 650 hands on board as Henry watched. The effort to raise the ship, which was said to be the world's most ambitious underwater archaeological operation, began in 1971 and cost $7 million.

Before the ship was raised, divers recovered more than 17,000 artifacts, including guns and other weapons, surgical and musical instruments, games, coins, clothing, cooking utensils, and pocket sundials. They also recovered numerous human skeletons. Scientists have begun studying the remains for information about disease and nutrition in the 1500s.

Roman ships. Workers digging the foundation for a hotel in Mainz, West Germany, uncovered two ancient Roman warships in the fall of 1982. Nine other ships had been found at the same site in late 1981. Although one ship was built in A.D. 81, the others were built about 300 years later. Few Roman ships have been found in northern Europe because wood rots quickly in damp climates. These ships survived because they were covered by thick layers of clay.

The ships show no sign of war damage, so West German archaeologists speculated that they had been abandoned in the early 400s when the Goths menaced northern Europe, and Romans in Germany fled to Italy for safety. [Geoffrey A. Clark]

Archaeology

Continued

New World. In December 1982, archaeologists from the Texas Department of Highways and Public Transportation discovered a human grave near Austin that may be among the oldest in the New World. Archaeologist Frank Weir reported in January 1983 that the grave contained a skeleton more than 10,000 years old.

Deposits at the site had already yielded significant data. Particularly important were the more than 100 spearpoints and at least 150 cooking areas discovered at a level estimated to be 10,200 years old. About 63 centimeters (28 inches) below that level, archaeologists found the skeleton buried in what had been a shallow pit. The skeleton was in a bent position, with its arms and legs folded and drawn up. A grinding stone and a fossilized shark's tooth had also been placed in the grave. Physical anthropologist Al Wesolowsky of the University of Texas at San Antonio identified the bones as those of a woman between 25 and 35 years old and about 160 centimeters (5 feet 3 inches) tall.

Archaeology at Monticello. In August 1982, a team of archaeologists led by William M. Kelso, resident archaeologist at Monticello, reported on a study of the Virginia home of President Thomas Jefferson. The research is being used to aid in the reconstruction of the landscape and outbuildings that formed a large part of the Monticello plantation. Although extensive documents and plans for the plantation dating from the late 1700s and early 1800s still exist, excavations were necessary in order to locate and trace the boundaries of Jefferson's experimental garden, several outbuildings, and a food-storage cellar.

Kelso's excavations turned up post molds — stains left in the earth by decayed wooden posts — that marked the perimeter of Jefferson's garden, known as Mulberry Row. Discarded tools, ceramic fragments, and food refuse indicated the location of storehouses and slave quarters. The research team also located part of the buried stone foundation of a pavilion, a decorative structure adjacent to the garden, also

The drawing of an owllike bird is one of a series of prehistoric images discovered on the mud walls of a cave in Tennessee. The Indian drawings, which are the only known cave art in North America, may have been made as long ago as A.D. 1100.

A symbol on a pottery fragment found at El Mirador in Guatemala and dated to the first or second century B.C. is one of the earliest known examples of Maya writing. The symbol stands for the Maya word meaning *lord*.

Archaeology

Continued

designed by Jefferson. Architects are currently rebuilding the pavilion using combined data from Jefferson's plans and the archaeological findings.

At one site, clusters of nails at various stages of completion indicated the location of a nail-making shop built in 1794. Archaeologists also found traces of a smokehouse and dairy built in the 1780s, and a deep cellar used to preserve food. The cellar was 4.8 meters (19 feet) deep and 11 square meters (121 square feet) in area.

Artifacts unearthed by the researchers included porcelain tableware fragments and seeds discarded from a nearby kitchen and five bottles, used as canning jars, sealed with airtight corks. These 200-year-old bottles contained cherries and cranberries grown on the plantation.

Modern Maya and ancient crafts. In January 1983, anthropologist James Nations of the Center for Human Ecology in Austin, and John E. Clark, a graduate student in archaeology at the University of Michigan at Ann Arbor, reported on their study of bow-

and-arrow making among the Lacandon Maya of the tropical rain forests of southeastern Mexico. Descendants of pre-Columbian Maya, the Lacandon still make bows and arrows. By studying the methods used by the modern Lacandon, researchers hoped to gain insight into the way this craft was practiced in the past.

The scientists found modern Lacandon often use lignum vitae, one of the hardest woods in the world, to make their bows and cane to make their arrows. The arrows are often tipped with points made of flint or obsidian.

The archaeologists were particularly interested in the techniques used to manufacture flint points. The Lacandon use a punch — a chisellike tool made of deer antler — to knock a flake from a cobble, or large rounded stone. The punch and cobble are held in the left hand, with the fingers balancing the punch against the cobble edge. The Indians then strike the punch with another stone to break off a piece of flint, which is sharpened into a point.   [Thomas R. Hester]

Astronomy

Solar System Astronomy. Research reported in March 1983 by Hartmut Holweger and W. Steenbock of the University of Kiel in West Germany and William C. Livingston of Kitt Peak National Observatory in Tucson, Ariz., shed new light on the Sun-Earth relationship. The solar astronomers' discovery may lead to proof of a physical link between variations in the Sun's temperature and weather patterns on Earth. Variability in the temperature of the Sun's photosphere — its surface, or visible part of its atmosphere — is caused by the Sun's magnetic activity cycle. That cycle controls sunspots, relatively cool, dark areas on the Sun.

During an 18-month period in 1980 and 1981, the astronomers used the Robert R. McMath solar telescope at Kitt Peak to make a series of measurements of the Sun's spectrum. The scientists then compared the data with measurements Livingston began making in 1975, when there were a minimum number of sunspots. They found that the strength of certain absorption lines — dark lines in the spectrum showing the presence of specific elements — varied systematically over periods of several years as the number of sunspots increased. These spectral absorption lines are sensitive indicators of temperatures and motions at particular levels in the Sun's atmosphere. Absorption lines associated with lower levels of the photosphere showed a cooling trend, while those typical of higher levels of the photosphere showed a warming trend. This indicated that the temperature structure of the Sun's atmosphere varies. Both these variations and the variations in the number of sunspots may be manifestations of the activity of the Sun's magnetic fields.

Overall, the solar research team found that the Sun's total energy output remains more or less constant. This confirmed measurements of total solar energy output made by the National Aeronautics and Space Administration's (NASA) Solar Maximum Mission (SMM) satellite during the same period. The SMM data showed

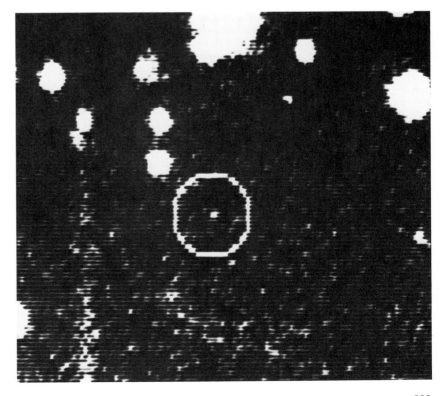

Halley's Comet – on the way toward its cyclical approach to the sun in 1986 – was first seen on Oct. 15, 1982, on Palomar Mountain in California with a telescope equipped with an advanced electronic detector system.

Astronomy

Continued

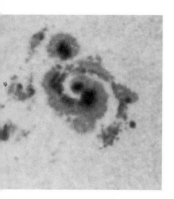

A spiral sunspot seen in February – the most striking example of this rare type ever observed – might be caused by hurricanelike activity within the Sun.

both rapid and long-term energy fluctuations, but the changes are so small that it is difficult to tell if they will affect worldwide weather patterns. However, Holweger and his colleagues found that the relative amount of ultraviolet and blue light from the Sun is decreasing, while the amount of red light is increasing.

The astronomers calculated that all the changes they observed on the Sun would result in an increase of about 0.2 per cent in the amount of energy reaching the Earth. Although this amount appears small, it is the largest variation of solar energy input to Earth yet reported, and may have an important effect on our climate.

Halley's Comet was "recovered," or sighted, for the first time in 72 years on Oct. 15, 1982. A group of astronomers from the California Institute of Technology (Caltech) in Pasadena led by G. Edward Danielson and graduate student David Jewitt used the 200-inch Hale telescope on Palomar Mountain to sight the comet on its way back to the vicinity of the Sun. The brightness of the comet was about 20 million times fainter than the faintest star the unaided eye can see.

Scientists were also able for the first time to accurately predict the orbit of the comet and therefore its position on the sky when first sighted. Past attempts to predict Halley's orbit before it was sighted usually were incorrect by about a week with regard to its closest approach to the Sun. Astronomer Donald K. Yeomans used extremely powerful computers at Caltech's Jet Propulsion Laboratory (JPL) to plot an orbit that turned out to be accurate to within a few hours.

First U.S. comet space mission. NASA will not send a spacecraft to observe Halley's Comet close up—as will the Europeans, the Soviets, and the Japanese. But the U.S. space agency did divert a space probe in June 1982 to examine Comet Giacobini-Zinner. That comet is surrounded by an extensive atmosphere and trails a long tail—the brilliant streak of gas molecules and dust particles swept back from the small nucleus, or body.

NASA took the opportunity to study this comet without mounting an expensive launch by sending a craft al-

ready in space—the third *International Sun-Earth Explorer* (*ISEE-3*)—toward a fly-by of Giacobini-Zinner in late 1985. *ISEE-3*, launched in 1978, had been hovering around a point between the Earth and Sun measuring electrical and magnetic fields in the solar wind.

Other cometary research revealed the first direct evidence confirming the long-held theory that a comet's nucleus is largely composed of water ice. When comets are bright enough to be found easily, observers have not been able to see their nuclei because their light is obscured by gases and dust in the cometary atmosphere.

Humberto Campins, George H. Reike, and Marcia J. Lebofsky of the University of Arizona's Steward Observatory in Tucson reported in February 1983 that they had succeeded in making some very difficult infrared spectroscopic observations of a comet. Their subject, Comet Bowell, seemed clearly to show the presence of water ice. When the astronomers observed the comet—moving in the asteroid belt between the orbits of Mars and Jupiter—it already appeared to show signs of developing an atmosphere. In fact, rather than observing the nucleus itself, the researchers reported that they most likely saw a cloud of water ice grains, which had been liberated from the nucleus.

On May 11, 1983, a newly discovered comet streaking across the skies above North America made an unusually close approach to Earth. The comet was named IRAS-Araki-Alcock for the *Infrared Astronomy Satellite* (*IRAS*) and the two amateur astronomers who detected it less than nine days later. The comet came within 4.6 million kilometers (2.9 million miles) of Earth, and was widely observed by astronomers in the United States. Very strong radar reflections obtained from the comet should improve our understanding of the composition of its nucleus.

Planetary ringlets. Continuing study of photographs and other data returned by NASA's *Voyager* space probes of Jupiter and Saturn from 1979 to 1981 yielded new insights on how gravitational and electrical forces act in the rings of Jupiter and in Saturn's rings.

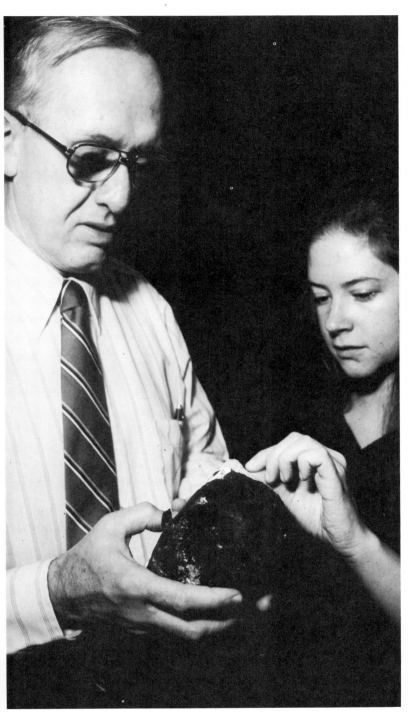

Smithsonian Institution scientists examine an L6 chondrite meteorite – the type most commonly found on earth – that fell through the roof of a Wethersfield, Conn., house in November 1982 after a galactic journey.

Our first impression of Jupiter's rings from spacecraft images was that the rings had a rather loose, spread-out structure unlike that of Saturn's well-defined bands or Uranus' narrow ringlets. This turned out to be a premature interpretation of pictures grossly smeared by spacecraft motion.

Caltech astronomy student Vance R. Haemmerle worked with space scientists G. Edward Danielson and Michael Ravinne, along with Douglas G. Currie of the University of Maryland in College Park and Artie Hatzes of the University of California in Santa Cruz, to enhance the *Voyager* photos. The team reported in October 1982 that they applied advanced image-processing techniques to the original photos, giving them the clarity they would have had if the spacecraft had been standing still while its cameras made the exposures. The enhanced pictures show Jupiter's ring made up of small ringlets. The astronomers think these ringlets were formed as the result of gravitational interactions with small natural satellites orbiting nearby.

Further analysis of *Voyager* data shed light on the cause of bursts of electromagnetic radiation on Saturn, similar to lightning, in information returned by the spacecraft. *Voyager*'s radio receivers heard and relayed these puzzling bursts at regular intervals of about 10 hours 11 minutes. In September 1982, scientists at Radiophysics Incorporated and the University of Colorado, both in Boulder, and at JPL reported finding the probable answer.

Photographs revealed a very narrow gap in the thickest part of Saturn's B ring — the most prominent part of the ring system, which at first seemed unbroken. The gap, which is barely 150 meters (500 feet) wide, occurs at the place in the ring that orbits Saturn every 10 hours 9 minutes 4 seconds. This timing coincides with the electrostatic discharges.

The scientists doubt that this is the result of chance, and assume that there must be a connection between the lightning and the gap in the ring. They speculated that the discharges are caused by an electrical interaction between ring particles and an object embedded in the ring. This object also created the gap. [Michael J. S. Belton]

Astronomy

Continued

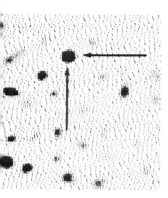

A faint red dwarf star whose light "flickers" rapidly may be the "millisecond pulsar" whose radio signals pulse at a rate 50 times faster than any known before.

Galactic Astronomy. The discovery of a remarkable pulsar was announced in December 1982 by Donald C. Backer, Shrinivas R. Kulkarni, and Carl Heiles of the University of California at Berkeley. They worked with scientists at the National Astronomy and Ionosphere Center in Arecibo, Puerto Rico, and the Kapteyn Laboratory in Groningen, the Netherlands.

The object's official name is PSR 1937 + 214, but it is called the "millisecond pulsar" because it emits an intense pulse of radio waves every 1.558 milliseconds. (A millisecond is equal to one-thousandth of a second.) PSR 1937 + 214 pulses almost 50 times faster than any of the more than 330 previously known pulsars, and is less highly magnetized than the others.

Most astronomers agree that pulsars are rapidly spinning neutron stars, the collapsed remnant cores of stars that underwent supernova explosions. A knot of magnetized material at the surface of a neutron star generates radio waves in a narrow beam. Astronomers observe a pulsed radio signal when this beam of radiation sweeps past the earth, like a searchlight beacon, as the neutron star rotates.

According to the simplest theories of neutron stars, the most rapid pulsars should be the youngest — that is, less than 10,000 years old. If the millisecond pulsar is as young as its short period of rotation implies, astronomers would expect it still to be associated with the gaseous remnant of its supernova explosion. The remnant would emit steady radio signals. But there was no evidence of such emissions.

In January 1983, radio astronomers at Nuffield Radio Astronomy Laboratory near Manchester, England, reported making precise timing measurements of a series of the pulses. These measurements were confirmed by Backer and Kulkarni, together with Joseph H. Taylor of Princeton University in New Jersey. Their surprising conclusion was that the millisecond pulsar is slowing down at the extremely slow rate of only a few trillionths of a second per year. This is unusual because the fastest pulsars tend to slow down at the greatest rate.

Theorists were not far behind observers in trying to interpret the data.

In March 1983, Jonathan Arons of the University of California at Berkeley suggested that such a short-period, weakly magnetized pulsar could have resulted from a supernova explosion between 100,000 and 1 million years ago. If Arons' theory is correct, the pulsar is not young, but very old, and this would explain why no gaseous supernova remnant is seen today.

The Infrared Astronomy Satellite (*IRAS*) was successfully launched on Jan. 25, 1983. This international observatory is sponsored by the Netherlands, Great Britain, and the National Aeronautics and Space Administration (NASA) of the United States. *IRAS* carries a 57-centimeter telescope designed to survey the entire sky in several bands of infrared light.

Because very little infrared energy penetrates earth's atmosphere to reach the surface, astronomers have detected infrared radiation by means of rockets, balloons, or high-altitude aircraft, or from the ground through a few "windows" in the atmosphere. *IRAS* now provides astronomers with a full-time infrared observatory, and is expected to reveal thousands of new infrared stars. It will be particularly effective in probing the clouds of gas and dust where stars form. Already *IRAS* helped to discover a new comet. See ASTRONOMY (Solar System Astronomy).

The center of the Milky Way continued to arouse great interest. John H. Lacy and Charles H. Townes of the University of California at Berkeley and David J. Hollenbach of NASA's Ames Research Center at Moffett Field, Calif., reported in November 1982 their interpretation of clouds at the center of the galaxy. Infrared observations have revealed rapidly moving, compact gas clouds spanning a few light-years at the center of the galaxy. (A light-year is the distance light travels in one year — about 9.5 trillion kilometers [6 trillion miles].) The clouds may be revolving around a massive central object. If so, that object must contain about 3 million times the mass of the sun in order to keep the gas clouds in orbit. Some scientists have suggested — though it is far from certain — that the central mass could be a giant black hole — a region so dense that not even light can escape it.

Lacy and his colleagues suggested that the moving gas clouds are left over from collisions between red giant stars in the crowded galactic center. They also proposed that an unseen cluster of hot stars supplies the energy that the gas clouds convert into infrared radiation. These very hot stars, which emit mostly ultraviolet light, could be hidden from view in the galactic center by the enormous amount of dusty material that litters interstellar space in that region.

However, such hot stars are usually found in association with very cool supergiant stars, which emit primarily infrared light. Because interstellar material blocks out a relatively small amount of infrared light, astronomers should be able to observe the cool supergiant stars even at the galactic center 30,000 light-years from earth.

In December 1982, Marcia J. Lebofsky and George H. Rieke of the University of Arizona's Steward Observatory in Tucson and Alan Tokunaga of the University of Hawaii in Honolulu announced the discovery of a "dramatic concentration" of cool supergiant stars at the center of the galaxy. Their observations, based on infrared spectroscopy, provided indirect support for Lacy's theory that there may be a large cluster of very hot stars in the galactic center.

Robert L. Brown of National Radio Astronomy Observatory (NRAO) in Charlottesville, Va., proposed an alternative explanation for the moving gas clouds in November 1982. Brown, along with Kenneth J. Johnston of the Naval Research Laboratory in Washington, D.C., and Kwok-Yung Lo of California Institute of Technology in Pasadena, used NRAO's Very Large Array near Socorro, N. Mex., to observe radio emissions from the area of the clouds. Brown suggested that the moving clouds arise in twin jets of gas blown out in opposite directions from an object at the center of the galaxy. He identified that central object with the compact core of a radio source at the galactic center known as Sagittarius A. Thus Brown's picture of the center of our galaxy resembles the ex-

Technicians check out the *Infrared Astronomy Satellite (IRAS)* before its launch on Jan. 25, 1983. *IRAS* allows astronomers to observe in the infrared range, which is normally blocked out by the earth's atmosphere.

Len Norris – *Vancouver Sun*, Canada

"Heavens! Crampton and Hutchings have
found yet another black hole in space!"

Astronomy

Continued

tremely violent cores of some radio galaxies — distant galaxies detectable most easily at radio wavelengths.

New light on an old nova. An international group of astronomers led by Michael V. Penston of the Royal Greenwich Observatory in England in March 1983 presented new observations of the slow nova RR Tel, located in the Southern Hemisphere constellation Telescopium. There are fast and slow novae. A fast nova is the more numerous type. It is a star — or more precisely, a binary star system — that explodes, sending off dust and gas. When this occurs, the nova suddenly brightens, then becomes fainter again over a period of days, weeks, or months. RR Tel, in contrast, is a rare slow nova, which became 10,000 times brighter than usual during its outburst in 1944. There is evidence that the outburst lasted for at least eight years. The envelope of gas that surrounds it has continued to expand, and the atoms of elements in the gas are continually being excited to increasingly higher energy levels.

Using the ultraviolet spectrograph on the *International Ultraviolet Explorer* satellite, Penston obtained measurements of 431 spectral lines radiated by atoms in the nova's gaseous envelope. After analyzing these data, Penston and his colleagues calculated what the temperature, density, and size of the envelope must be. For example, they suggested that one star in the RR Tel binary system has a temperature higher than 70,000°C. The ultraviolet spectrum of RR Tel is so rich in emission lines from the unusually excited atoms that the astronomers were able to use these data to make measurements better than obtained in laboratories of some basic properties of neon, argon, magnesium, and calcium.

Astronomers at the South African Astronomical Observatory in Cape Province, South Africa, under the direction of Michael W. Feast, also observed RR Tel. In March 1983, they reported finding definite evidence that RR Tel is a binary star system containing a type of cool giant star called a Mira variable. [John H. Black]

Astronomy

Continued

Extragalactic Astronomy. Astronomers specializing in extragalactic studies met at an International Astronomical Union (IAU) symposium in the Greek islands from June through August 1982 to discuss the early evolution of the universe and its present state. At the meeting, John P. Huchra, Marc Davis, and David W. Latham of Harvard-Smithsonian Center for Astrophysics (CfA) in Cambridge, Mass., reported results from the CfA Redshift Survey, a four-year program of observing red shifts of galaxies in the Northern Hemisphere. Light coming from a celestial object is shifted toward the red, or longer wavelength, end of the electromagnetic spectrum when the object is moving away from the earth. The greater the object's velocity, the more its light is red-shifted.

The CfA team measured the velocities of 2,400 galaxies almost 300 times fainter than the farthest object the unaided eye can see. For this survey, the astronomers used the 60-inch telescope of the Fred L. Whipple Observatory at Mount Hopkins in Arizona.

Data from the Redshift Survey provided a three-dimensional view of space that allowed astronomers to observe the position of large structures, or associations of galaxies. One surprising observation involved the Local Group, the small group of galaxies that includes the Milky Way. The astronomers found that it is falling toward the center of the Local Supercluster, the very large structure of which it forms a part. Marc Aaronson and his colleagues at Kitt Peak National Observatory near Tucson, Ariz., used CfA Redshift Survey data to measure the speed at which the Local Group is falling inward.

Aaronson's measurement provided more evidence in a key cosmological argument: Will the universe expand forever or collapse? Huchra and Davis used the measurement to compute a value for the average density of the universe — the amount of matter it contains per cubic centimeter. According to their calculations, that figure is only 20 per cent of the so-called closure density — the amount of matter

The rare ring nebula RCW 58 consists of a very hot central star and hydrogen gas in the interstellar medium ionized by ultraviolet emission from that star. RCW 58 may be similar to ring nebulae in our neighbor galaxy, the Large Magellanic Cloud.

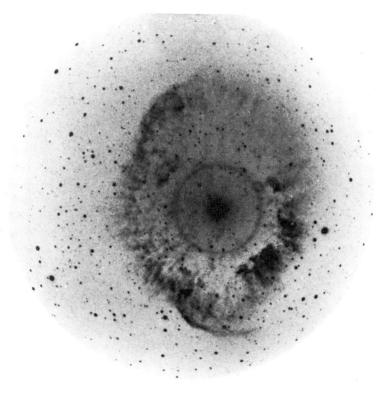

Astronomy

Continued

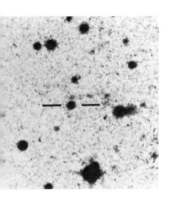

The quasar PKS 2000-330, estimated to be at least 12 billion light-years away, is the most distant object yet observed in the universe.

needed to allow the force of gravity to counteract the expansion of the universe and cause it to collapse. The astronomers concluded, therefore, that the universe will expand forever. See MAPPING THE UNIVERSE.

Cosmic structures. Neta A. Bahcall and Ray Soniera of Princeton University in New Jersey reported in January 1983 that they had studied the distribution of clusters of galaxies in the universe and found evidence for the existence of large-scale structures as many light-years in diameter as they are distant from the earth. The huge structures are hundreds of millions of light-years away. (A light-year is the distance light travels in a year—about 9.5 trillion kilometers [6 trillion miles].) These clusters of clusters, or superclusters, are irregular in shape and often appear to have a wispy, threadlike form.

A good example of such an object is the Local Supercluster, on which R. Brent Tully of the University of Hawaii's Institute for Astronomy in Honolulu reported in June 1982. Tully based his analysis partly on data from the CfA Redshift Survey and partly on other sources of information. He concluded that the Local Supercluster has three main components—a dense core, which is surrounded by a flat disk, and a small number of clouds of galaxies in a halo around the core and disk.

A quantity of quasars made news during 1982 and 1983. One that was discussed at the IAU meeting was the new candidate for the title of most distant quasar, PKS 2000-330. Quasars are highly energetic but little understood emitters of energy, and are generally considered to be the farthest objects in the universe we can observe from earth. Bruce A. Peterson of the Australian National University's Mount Stromlo Observatory and Siding Spring Observatory reported that he and his colleagues had used the Anglo-Australian 3.9-meter telescope in March 1982 to measure the spectrum of PKS 2000-330. They found that the quasar had a red shift that indicated it is at least 12 billion—and very likely up to 20 billion—light-years away.

Astronomer Susan Wyckoff of Arizona State University in Tempe and her colleagues reported in June 1982

that they had detected nebulosity—a faint "fuzziness"—around another quasar, 3C273. They used the 1.8-meter telescope of the Lowell Observatory in Flagstaff, Ariz., equipped with a special electronic light detector called a charge-coupled device. The detector enabled the astronomers to separate the bright central object they observed—the quasar—from the fuzzy underlying image. When Wyckoff and her team analyzed the data, they noted that the nebulous object decreased in brightness outward from the center just as they would have expected a bright elliptical galaxy to do—implying that the quasar is part of a galaxy.

One of the long-standing questions about quasars has to do with the size of the core, or active energy-emitting region, responsible for the radiation they give off. This radiation varies. Astrophysicist Terry A. Matilsky and graduate student Chris Shrader of Rutgers University in New Brunswick, N.J., and Harvey D. Tananbaum of CfA reported in July 1982 that they had used the varying emissions from a quasar to set limits on the size of its core. The scientists used data from the second High Energy Astronomy Observatory (the *Einstein* Observatory) in orbit around earth. The *Einstein* X-ray telescope detected X rays from quasar 1525 + 227 that "flickered on and off" within about 200 seconds. This timing meant that the quasar's core could be no more than 200 light-seconds across—less than 60 million kilometers (37 million miles). The astronomers concluded that in a region of space less than the distance from the sun to the earth, some unknown source is responsible for an energy output 1 million times that of the Milky Way galaxy. See THE BRIGHTEST BEACONS, *Science Year*, 1983.

From their observations, the astronomers deduced that the mass of the quasar core must be between 1 million and 20 million times the mass of the sun. The very rapid flickering combined with its extreme intensity convinced the astronomers that the emitting process in quasars must be unlike that of such objects as stars, which emit X rays uniformly in all directions. Quasars more likely have some sort of focused beam, similar to a lighthouse

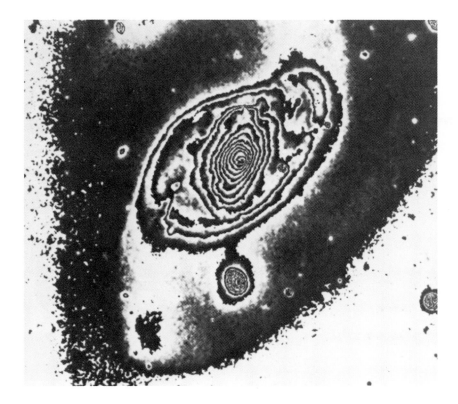

A computer-enhanced image seems to show a quasar (small circular object) tied by a "bridge" to a known nearby galaxy, NGC 4319 (large oval). This seemed to lend support to the view of a few dissenting astronomers that quasars are not really as far away as most astronomers believe.

Astronomy

Continued

beacon. Such beaconlike beams of radio waves have been detected in quasar 1525 + 227 and some others. Matilsky, Shrader, and Tananbaum think that a similar process may be responsible for the flickering radiation in the X-ray range.

A new class of galaxies was the subject of a June 1982 report by astronomer Hyron Spinrad of the University of California at Berkeley. Using the 3-meter optical telescope at Lick Observatory on Mount Hamilton in California, Spinrad discovered about a dozen very distant galaxies that had previously been known only as unidentified sources of radio waves. The galaxies have extremely strong emission lines—bright features in their spectra indicating the presence of specific elements. These lines in the galaxies' spectra are characteristic of ionized oxygen. By calculating the red shift of the strong emission lines of oxygen, as well as those of other elements in the galaxies' spectra, Spinrad determined that the galaxies are 6 billion to 10 billion light-years from earth.

Spinrad also concluded that the strong emission lines come from gas heated by shock waves, such as those produced by exploding stars. However, gas heated that way would cool down so quickly that there is little likelihood of observing its emission lines. One possible reason why Spinrad was able to observe the emission lines in the spectra of these galaxies is that the galaxies may be part of clusters surrounded by a great deal of gas from the intracluster medium.

New look at the jet set. Astronomers have known for about 60 years that the giant elliptical galaxy M87 has a jet shooting out from it—a stream of hot gas, or energetic particles, emerging from a very active center. They know the high-energy radiation from the jet detected by optical and radio telescopes must be due to synchrotron radiation—energy produced by so-called relativistic electrons spiraling around magnetic lines of force at velocities near the speed of light. But no one had observed M87 in enough detail to learn how the energy in its center

Astronomy

Continued

The 10-meter optical reflector at Whipple Observatory in Arizona has been modified to pinpoint sources of high-energy gamma rays in our galaxy and beyond by detecting the tiny flashes of light that result when these cosmic particles strike earth's atmosphere. A concave dish made of 248 adjustable mirrors serves as the focusing lens, and 37 phototubes in a focus box, at right, replace camera film. The wheeled platform permits adjustment or change of the phototubes.

could be transferred to the jet. Now, two teams of researchers have clarified the situation by analyzing observations made with high-resolution telescopes.

J. L. Nieto used the 3.6-meter Canada-France-Hawaii telescope on Mauna Kea and G. Lelievre used the Pic du Midi Observatory 1-meter telescope in the Pyrenees mountains in southwestern France to obtain data in the ultraviolet range of the spectrum. The astronomers reported in May 1982 that the M87 jet consists of groups of knots, or dense clumps of gas. There appears to be no material between the knots. Nieto and Lelievre found that the groups are regularly spaced, implying that they are ejected at a periodic rate by some process that scientists do not yet understand.

In January 1983, Ethan J. Schreier of Space Telescope Science Institute in Baltimore and Eric D. Feigelson of Massachusetts Institute of Technology in Cambridge, Mass., reported that they had analyzed X-ray data from *Einstein* Observatory studies of M87 and also made calculations that indi-

cate the relativistic electrons in the jet are not made in the galaxy's center.

The X-ray image is similar to that of the brightest radio and optical images of the galaxy and its jet. The scientists assumed that the X-ray energy, like that detected at radio and optical wavelengths, is produced by synchrotron radiation. Schreier and Feigelson then calculated that it takes these electrons, traveling at close to the speed of light, about 200 years to radiate away their energy. But it would take them more than 3,000 years to travel from the center of M87 to the jet. Therefore, the researchers deduced, the high-energy electrons responsible for radiation from the M87 jet must be produced in the jet itself.

The astronomers theorized that energy is carried from the center of the galaxy in the material that makes up the jet. That flow becomes turbulent as it leaves the galaxy and shock waves form in it, accelerating electrons to near the speed of light. Thus, high-energy electrons are produced along the jet.

[Stephen S. Murray]

Books of Science

Here are 25 outstanding new science books suitable for the general reader. They have been selected from books published in 1982 and 1983.

Archaeology. *Martin's Hundred* by Ivor Noël Hume describes excavations in Virginia that led to the discovery of a 17th-century settlement known as Wolstenholme Towne. (Knopf, 1982. 343 pp. illus. $17.95)

Astronomy. *The Cambridge Photographic Atlas of the Planets* by Geoffrey Briggs and Fredric Taylor presents about 200 excellent photographs of the planets from Mercury to Saturn. It also includes maps and text summarizing discoveries about the planets. (Cambridge Univ. Press, 1982. 255 pp. illus. $24.95)

Searching Between the Stars by Lyman Spitzer, Jr., extends our knowledge of the materials that fill interstellar space and of the cosmic cycle leading to the birth of stars and their eventual destruction. Many of the discoveries reported were collected by the United States satellite *Copernicus*. (Yale Univ. Press, 1982. 179 pp. illus. $25)

Biology. *The Growth of Biological Thought: Diversity, Evolution and Inheritance* by Ernst Mayr is a monumental study of the major ideas that have shaped modern approaches to biology. The author answers basic questions about the study of biology, its place in scientific thought, and the nature of science itself. (Belknap Press, 1982. 974 pp. $30)

How Life Learned to Live: Adaptation in Nature by Helmut Tributsch looks at creatures that live at extremes of temperature and pressure, and describes how they use principles of physics to move, to see, and to survive. (MIT Press, 1982. 218 pp. illus. $19.95)

Man-Made Life: An Overview of the Science, Technology and Commerce of Genetic Engineering by Jeremy Cherfas. Incredible strides in genetic engineering have been made in the past 10 years. This book gives the background and brings the reader up to date on these developments, including the role of commercial enterprise and possible uses in biological warfare. (Pantheon Bks., 1983. 270 pp. illus. $15.95)

The Youngest Science: Notes of a Medicine-Watcher by Lewis Thomas, a physician, analyzes discoveries in medical science and the author's role as a practitioner. The book, which is autobiographical, also recounts Thomas' own experience with a serious illness and its effect on his thinking. (Viking, 1983. 270 pp. $14.75)

Earth Sciences. *Earthfire: The Eruption of Mount St. Helens* by Charles Rosenfeld and Robert Cooke discusses the 1980 eruption of Mount St. Helens as it relates to other peaks in the Cascade Mountains and the worldwide volcanic system. The text is interspersed with spectacular photographs and with "technical vignettes" that describe the eruption from the viewpoint of various specialists. (MIT Press, 1982. 155 pp. illus. $25)

Fossils: The Key to the Past by Richard Fortey explains how fossils are used in reconstructing the history of the earth and the biology of the organisms whose existence the fossils record. The book also tells how to recognize fossils and begin a collection. (Van Nostrand Reinhold, 1982. 172 pp. illus. $24.95)

The Mysterious Carolina Bays by Henry Savage, Jr., reviews the evidence for the theory that the many shallow, oval marshes throughout coastal North and South Carolina were formed by the impact of a comet striking the earth. Savage includes numerous aerial photographs and an extensive bibliography. (University of South Carolina Press, 1982. 121 pp. illus. $14.95)

The Road to Jaramillo: Critical Years of the Revolution in Earth Science by William Glen is a history of discoveries about changes in the earth's magnetic poles, their record in the earth's rocks, and their contribution to the theory of plate tectonics — the idea that the earth's crust consists of about 20 rigid plates in slow, continuous motion. (Stanford Univ. Press, 1982. 459 pp. illus. $37.50)

Environment. *Fire in America: A Cultural History of Wildland and Rural Fire* by Stephen J. Pyne is an account of the complex relationship between fire as a natural force and human beings, whose responses and attempts to manage it have varied over the centuries. (Princeton Univ. Press, 1982. 654 pp. illus. $35)

Of Mice and Molecules: Technology and Human Survival by Eric Skjei and M.

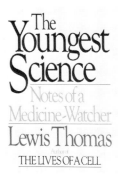

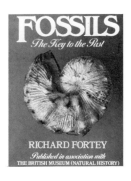

Books of Science

Continued

Donald Whorton identifies the major sources of pollution present in the food we eat, the air we breathe, and the water we drink. The authors show the origin of these problems and describe the steps needed to alleviate them. (Dial Press, 1983. 347 pp. illus. $27.95)

Mathematics. *The Fractal Geometry of Nature* by Benoit B. Mandelbrot describes the author's efforts to invent a new geometry that can account for the fractal, or irregular, shapes of such objects as clouds, mountains, coastlines, and trees. (W. H. Freeman, 1982. 460 pp. illus. $32.50)

Infinity and the Mind: The Science and Philosophy of the Infinite by Rudy Rucker explores every kind of infinity — logical, theological, mathematical — and the paradoxes to which the notion of infinity can lead. Rucker also discusses the work of Czech-born logician Kurt Gödel and describes personal encounters with him. (Birkhäuser, 1982. 342 pp. illus. $15.95)

Mathematical Fallacies and Paradoxes by Bryan H. Bunch is a collection of the most interesting fallacies and paradoxes from mathematics, logic, physics, and language. The author encourages readers to solve various problems and provides clues before supplying the answers. (Van Nostrand Reinhold, 1982. 216 pp. illus. $16.95)

Philosophy of Science. *Grammatical Man: Information, Entropy, Language, and Life* by Jeremy Campbell discusses mathematician Claude E. Shannon's development of information theory and shows how it has been applied to problems in biology, psychology, philosophy, language, and art. (Simon & Schuster, 1982. 319 pp. $16.50)

The Possible and the Actual by François Jacob is a collection of essays that demonstrates how the theory of evolution can be used to help us understand what has happened in the past and what may happen in the future. The three essays focus on science and myth, the process of evolutionary change, and time and the future. (University of Washington Press, 1982. 71 pp. $8.95)

Physics. *Haphazard Reality: Half a Century of Science* by Hendrik B. G. Casimir is the autobiography of a Dutch scientist who worked with such leading physicists as Niels Bohr of Denmark

and Wolfgang Pauli and Paul Ehrenfest of Austria. Casimir, who was an industrial manager for a leading manufacturer of electric products, discusses how science contributes to advances in technology and vice versa. (Harper & Row, 1983. 356 pp. $15)

The Lighter Side of Gravity by Jayant V. Narlikar is a nonmathematical approach to this fundamental force of nature. The discussion includes falling apples, nuclear fusion, and black holes — astronomical objects with such strong gravitational force that not even light escapes from them. (W. H. Freeman, 1982. 194 pp. illus. $17.95)

Psychology. *Psychological Life: From Science to Metaphor* by Robert D. Romanyshyn discusses how specific scientific discoveries shape our understanding of reality. For example, the author shows how English physician William Harvey's discovery that the heart is a pump changed scientific thinking about the body. (University of Tex. Press, 1982. 209 pp. illus. $19.95)

Technology. *The Better Mousetrap: A Miscellany of Gadgets, Labor-Saving Devices, and Inventions That Intrigue* by Aaron E. Klein and Cynthia L. Klein uses 200 patent drawings as the basis of a history of invention in the United States from 1790 to 1840. (Beaufort Bks., 1982. 400 pp. illus. $19.95)

Experiments in Gothic Structure by Robert Mark explores the complex technology underlying the construction of Europe's monumental Gothic cathedrals between the 1100s and the 1400s. (MIT Press, 1982. 135 pp. illus. $15)

The Power of Steam: An Illustrated History of the World's Steam Age by Asa Briggs shows how steam was used to power machines of all types, beginning with the Industrial Revolution in the 18th century, culminating in the late 19th century, and declining in use but still widespread in the 20th. (University of Chicago Press, 1982. 208 pp. illus. $22.50)

A Short History of Twentieth Century Technology: c. 1900-c. 1950 by Trevor I. Williams outlines the development of technology in the first half of the 20th century and the social, economic, and political factors that influenced it. (Oxford Univ. Press, 1982. 411 pp. illus. $19.95)   [William G. Jones]

Botany

Botanists have long known that pine tree pollen is carried by the wind. And they assumed that how much pollen fell on a pine cone was a result of chance. However, in July 1982, botanists Karl J. Niklas of Cornell University in Ithaca, N.Y., and Kyaw That Paw U of Purdue University in West Lafayette, Ind., reported that pine cone ovules attract a greater number of pollen grains of their own species than would occur at random. (An ovule is the part of a female pine cone that develops into a seed.)

Pine tree pollination occurs when pollen grains containing sperm cells from the small, male cones are carried by air currents and deposited on ovules, which are located on the scales of the larger, female cones. Each grain then sprouts a tube, which carries the sperm cell to the egg cell — the female reproductive cell within the ovule. This leads to the formation of a pine seed if the pollen grain and the ovule are of the same species.

Pine trees produce large quantities of pollen because pollination that de-pends upon air currents is an inefficient process. It would be somewhat more efficient if pollen from a given variety of pine were more likely to land on ovules of the same species than on the ovules of other species. The two botanists discovered that this is exactly what happens.

In a wind tunnel, they blew equal numbers of pollen grains from seven species of pine past female cones from each of the species. Then, with a microscope, they counted the number of pollen grains adhering to the ovules on the cone scales. They found that each cone had more pollen of its own species adhering to its ovules than pollen of any other species. A totally random distribution of pollen would cause about 14 per cent of each pollen type (100 per cent divided by 7) to adhere to an ovule. But, 23 to 31 per cent of the pollen grains on each ovule were of the same species as the ovule.

Why should pollen tend to adhere to ovules of its own species? The experimenters found that part of the reason was the settling velocities — the "land-

A parasitic nematode, which destroys plant roots, is held in the coils of the carnivorous fungus *arthrobotrys*. This and other predatory fungi may prove useful in combating the many enemies of plants.

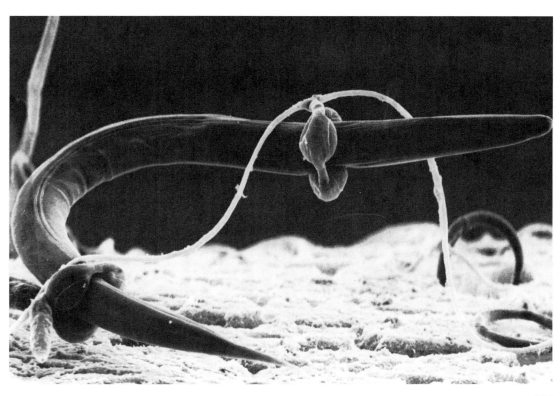

Botany

Continued

ing speeds" — of the pollen grains and the airflow patterns around the female cones. The structure of a cone causes wind eddies whose speed is the same as the settling velocities for pollen of the same species. However, the settling velocities of two of the seven pollen species were found to be identical, leading the researchers to suggest that other qualities of the cones, such as roughness, must also play a role.

Water stress. Botanists at Yale University in New Haven, Conn., reported in September 1982 that they had found a compound used by plants to cope with water stress, the loss of water from cells. This can be caused by drought, freezing temperatures, or exposure to external salt water.

Plants counteract water stress by forming soluble molecules in their cells. These molecules increase the concentration of the water in the cells, thereby lessening its tendency to evaporate, freeze, or leak out of the cells. Botanists knew of only a few such compounds. The Yale researchers, Hector E. Flores and Arthur W. Galston, discovered another one named putrescine.

Flores and Galston found that putrescine, so called because it is also produced in putrid animal tissues, increases to 60 times its normal concentration in oat leaves subjected to water stress. Like the other compounds that plants use to combat water stress, putrescine is a so-called compatible solute — it can build up to high concentrations in plant cells without damaging the cell's proteins.

Venus's flytrap. The mechanism that causes the Venus's flytrap to close has never been well understood. But in December 1982, two botanists working at Cornell University — Stephen E. Williams of Lebanon Valley College in Annville, Pa., and Alan B. Bennett of Cornell — reported that they had discovered how it works. According to the researchers, the plant's insect-trapping leaves snap shut because the cells on the leaves' outer surfaces undergo rapid acid growth — the nearly instantaneous expansion of the cells caused by the acidification and stretching of the cell's walls.

The Venus's flytrap leaf has two opposed lobes, each of which has several

A green peach aphid is trapped in the sticky hairs of a new hybrid potato plant, a cross between American potatoes and a potato that grows wild in Bolivia. Pouches on the tips of the hairs break open, spilling a sort of glue that immobilizes the insect's feet.

trigger hairs on its upper surface. When an insect brushes against the hairs, an electrical impulse is transmitted to the leaves, causing them to close in one to three seconds. Scientists previously had thought that the impulse from the trigger hairs caused the cells on the outside of the leaves to rapidly absorb water and expand, forcing the lobes together.

But Williams and Bennett observed that the outside tissue of a closed leaf seems limp rather than tight and swollen. The botanists theorized that instead of the interior of the cells becoming engorged with liquid, the walls of the cells increase in size.

To prove their hypothesis, Williams and Bennett conducted several tests with Venus's flytraps. First, they marked the outside and inside of the lobes with a row of precisely measured ink dots. They found that when a flytrap's leaves closed, the distance between the dots on the outside of the lobes increased by about 28 per cent. This finding, along with the fact that the outside of the leaf seemed flabby, supported the idea that the walls of the cells had gotten larger.

The botanists reasoned that if the closing of the trap is caused by acid growth of the cells, then neutralizing the acid would prevent the leaves from closing. To confirm that, they applied buffering agents — solutions that absorb acids — to the leaves. The buffered leaves would not close when the trigger hairs were stimulated. The investigators then made an opposite prediction — that leaves treated with acid solutions would close even when their trigger hairs were not stimulated. That is precisely what happened.

Finally, since the acidification of a plant requires energy, Williams and Bennett theorized that trap lobes should lose large amounts of high-energy compounds when they closed if rapid acid growth was indeed occurring. The most important energy compound in most cells is adenosine triphosphate (ATP). The scientists froze flytrap lobes with liquid nitrogen before and after closing and analyzed their ATP content. They found that closed lobes did indeed lose energy. They contained 29 per cent less ATP than open lobes. [Frank B. Salisbury]

Chemistry

In March 1983, chemists at Northwestern University in Evanston, Ill., reported preparing the first solution to contain a silylenium ion—a positively charged silicon atom. Silicon is normally bonded to four other atoms or groups of atoms. The silylenium ion was attached to only three groups.

To prepare the silylenium solution, chemists Joseph B. Lambert and William J. Schulz, Jr., synthesized tris-(2-propylthio)silane, or silane, a chemical compound that has three sulfur-containing groups of atoms and a single hydrogen atom attached directly to a silicon atom. They then mixed the silane and a compound called trityl perchlorate into the solvent dichloromethane at room temperature. The single hydrogen atom detached from the silicon atom, creating the silylenium ion.

The chemists used several techniques to prove that they had formed the ion. They showed that the ability of the solution to conduct electricity was the same as that expected from a fully ionized substance. More evidence

came from nuclear magnetic resonance (NMR) spectroscopy, a technique that uses magnetic fields and radio waves of various frequencies to distinguish among atoms in a molecule. NMR showed that the three groups of atoms attached to the silicon were identical and absorbed energy as if they were attached to a positively charged silicon atom. It also revealed that the hydrogen atom was no longer attached to the silicon. Lambert and Schulz are now trying to make the silicon ion react with other substances and thus produce entirely new chemicals that might be of industrial value.

Highly strained compound. Chemists at Yale University in New Haven, Conn., reported in September 1982 that they had synthesized a molecule that is the most strained of any known organic, or carbon-containing, compound. Strain is the bending of chemical bonds between atoms from their normal orientations within a molecule.

Kenneth B. Wiberg and Frederick H. Walker made the highly strained molecule tricyclo[1.1.1.0]pentane, or

A laser beam enters the sample chamber of a mass spectrometer, where it charges atoms of only one element so that the spectrometer can sort them out by mass. The technique, developed at Los Alamos National Laboratory in New Mexico, allows the spectrometer to distinguish among equally heavy isotopes of different elements.

[1.1.1]propellane. The molecule, which is made up of five carbon atoms and six hydrogen atoms, resembles a three-bladed propeller. Two carbons make up the propeller "shaft."

In the most stable normal arrangement of a carbon atom bonded to four other atoms, the carbon atom is at the center of a tetrahedron. In the [1.1.1] propellane shaft, however, the four bonds between carbon and the other atoms are bent back sharply, all in the same direction. This bending causes a great distortion from the normal orientation and creates what chemists call an angle strain. This contains a destabilizing type of energy, much like the energy in a tightly coiled spring.

The chemists therefore expected [1.1.1]propellane to be unstable at room temperature. However, it turned out to be perfectly stable. Wiberg theorized that the molecule remained stable because the only chemical reactions it could undergo would lead to even more angle strain.

The surprising stability despite distorted bonds in the two carbons of the [1.1.1]propellane shaft caused chemists to ask new questions about the nature of the carbon-carbon bond. Until the Yale experiment, chemists had always found that the bond angle of a carbon atom attached to four other atoms was close to 109.5 degrees. Molecules whose bond angles deviated greatly from this angle had only a fleeting existence. Consequently, chemists had believed that the high energy caused by such strained bonds would make all such molecules unstable. Chemists have not yet measured the bond angle of propellane, but they know that it deviates greatly from 109.5 degrees.

Dodecahedrane. Chemists at Ohio State University in Columbus culminated a 20-year effort in August 1982 by synthesizing dodecahedrane. This artificial compound contains 20 carbon atoms and 20 hydrogen atoms arranged in the shape of a polyhedron with 12 pentagon-shaped sides. The effect is an almost spherical molecule.

Chemists Leo A. Paquette, Douglas W. Balogh, and Robert J. Ternansky started with the pentagon-shaped five-carbon-ring compound, cyclopentadiene. Twenty-three reactions later,

they had two milligrams of dodecahedrane. Researchers will need larger amounts of the molecule in order to study its physical and chemical properties. However, they have already found that dodecahedrane does not melt at temperatures up to 450°C (842°F.), unlike other compounds containing only carbon and hydrogen.

In 1981, researchers led by Paquette had synthesized a dodecahedrane molecule, but they were unable to build it without two methyl groups — each made up of one carbon atom and three hydrogen atoms — on the outside of the molecule.

The new molecule is too small to enclose any but the smallest ions, but it may eventually find medical uses. Medical scientists use similar closed molecules to carry ions for treating body cells. Such molecules do not dissolve in blood, so they keep the ions trapped as they flow through the bloodstream. But the closed molecules do break up inside body cells, releasing the ions.

Measuring attograms. In February 1983, chemists Norman J. Dovichi, John C. Martin, James H. Jett, and Richard A. Keller of Los Alamos National Laboratory in New Mexico reported making the smallest measurement to date of a chemical substance. They measured 28 attograms of a dye dissolved in a liquid. (One attogram is 10^{-18} gram — a billionth of a billionth of a gram.)

The chemists used a technique called laser-induced fluorescence to measure the dye. Chemicals fluoresce by absorbing high-energy light and then emitting heat and lower-energy light. The color of the light that a substance emits depends upon its composition, so scientists use fluorescence to determine the makeup of certain substances. Ordinarily, they use an ultraviolet lamp to supply the high-energy light. However, such a lamp would not have caused enough of the dye molecules to fluoresce. The powerful laser beam that the Los Alamos scientists used caused almost all the molecules in the sample to fluoresce.

The new technique will enable technicians to analyze very small samples of other substances. This could prove useful in such medical tests as fluo-

Chemistry

Continued

A mixture of metal powders and sodium azide packed into a cylinder reacts in a blaze that engulfs the entire cylinder in seconds. This forms compounds called nitrides that are extremely hard and have high melting points.

roimmunoassays, which determine whether a chemical is poisonous by measuring how much of it binds to substances produced by the blood.

Water splitting. Chemists have been working since the early 1970s to improve the efficiency of devices that convert sunlight into usable energy. In December 1982, chemists Adam Heller and Eliezer Aharon-Shalom of Bell Laboratories in Murray Hill, N.J., announced the development of an electrochemical cell with the highest efficiency yet reported, 16 per cent. The cell uses solar energy combined with electrical energy to split water into oxygen and hydrogen gas, a useful fuel.

The cell consists of two electrodes— an anode and a cathode—connected by a wire. The anode is made of titanium metal coated with ruthenium dioxide; the cathode, of indium phosphide coated with a layer of either rhodium or rhenium metal. The coating's average thickness is only one-billionth of a meter.

The chemists placed the electrodes in water containing perchloric acid and switched on a current, making the anode positive and the cathode negative. The anode's positive charge was so strong that the anode took electrons, which are negatively charged, from water molecules. This loss of electrons caused the water molecules to break apart, forming oxygen gas and positively charged hydrogen ions.

The now positively charged ions next traveled to the negatively charged cathode, where they picked up electrons. This gain of electrons caused the hydrogen ions to lose their charge and combine in pairs to form molecules of hydrogen gas. The scientists then separated this gas from the oxygen and measured how much of the two gases had been produced.

Finally, the Bell chemists repeated the experiment with sunlight shining on the cell. In sunlight, the electrodes required less voltage to split water into the same amounts of oxygen and hydrogen. The researchers calculated that the sunlight contributed 16 per cent of its energy to the splitting of water. In the summer of 1983, the Bell cell was still in the laboratory stage, but the experiment may serve as the basis for the future production of hydrogen fuel from water.

Chorismic acid synthesized. Two groups of chemists independently reported the laboratory synthesis of chorismic acid in 1982. Green plants synthesize chorismic acid and use it to make several amino acids and other substances crucial to their growth.

In the spring, chemists Glenn A. Berchtold and Donald A. McGowan of Massachusetts Institute of Technology in Cambridge reported that they had synthesized chorismic acid; and, in November, chemists Bruce Ganem, Nobuo Ikota, V. B. Muralidharan, Stanley D. Young, Yusuke Yukimoto, and Warren S. Wade of Cornell University in Ithaca, N.Y., also reported the synthesis of the acid.

The synthesis of chorismic acid may enable researchers to develop herbicides that prevent unwanted plants from forming the acid, thus preventing their growth. This type of herbicide would not harm animals.

New reaction. Dutch researchers reported in April 1983 that they had converted cheap and readily available carbon monoxide (CO) into glycolic acid under relatively low temperature and pressure. Glycolic acid can be converted to ethylene glycol, an important industrial chemical widely used in plastics and as antifreeze. Ethylene glycol presently is made from petroleum-based chemicals, but CO is obtained industrially from coal.

Chemists Peter W. Lednor and Peterina C. Versloot of the Royal Dutch Shell Company in Amsterdam, the Netherlands, bubbled CO into a deep-blue organic solvent containing sodium and potassium.

When the carbon monoxide was added, the color of the solution faded, indicating that a reaction had taken place. The researchers then added water to the mixture and analyzed the products. Glycolic acid accounted for three-quarters of the total product of the reaction. Further work will determine whether the low temperature and pressure of the Dutch process will make it industrially useful.

Oxygen carrier. As part of an effort to make a synthetic hemoglobin, chemists at Ohio State University reported in January 1983 that they had made new, organic, iron-containing compounds that accept and give off oxygen much as natural hemoglobin does. Hemoglobin is an iron-containing organic molecule that carries oxygen in the bloodstream from the lungs to the tissues.

Each iron atom in hemoglobin is surrounded by a flat circular molecule called a porphyrin ring. The complete unit is called a heme group. Hemoglobin contains four identical heme groups. Each heme group fits into a water-repelling, V-shaped cavity in a coiled and twisted protein molecule, much as a large coin fits into a cupped hand. There is just enough room for the oxygen molecule to get into the cavity and bind to the iron. In the absence of water, no chemical reaction occurs between the normally reactive iron and oxygen, so the two atoms are not strongly bound to each other. The oxygen is therefore easily released to the tissue.

The Ohio State chemists—Daryle Busch, Norman Herron, James H. Cameron, and Gay L. Neer—have made five different but chemically related nonheme iron compounds that bind and release oxygen under conditions similar to those of natural hemoglobin in the bloodstream. The synthetic oxygen carriers contain bulky organic groups that surround the iron atom on one side, forming a cavity. The other side of the iron atom is blocked by a solvent molecule or by another organic group. The molecular shape allows oxygen to bind to iron in the hollow region without causing a chemical reaction. Although the oxygen's attraction to iron resembles that in hemoglobin, the synthetic compounds are not as stable as hemoglobin at body temperature.

The new compounds open several research possibilities. Chemists will try to modify them to form compounds whose ability to carry oxygen more closely resembles that of hemoglobin. They also can synthesize similar compounds that may be efficient industrial catalysts, substances that change the rates of certain chemical reactions while themselves remaining practically unaltered.   [Lawrence P. Verbit]

Deaths of Scientists

Notable scientists and engineers who died between June 1, 1982, and June 1, 1983, are listed below. An asterisk (*) indicates that a biography appears in *The World Book Encyclopedia*.

Belyakov, Aleksandr V. (1897-Dec. 2, 1982), Soviet aviation pioneer who navigated the first flight from Russia to the United States in 1937.

Bond, George F. (1915-Jan. 3, 1983), United States Navy physician who pioneered the Sealab program in the 1960s. He was an authority on the medical effects of deep-sea diving and undersea pressure.

Boyd, William C. (1903-Feb. 19, 1983), immunochemist who in 1945 discovered lectins — natural chemicals related to certain blood types, important in immunology.

Braestrup, Carl (1897-Aug. 4, 1982), physicist who sounded early alarms about the dangers of radiation, and invented the Theratron, a cobalt-therapy machine, in 1953.

Cattell, McKeen (1891-Feb. 8, 1983), pharmacologist whose research showed the specific effect of digitalis on increasing the strength of contractions of the heart muscle.

Chapman, Colin (1928-Dec. 16, 1982), British automotive engineer whose innovations in race-car design included the first in which the engine and framework were integrated.

Chipman, John (1897-May 4, 1983), metals expert noted for his studies of the chemical reactions of steel production. During World War II, he developed a method for converting powdered uranium into solid castings when the solid uranium supply was scarce.

Claude, Albert (1898-May 23, 1983), Belgian-born biologist, co-winner of the 1974 Nobel Prize for physiology or medicine for his work in cell biology.

DeGraff, Arthur C. (1899-May 25, 1982), cardiologist best known for his contributions to the treatment of heart diseases and disorders, using digitalis and diuretics. He founded the Committee for the Promotion of Medical Research in 1944.

Dorfman, Albert (1916-July 27, 1982), physician and medical researcher who discovered the cause of Hurler's syndrome, a genetic defect that leads to mental retardation.

Fleischer, Andrew W. (1882-Jan. 11, 1983), pharmacist who developed a device to measure blood pressure in 1911 and an improved stethoscope in 1913.

*Freud, Anna (1895-Oct. 9, 1982), Austrian-born psychoanalyst, daughter of Sigmund Freud. She was a leader in the treatment of mental illness in children.

Godowsky, Leopold, II (1900-Feb. 18, 1983), co-developer of the Kodachrome color photography process.

*Grumman, Leroy R. (1895-Oct. 4, 1982), astronautical engineer who founded the Grumman Aircraft Corporation, one of America's largest defense contractors, in 1929.

Hartline, H. Keffer (1903-March 17, 1983), physiologist, co-winner of the 1967 Nobel Prize for physiology or medicine for "discoveries concerning the primary chemical and physiological processes of the eye." His basic studies on the integrative action of the retina are considered the foundation for practically every advance in the neurophysiology of vision.

Heidelberger, Charles (1920-Jan. 18, 1983), chemist and educator who developed 5-fluorouracil, a powerful anticancer drug. Heidelberger was noted for his research into chemical processes of malignancy.

Hildebrand, Joel H. (1881-April 30, 1983), chemist and educator who taught 40,000 freshmen during 68 years at the University of California, Berkeley. His research included discoveries about the absorption of gas into liquids under pressure that led to ways of protecting deep-sea divers from the bends.

Izotov, Sergei (1918-May 6, 1983), one of Russia's leading aeronautical engineers. He helped develop the turboprop engine of the Antonov-28, a large transport plane.

Kistiakowski, George B. (1900-Dec. 7, 1982), Russian-born chemist who developed the conventional explosives used to detonate the first atomic bomb in 1945. He later became a leading advocate of nuclear disarmament.

Kline, Nathan S. (1916-Feb. 11, 1983), psychiatrist who pioneered in the use of tranquilizers and antidepressants in the treatment of mental illness.

Anna Freud

H. Keffer Hartline

Stanford Moore

Deaths of Scientists

Continued

Hans Selye

Hugo Theorell

Ulf S. von Euler

Kollsman, Paul (1900-Sept. 26, 1982), aeronautical engineer who, in the 1920s, invented the altimeter, a device that measures a plane's altitude.

Kono, Fumihiko (1896-Aug. 11, 1982), Japanese engineer who led the team that developed the Zero fighter plane used by Japan during World War II.

Krueger, Albert P. (1902-Dec. 8, 1982), bacteriologist, best known for his research on air ions.

Lawler, Richard H. (1886-July 24, 1982), surgeon who performed the world's first kidney transplant in 1950.

Mitscherlich, Alexander (1908-June 26, 1982), West German psychoanalyst noted for his studies of aggression and his use of Freudian psychology to explain social institutions.

Moore, Stanford (1913-Aug. 21, 1982), biochemist who shared the 1972 Nobel Prize for chemistry in recognition of his work on the chemical structure of pancreatic nuclease.

Pearse, Herman E. (1899-May 2, 1982), surgeon who worked on the Manhattan Project during World War II. He was noted for his research on the treatment of flash burns from radiation in Hiroshima, Japan.

Pei, Wenzhong (1903-Sept. 18, 1982), Chinese archaeologist who in 1929 discovered the skull of Peking man, furnishing the first strong evidence of the evolution of humans from less advanced species.

Pilyugin, Nikolay A. (1908-Aug. 2, 1982), Russian aeronautical engineer who developed control systems for launch vehicles and spacecraft.

Reichelderfer, Francis W. (1895-Jan. 26, 1983), meteorologist, chairman of the U.S. Weather Bureau from 1938 to 1963. He presided over the bureau's development into the world's most scientific and sophisticated meteorological agency.

***Selye, Hans** (1907-Oct. 16, 1982), Canadian endocrinologist, born in Austria, helped develop the concept of stress as it affects the human body. His research showed how the body reacts to stress, how stress can bring on physical and emotional illness, and what can be done to alleviate the harmful effects of stress.

Spiegelman, Sol (1914-Jan. 21, 1983), biologist noted for his research on genetics and on the molecular basis of cancer.

Szmuness, Wolf (1919-June 6, 1982), Polish-born epidemiologist who directed the New York Blood Center studies that documented the effectiveness of the first hepatitis vaccine.

Terman, Frederick E. (1900-Dec. 19, 1982), electronics engineer and provost emeritus of Stanford University. He was a major influence in the development of Stanford's electronics program and in the growth of northern California's electronics industry. He won the 1976 National Medal of Science.

Theorell, Hugo (1903-Aug. 15, 1982), Swedish scientist who won the 1955 Nobel Prize for physiology or medicine for his research on oxidative enzymes and the body's conversion of food to energy.

Tolstoi, Edward (1897-May 22, 1983), physician noted for his work on diabetes. His books include *Living With Diabetes*.

Vinogradov, Ivan M. (1891-March 20, 1983), Russian mathematician, one of the world's foremost experts in the analytical theory of numbers. He was director of the Soviet Institute of Mathematics since 1932.

Von Euler, Ulf S. (1905-March 10, 1983), Swedish biochemist who in the 1950s discovered prostaglandins, the hormones used in birth control pills. He was co-winner of the 1970 Nobel Prize for physiology or medicine for his work in detecting noradrenaline, a key neurotransmitter that controls such involuntary actions as the heartbeat.

Voyat, Gilbert E. (1940-May 28, 1983), Swiss-born psychologist and educator noted for his work with autistic children and his studies of American Indian children in the Southwestern United States.

Wilson, Carroll L. (1910-Jan. 13, 1983) engineer, first general manager of the U.S. Atomic Energy Commission from 1947 to 1951.

***Zworykin, Vladimir K.** (1889-July 29, 1982), Russian-born physicist who was responsible for many scientific advances in radio and television, including the electron microscope and the iconoscope. This electronic tube converts light rays into electrical signals, and was pivotal to the development of television.   [Irene B. Keller]

Drugs

New combinations of drugs and adjustments of dosages were responsible for some success in treating two major diseases — cancer and heart disease — in 1982 and 1983.

Swedish medical researchers Stig Borgstrom, Finn Edler von Eyben, Per Flodgren, Burgt Axelsson, and Homs O. Sjogren reported in October 1982 that adding cimetidine to interferon caused remissions of melanoma — a skin cancer. They had been giving 4 million to 12 million units of interferon daily (a rather low dose) to 6 melanoma patients with no effect. They then added 100 milligrams (mg) of cimetidine to the daily dosage and remissions occurred in 3 of the patients.

After initial encouraging results, interferon has had very limited success in treating cancer. It has proved to be toxic, causing fever, aches and pains, and loss of appetite. In some cases, it has been associated with seizures or abnormal rhythms of the heart.

Cimetidine is a histamine-blocking drug used to treat peptic ulcers. The researchers believe that cimetidine decreases the number of cells that act to suppress the immune system. This enables the patients to mount a stronger immune response to the cancer and thus improve.

R. D. Thornes and G. Lynch of St. Laurence's Hospital in Dublin, Ireland, reported success in melanoma remissions by treating three patients with a combination of cimetidine and coumarin. Coumarin stimulates the production of macrophages — cells in the body's immune system. The combination of this stimulant with cimetidine's role in removing suppressor cells may strongly enhance the body's immunological defenses against this type of cancer.

In the past, drugs used to enhance the response of the immune system to melanoma have not proved out. Also, none of the interferon- or coumarin-treated patients have been observed for very long. So researchers do not know the long-term effects of these therapies. Nevertheless, this use of cimetidine in conjunction with other drugs is a cancer treatment to watch.

"Personally, I never take anything but aspirin."

New Rules
for Drug
Packaging

Nonprescription drugs are now packaged in an ingenious variety of tamper-resistant containers including, from left to right, a pop-top can, foil-sealed bottle, plastic-wrapped container, warning seal, and plastic bubbles surrounding individual pills.

When you buy a nonprescription medicine anywhere in the United States today, you will find it enclosed in a "tamper-resistant" package. This is due primarily to the deaths of seven people in the Chicago area in September and October 1982. A person or persons unknown had laced capsules of Extra-Strength Tylenol, a nonprescription painkiller, with a deadly chemical—cyanide. Seven unsuspecting consumers swallowed the poisoned capsules and died. Authorities took immediate steps to prevent such a tragedy from recurring.

The Food and Drug Administration (FDA)—the federal agency responsible for overseeing the purity and safety of all foods, drugs, and cosmetics sold in the United States—backed pharmaceutical manufacturer Johnson & Johnson's nationwide recall of Tylenol products as people in many parts of the United States reported suffering ill effects after using drugs that seemed to have been tampered with.

The FDA drafted a packaging regulation for all nonprescription drugs,

contact lens solutions, liquid mouthwashes, and certain types of liquid cosmetics. Recognizing that no package can be absolutely tamper-*proof*, the FDA rules require tamper-*resistant* packages designed to alert the consumer if they have been opened. The FDA defines a tamper-resistant package as "having an indicator or barrier to entry which, if breached or missing, can reasonably be expected to provide visible evidence to consumers that tampering has occurred."

Manufacturers have responded with a variety of barriers, including plastic wraps, glued or taped boxes, shrink bands around bottlenecks, steel cans, breakable caps, inner membrane seals like those on coffee jars, and blister packs—plastic sheets that encase each capsule in its own bubble.

Initial FDA rules went into effect in February 1983 and by February 1984 all over-the-counter drugs sold in the United States—even those produced in other countries—must comply. But the consumer must still be alert for evidence of tampering. [Ben Miyares]

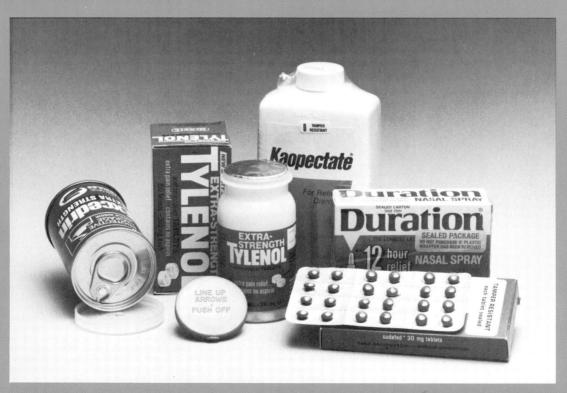

Drugs
Continued

Aspirin and arteries. Babette B. Weksler and other medical researchers at Cornell University Medical College in New York City have an explanation for the failure of aspirin to ward off coronary artery disease in clinical trials, as theory says it should. Aspirin should help because it inhibits the enzymes in platelets that make thromboxane. This substance causes platelets to clump together and block blood vessels.

The researchers gave aspirin to patients prior to coronary artery by-pass surgery and then examined tissues removed from arteries and veins. They also examined the platelets. They found that aspirin in doses of 40, 80, or 320 milligrams taken 12 to 16 hours before the surgery inhibited platelet clumping. At the same time, the 320-milligram dose also inhibited enzymes in the blood vessels that make prostacyclin. This is a substance that keeps the blood vessels dilated and prevents platelets from sticking to the inner lining of vessels and blocking blood flow.

A high dose of aspirin seems to have two effects, which tend to cancel each other. The dose of 320 milligrams (equal to 1 regular aspirin tablet) decreases the ability of platelets to obstruct small blood vessels. At the same time, it inhibits the normal mechanisms of the blood vessel that help maintain a free flow of blood through the vessel. Clinical trials using much lower doses of aspirin than those used in past trials are needed to assess aspirin's real effect on heart disease.

Heparin, a drug that inhibits blood coagulation, has been used in low doses to prevent thrombosis, or emboli that obstruct blood vessels, in hospital patients recovering from heart attacks, strokes, and certain types of surgery. Israeli medical researchers Hillel Halkin, Joel Goldberg, Michaela Modan, and Boruch Modan reported in 1982 on a program they conducted in which selected patients admitted to hospitals, no matter the reason, were given heparin as a clot preventive.

The researchers assigned 669 patients to a heparin-treatment group. A control group of 689 patients did not receive heparin. Only 7.8 per cent of the patients in the heparin-treatment group died while hospitalized, compared with 10.7 per cent of those in the control group. Since the two groups appeared to be comparable at admission, the difference in mortality rates was probably due to the heparin.

Estrogen therapy — is it, on balance, good or bad? Medical researcher Trudy L. Bush of the Oklahoma Medical Research Foundation in Oklahoma City and others reported in February 1983 on a study indicating that estrogen has a positive effect on postmenopausal women.

There has been much controversy over the use of estrogen to treat the symptoms of menopause. Some researchers consider that the estrogen secreted naturally by premenopausal women is responsible for their lower cardiovascular disease and death rate compared with men of the same age. Others think that estrogen is important in maintaining normal bone structure and its lack in elderly women is why so many of them seem to break their hips easily. On the other hand, prescribing estrogen is risky because it appears to increase uterine cancer.

The researchers found during a 5½-year follow-up period of estrogen users that the overall mortality rate was one-third that of nonusers. The subjects of the study were women between the ages of 40 and 69 at the start of the observation period. The estrogen was prescribed by the patients' physicians for reasons unrelated to the study. Thus the study had a weakness — if the groups were not truly identical except for estrogen use, the difference in mortality could be due to other factors.

Slipped disk relief. A new treatment for herniated intervertebral disk — slipped spinal disk — was approved by the Food and Drug Administration in November 1982. The treatment consists of injecting the enzyme, collagenase, into the disk.

A slipped disk causes low back pain that can be severe enough to be disabling. Standard treatment is bed rest, pain relievers, and muscle relaxants. If these treatments are not effective, surgeons may operate to remove the disk. Collagenase works by dissolving the central collagen portion of the disk. This apparently relieves the pressure on the nerve roots, which can cause pain. [Marcus M. Reidenberg]

245

Earth Sciences

Geology. During 1982 and 1983, geologists measured earth tremors and other geologic signs that may foretell a large-scale volcanic eruption near Mammoth Lakes, Calif., in the eastern Sierra Nevada.

By 1982, fingers of magma—molten rock—that had caused internal earthquakes at depths of 7 to 8 kilometers (4 to 5 miles) in 1978 had welled up to within 3 kilometers (2 miles) of the earth's surface.

Throughout 1982 and early 1983, the magma continued to generate swarms, or clusters, of small earthquakes in the area. Although the largest of the earthquakes were felt throughout the area, they caused little property damage.

Some of the earthquake swarms were centered on the southern edge of Long Valley—a large caldera, or volcanic depression—and along a line of lava domes called the Inyo domes. The youngest dome formed about 700 years ago when molten magma oozed out of the earth along a series of faults, or cracks, in its crust. These domes

were the sites of the most recent volcanic activity in the caldera.

In May 1982, the increasingly shallow spasmodic tremors led the United States Geological Survey (USGS) to issue a volcanic hazard notice, the first precautionary stage of alert, for the Mammoth Lakes region. Scientists also stepped up their observations of changes within the earth. They monitored patterns of seismic activity—movement within the earth's crust—and measured the temperatures of the area's hot springs. These temperatures increase as magma rises to the surface. The researchers also monitored increases in elevation and tilt of the land. Geophysicist James Savage of the USGS reported in January that some regions within the caldera had risen 24 centimeters (9 inches) because of the growth of the underlying magma chamber as new magma welled up from deeper regions within the earth.

The USGS reported in January 1983 that the number of small, shallow earthquakes measuring at least 1 on the Richter scale had increased to 80

A meteorite found in Antarctica in 1982, *below,* is the first moon rock found on earth, the first meteorite whose source has been identified, and the first known meteorite from outside the asteroid belt. Another meteorite found in Antarctica, *below right,* could be from Mars because its chemical composition resembles that of the Martian atmosphere.

to 100 per hour, well above the usual level of 2 per hour. In addition, several earthquakes measuring 5 to 6 on the Richter scale were recorded.

While the seismic activity at Mammoth Lakes continues, geologists debate the possibility of a large destructive earthquake such as the great earthquake of 1872 in nearby Owens Valley that had a magnitude of more than 8 points on the Richter scale. The upwelling magma may also break through to the surface or penetrate the water table, leading to steam explosions or a volcanic eruption.

Ups and downs. The ability of geologists to predict earthquakes by measuring rapid changes in the elevation of the earth's crust was complicated by observations reported in March 1983. A team of scientists led by geophysicist Robert C. Jachens of the USGS in Menlo Park, Calif., measured the elevation of several areas in southern California along the San Andreas Fault from 1977 to 1982.

The researchers found that during this period, the land near Palmdale rose then fell to its original level. However, this motion, up to 10 centimeters (4 inches) per year, was not accompanied by any large earthquakes.

The scientists do not know what caused the Palmdale swelling or why it should occur along an active fault where two plates are moving alongside each other without an earthquake. The scientists noted that attempts to forecast earthquakes by measuring land motion will have to take into account these aseismic swellings, which make earthquake prediction more difficult.

Ocean geology. Important advances in understanding the geology of ocean basins based on new technology were reported in 1983. In January, earth scientists announced that data from the *Seasat* satellite, which was used in 1978 to study waves and tides on ocean surfaces, are being used to map the ocean floor. See EARTH SCIENCES (Oceanography).

, In March, using a sophisticated new sonar system, marine geologist Kenneth C. Macdonald of the University of California at Santa Barbara and Paul J. Fox of the University of Rhode Island in Kingston reported finding evidence of so-called overlapping spreading ridges — pairs of ridges running almost parallel to each other — in the floor of the southeast Pacific Ocean. At spreading ridges, molten rock wells up through cracks in the ocean floor, forming new crust. Previously, geologists believed that oceanic ridges followed a single jagged path through the earth's ocean basins.

The new sonar system detects features on the ocean floor over a wider area than does older echo-sounding sonar equipment. The system also provides a much sharper, more detailed picture of the ocean floor.

Macdonald and Fox found eight areas where two spreading ridges curve toward each other and overlap. In one area, the ridges run alongside each other for 25 to 35 kilometers (15 to 22 miles). Between the two ridges lies a basin more than 500 meters (1,650 feet) deep.

Tracking tectites. In September 1982, geophysicists Henry Shaw and Gerald Wasserburg of the California Institute of Technology in Pasadena reported new evidence for the terrestrial origin of tectites — tiny glassy spheres found in only eight areas on earth. Scientists have debated the origin of tectites since the early 1900s. Some have argued that the tectites are volcanic material ejected from the moon. Others theorized that the tectites formed on earth from rock melted by heat produced by the impact of a meteorite or comet.

Shaw and Wasserburg analyzed the ratios of two isotopes, or forms, of the element strontium and two isotopes of the element neodymium in tectites from all eight areas. They found that the proportions of these isotopes matched the ratios in sediment from 950-million-year-old earth rock. However, the ratios were completely different from those in meteorites or lunar rocks. Although the evidence suggests that the meteorite impact theory is a better explanation for the tectites' origin, scientists have not yet discovered any craters the meteorites would have made when crashing into the earth.

Vagabond rocks. In March 1983, earth scientists from the National Aeronautics and Space Administration (NASA) and the National Science Foundation verified that a greenish-

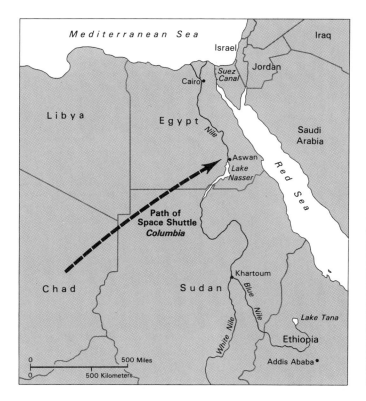

Earth Sciences

Continued

Deserted Rivers
Radar pictures, *above right,* of a strip of the Sahara in Egypt and the Sudan from the space shuttle *Columbia* reveal prehistoric river valleys now covered by barren and nearly featureless terrain.

brown meteorite found in Antarctica in January 1982 is a fragment of the moon. A team of U.S. scientists led by William Cassidy of the University of Pittsburgh discovered the 31-gram (1-ounce) meteorite, known as ALHA 81005, in the Allen Hills region.

The meteorite looks like samples of lunar breccia—a conglomeration of rock fragments rich in the mineral plagioclase—collected by the *Apollo 16* astronauts in the lunar highlands. Twenty teams of scientists from the United States and other countries found the chemical composition of the meteorite to be identical to that of lunar rocks.

This meteorite marks a number of firsts. It is the first moon rock found on earth, the first meteorite whose source has been identified, and the first proof that meteorites come from planet-sized bodies as well as from the asteroid belt. Geophysicist Jay Melosh of the University of Arizona in Tucson theorized that ALHA 81005 was ejected into space when a much larger meteorite crashed into the moon.

Also in March 1983, geochemist Donald Bogard of the Lyndon B. Johnson Space Center in Houston reported that other unusual meteorites called SNCs may be from Mars. Scientists have found nine SNCs, including two in Antarctica in 1979.

Unlike other meteorites, which are 4.5 billion years old, the SNCs are only 1.3 billion years old. Bogard found that the ratios of argon and xenon isotopes in one of the Antarctic SNCs strongly resemble the ratios of these isotopes in the Martian atmosphere tested by the *Viking* spacecraft. He speculated that the gases were trapped among mineral grains in the rocks when they blasted from the Martian surface and were preserved in the Antarctic ice sheet.

Additional evidence that the meteorites are from Mars and not the moon is that the meteorites appear to be volcanic rocks and, by the time they were formed, the moon had cooled to the point where volcanic activity had ended. Volcanic activity was still taking place on Mars, however.

Earth Sciences

Continued

Plate forms. In December 1982, seismologist Paul Tapponnier and his colleagues at the Institute for Earth Physics in Paris proposed a model to explain how the collision of India with western Asia caused the movement of land masses in eastern Asia to form certain features of Asia's geology, such as mountains.

In their model, Tapponnier's team used a rigid block to represent India and a sheet of plasticine—a flexible material resembling modeling clay—to represent Asia. Scientists are uncertain why Asia's crust is less rigid than India's. It may be because Asia consists of smaller land masses called terranes (see THE PATCHWORK EARTH). Or Asia's crust may still be relatively warm and soft because of the volcanic activity that has occurred north of the Himalaya throughout the past 50 million years.

When the French scientists pushed the rigid block into the plasticine, they found that structural changes in the plasticine resembled major geologic features that have formed on the Asian continent since the collision with India about 50 million years ago. The most obvious result of India's push into Asia was the buckling of the western edge of the Asian Plate and the formation of the Himalaya. According to the scientists, India's relentless pressure on Asia also caused Indochina in Southeast Asia to rotate clockwise along a major fault in the earth's crust. As Indochina moved, the crust split and the South China Sea opened.

According to the model, continuing pressure by India then pushed parts of South China up to 800 kilometers (500 miles) eastward, causing the formation of another fault and the opening of the Andaman Sea west of Indochina. The French scientists theorized that if India continues to push into Asia, another fault in northwestern Asia will extend to the Sea of Okhotsk. As this fault forms, another section of east Asia will begin to rotate clockwise, pushing South China southward. This model has lent new support to the theory that the earth's lithospheric plates—huge segments of the earth's crust on which the continents and oceans ride—are much less rigid than previously believed. [Robert W. Kay]

Paleontology. Two scientists in August 1982 proposed the establishment of a new geologic period. Geologists Preston Cloud, Jr., of the University of California at Santa Barbara and Martin F. Glaessner of the University of Adelaide in Australia suggested that the new period, the first to be proposed in nearly 100 years, should be called the Ediacarian Period. It would be named for the Ediacara Hills in Australia where the oldest known fossils of animals with soft bodies were first discovered in 1947. The new period would extend from about 670 million years ago, when the first Ediacarian fossils appeared, to about 560 million years ago, at the beginning of the Cambrian Period.

Until 1947, scientists believed that no animal life existed during the Precambrian time, which includes the almost 4 billion years from the formation of the earth to the beginning of the Cambrian Period. However, since 1947, scientists have found Precambrian fossil impressions in the Ediacara Hills of about 26 species of invertebrates, or animals without backbones. Similar Precambrian fossils have also been found in South Africa, Great Britain, Siberia, and Newfoundland, Canada.

Although official scientific approval for the establishment of the new period seems certain, the choice of a name may cause some debate. Scientists in a number of countries, including the Soviet Union, use the name Vendian for this period.

Mass extinctions. In March 1982, paleontologists David M. Raup and J. John Sepkoski, Jr., of the University of Chicago published a statistical study of the extinction rates of marine organisms during various periods of the Phanerozoic Eon—the last 600 million years of earth's history.

The scientists found that the extinction rates for families of marine species have declined over that time span, from 4.6 families per 1 million years during the Cambrian Period to 2 families per 1 million years at present. During that same time, the number of marine families has increased. The increase in the diversity of marine families may have occurred because of the decline in their extinction rate.

Earth Sciences

Continued

The fossil foot bones of the earliest known primate, *above,* discovered in Wyoming and dated to 50 million years ago, indicate that the creature had a grasping big toe. The animal, *above right,* classified as *Cantius trigonodus,* may have used the toe to climb trees more easily and thus escape from predators.

Raup and Sepkoski also identified four short intervals with high marine family extinction rates. They included one about 225 million years ago at the end of the Paleozoic Era and one about 65 million years ago at the end of the Mesozoic Era.

In 1982, scientists continued to debate the possible relationship between sudden mass extinctions of species and bombardment by meteorites. In May, geochemist Ramachandran Ganapathy of the J. T. Baker Chemical Company in Phillipsburg, N.J., and a team of scientists led by geologist Walter Alvarez of the University of California, Berkeley, reported evidence that a large meteorite collided with the earth 34 million years ago. At that time, the fossil record shows that many species of microscopic marine animals died.

In 1979, Alvarez and other scientists proposed that another giant meteorite collided with the earth about 65 million years ago, causing the extinction of many plant and animal species, including dinosaurs. Both the 1979 and 1982 claims were based on the presence in ancient sediments of concentrations of iridium, an element rare on earth but plentiful in celestial bodies.

In 1982, Ganapathy and the Alvarez team reported on their study of a deepsea sedimentary core from the Caribbean Sea. A zone in the core 20 to 30 centimeters (8 to 12 inches) thick contained a concentration of microtectites — tiny, glassy spheres believed to form from rock melted by the heat of a meteorite impact. The researchers found that the sediment immediately above the microtectite level contained high levels of iridium. They dated the microtectites at 34 million years old. The researchers believe there is a link between the abrupt disappearance of many species at that time and the evidence of the meteorite impact.

Conodont mystery solved? In August 1982, three British paleontologists announced the discovery of remains of a fossil animal containing conodonts — microscopic toothlike fossils. Although hundreds of different types of conodonts had been found in rocks from 600 million to 190 million years old,

Earth Sciences

Continued

the animal they came from had previously been unknown.

Euan N. K. Clarkson of the University of Edinburgh found the fossil and collaborated with Derek E. G. Briggs of the University of London and Richard J. Aldridge of the University of Nottingham in describing it. The animal was about 4 centimeters (1½ inches) long, with a slender, eel-shaped body. It probably belongs to a new phylum, or major group of animals. The scientists speculated that the conodonts were the teeth of these eellike creatures.

Antarctic mammals. The first fossil evidence of land mammals in Antarctica was reported in October 1982 by paleontologists Michael O. Woodburne of the University of California, Riverside, and William J. Zinsmeister of Ohio State University in Columbus. The scientists found the fossil jawbones and teeth of an extinct marsupial in 40-million-year-old sediments in the northern Antarctic Peninsula.

Until this discovery, the remains of the family of animals to which this marsupial belonged had been found only in South America. The fossils provide support for the theory that marsupials originated in South America then migrated to Australia by way of Antarctica when the three continents were joined, about 56 million years ago.

Other finds. In July 1982, paleontologist Robert T. Bakker of Johns Hopkins University in Baltimore reported on an intriguing pattern in the distribution of fossil amphibian and reptile bones in deposits in west Texas from the Permian Period, about 280 million years ago. Bakker speculated that the young of these species spent most of their time in swampy habitats, possibly for protection from predators. The adults, however, tended to migrate to more open sites.

Paleontologist Kenneth D. Rose, also of Johns Hopkins, reported in May 1982 on the discovery of a nearly complete fossilized skeleton of the oldest known artiodactyl. This group includes modern cloven-hoofed animals, such as cattle, sheep, and hogs. Rose found the fossilized animal bones in rocks about 55 million years old in Wyoming. [Carlton E. Brett]

Meteorology. Unusual weather occurred across much of the Pacific Ocean, parts of South America, and most of North America during the winter of 1982-1983. There were rare hurricanes in Hawaii; searing drought in Australia; floods and landslides in Ecuador and Peru; and severe snow and cold over much of the United States along with record rainfall, wind, and waves in California.

The weather was not only anomalous — departing from the general rules of behavior — with regard to temperature and precipitation, but the extreme conditions were also unusually widespread and long-lasting. The bad weather appeared to be connected in a pattern stretching from Indonesia to the Atlantic seaboard. Distressing as it was to most people, the unusual weather came at just the right time to provide scientists with dramatic new evidence for a still-developing theory. The theory proposes that a series of teleconnections — interactions at a distance — exists between the oceans in low latitudes and the earth's atmosphere in tropical and subtropical regions around the world.

A phenomenon called El Niño is believed to play a leading role in these events. El Niño is a warm water current from the northwest that usually arrives off South America in December. Scientists do not yet understand the exact cause of El Niño but they suspect changes in trade winds may be involved. Under normal conditions, relatively cold water is found along the equator between the central Pacific Ocean and the coast of South America as a result of the upwelling of deep ocean water. The usually persistent easterly trade winds push the warmer surface water toward the central Pacific. When these trade winds collapse, the cold water is overrun by warmer water flowing eastward. While this sequence occurs to some extent every year, a true El Niño is now regarded as a long-lasting, widespread event.

In March 1983, atmospheric scientist George Philander of the National Oceanic and Atmospheric Administration's (NOAA) Geophysical Fluid Dynamics Laboratory in Princeton, N.J., reported on studies of El Niño conducted by a number of researchers

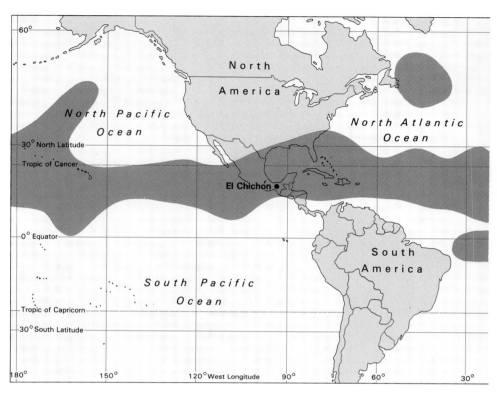

A Stratospheric Sash
Volcanic particles spewed as high as 25 kilometers (15.5 miles) into the earth's atmosphere by the eruption of Mexico's El Chichón volcano in March 1982, formed a globe-girdling cloud belt by June.

Map labels: 60°, North America, North Pacific Ocean, North Atlantic Ocean, 30° North Latitude, Tropic of Cancer, El Chichón, 0° Equator, South America, South Pacific Ocean, Tropic of Capricorn, 30° South Latitude, 180°, 150°, 120° West Longitude, 90°, 60°, 30°

Earth Sciences

Continued

over more than 30 years. The scientists concluded that El Niño is the result of large-scale shifts in atmospheric circulation over tropical oceans called the Southern Oscillation. A good example of these shifts is the seesaw relationship between the atmospheric pressure zone over northern Australia and Indonesia and the one over the eastern South Pacific Ocean—when one is low, the other is high. The Southern Oscillation is linked to sharp changes in rainfall, sea-surface temperature, and the intensity of trade winds. It is also connected with droughts in India, severe winter weather over North America, and shifts in the average air temperature over North America.

In May 1982, meteorologists Eugene M. Rasmusson and Thomas H. Carpenter of NOAA's Climate Analysis Center in Washington, D.C., summarized the sequence of El Niño-Southern Oscillation (ENSO) events from 1950 through 1972 in terms of air circulation and sea-surface temperature.

Most ENSO events occurred at intervals of 2 to 10 years. They began in

February and March with unusually warm sea-surface temperatures in the eastern tropical Pacific—the ocean within 20 degrees of the equator on either side—or with the prolonged appearance of intense eastward winds in the western tropical Pacific. Excessive rainfall caused by warming of the sea surface was part of the pattern. At the same time, there was a southward shift of the intertropical convergence zone (ITCZ)—the region where the southwest and southeast trade winds converge—and a shift eastward of the low pressure zone in the western Pacific.

These conditions intensified during the years that El Niño developed. By December, sea-surface temperatures over the entire eastern tropical Pacific were unusually warm, the ITCZ was farther south than normal, and the low atmospheric pressure zone in the western Pacific was at its most intense. Conditions began to ease in January, returning to normal by June.

The 1982-1983 event, however, did not follow the normal sequence. The ENSO originated in warm sea-surface

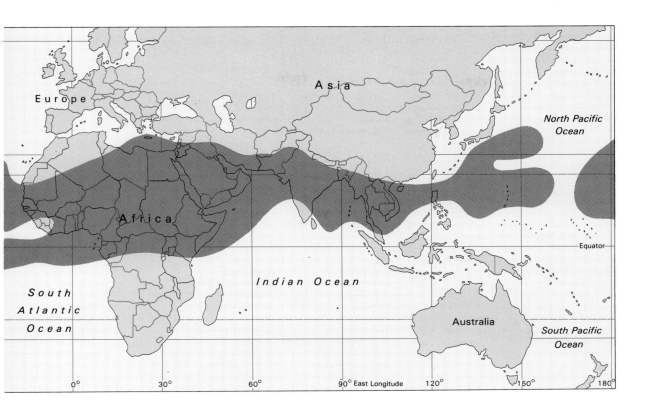

Earth Sciences

Continued

temperatures that had developed in the western rather than eastern tropical Pacific by April 1982. By January 1983, the NOAA Climate Analysis Center reported that the center of warm water along with heavy rain had moved eastward to the central Pacific accompanied by a fully developed El Niño. This shift of warm ocean water and its associated rainfall from the western to the central Pacific caused the drought that devastated Indonesia and Australia and brought very heavy rain to Peru early in 1983.

Scientists theorized that the teleconnections between these events and the unusual winter of 1982-1983 in much of the United States resulted from the atmosphere's response to this unusual pattern of tropical sea-surface temperatures. The heating of water in the central Pacific altered the large-scale airflow pattern over North America and, thus, winter storm development.

Meteorologists at the University of Washington in Seattle and Goddard Space Flight Center in Greenbelt, Md., reported in December 1982 that

they had confirmed the likelihood of such teleconnections using computer models of the general atmospheric circulation. Atmospheric scientists at the National Center for Atmospheric Research in Boulder, Colo., and Oregon State University in Corvallis reported in January 1983 that they had found similar results.

Of course, not all severe winter weather over North America is associated with ENSO events. Nevertheless, the winter of 1982-1983 provided the strongest evidence yet that unusual winters may be connected with earlier events in distant parts of the world and may thus in part be predictable a season or more in advance.

El Chichón, a volcano in Mexico's Yucatán Peninsula, began to erupt on March 28, 1982, spewing huge amounts of dust and gases into the stratosphere at the unprecedented heights of 22 to 32 kilometers (14 to 20 miles) above the earth. At first, scientists thought its effects on weather might be as far-reaching as those of El Niño. Within months, the El Chichón

Earth Sciences

Continued

cloud of volcanic particles had spread around the world in tropical latitudes from the equator to 30 degrees north latitude, and was the cause of unusually long and colorful sunsets seen in many locations. High concentrations of sulfur dioxide gas and sulfuric acid droplets in the cloud reduced the amount of sunlight reaching the earth's surface by as much as 30 per cent and caused a slight cooling of the earth's lower atmosphere. By mid-1983, however, meteorologists had not shown that this had directly affected the worldwide weather pattern.

Local storm watchers. On much smaller scales of space and time, other U.S. meteorologists turned their attention to severe local storms. It has usually been impossible for meteorologists to observe — let alone forecast — details of local weather connected with violent downdrafts, tornadoes, heavy rain, and hail. But such forecasting is highly desirable, because violent mesoscale phenomena — events occurring within an area 16 to 32 kilometers (10 to 20 miles) in diameter — affect such activities as agriculture and aviation.

Research meteorologist Robert A. Maddox of NOAA in Boulder reported in July 1982 on his study of mesoscale convective complexes — large storm cloud systems formed when warm air rises, expands, and cools. Maddox used enhanced infrared photos made by weather satellites to study the structure of these convective complexes, which are often seen over oceans in winter and over continents in summer. He concluded that these structures are probably responsible for much of the observed precipitation.

Other studies of mesoscale precipitation were reported in July 1982 by atmospheric scientist Peter V. Hobbs of the University of Washington in Seattle. Using a portable Doppler radar system, which tracks the motion of precipitation particles within storms, Hobbs and his colleagues traced the structure and movement of rain bands associated with cold fronts moving into the Northwest from the Pacific Ocean. They found that the precipitation in these bands occurs in a series of cells about 5 kilometers (3 miles) across that drift sideways along the moving cold front. [W. Lawrence Gates]

Oceanography. Extremely accurate measurements from space of variations in the height of the sea surface have provided marine geologists with a new tool for mapping the sea floor. In December 1982, William Haxby of Columbia University's Lamont-Doherty Geological Observatory in Palisades, N.Y., reported that he had developed a charting technique called geotectonic imagery (GTI), which relies on measurements made by the ocean research satellite *Seasat*.

For 70 days in 1978, instruments on *Seasat* measured small variations in the distance between the satellite's orbit 800 kilometers (500 miles) above the earth and the ocean surface to an accuracy within 10 centimeters (4 inches). The more than 50 million resulting measurements were then processed by computer to provide highly detailed data on the variation in height of the ocean surface. Using these data, Haxby and his colleagues were able to deduce the topography, or physical features, of the ocean floor.

A seamount, or underwater mountain, draws enough water over it to produce a bump several inches high in the sea surface. Likewise, a trench produces a small depression in the surface, and such extensive submarine features as ridges produce wide variations in the height of water.

With this type of data, Haxby was able to create maps showing detailed contours of seamounts, ridges, and trenches in all of the major ocean basins on earth.

Marine geologist Timothy H. Dixon and oceanographer Michael E. Parke of the Jet Propulsion Laboratory (JPL) in Pasadena, Calif., also reported in December that they had analyzed *Seasat* data to learn more about large-scale features of the Pacific Ocean floor. For example, the JPL scientists found that the *Seasat* measurements revealed a previously unknown submarine plateau as large as California and more than 1.6 kilometers (1 mile) high in the southwest Pacific Ocean. They also determined from the *Seasat* data that the Louisville Ridge in the southwest Pacific is a nearly continuous mountain chain, not a string of disconnected mountains as marine geologists previously believed.

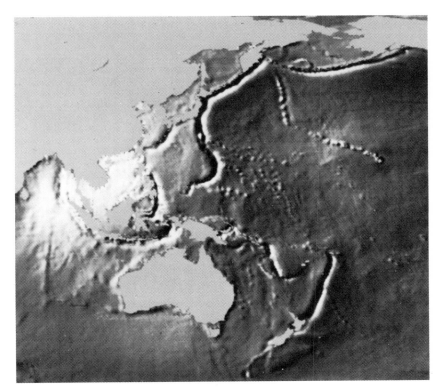

A new map of the South Pacific Ocean floor near Australia on which ridges and trenches stand out clearly was made from measurements of sea-surface height gathered by the oceanographic research satellite *Seasat*.

Earth Sciences

Continued

Ancient whales. Evidence accumulating for the past several years has indicated that the primitive ancestors of cetaceans, or whales, were amphibious creatures, representing a step in the evolution of land-dwelling animals to sea dwellers. A team of scientists from the University of Michigan in Ann Arbor, the National Museum of Natural History in Paris, and the Geological Survey of Pakistan in Quetta provided new support for this view in April 1983. The researchers based their conclusions on a study of fossil skull and tooth remains found in the Kohat District of Pakistan. The remains dated from the early Eocene Epoch 55 million to 35 million years ago. This made *Pakicetus*, as the researchers named the animal from which the fossils came, the oldest cetacean known.

Close examination of the skull indicated that *Pakicetus* probably could not dive to any great depth, and that it was more like land mammals than marine mammals. Moreover, other fossil remains near the skull fragment were those of land animals. The geologic record also suggests that the region where the fossil was found once had many salty lakes and bays rich in plankton and fish.

The researchers speculated that the primitive land-dwelling ancestors of modern whales first entered shallow seas in the early Eocene Epoch to feed on schools of herringlike and larger fish. At first, they probably formed colonies near shore, then moved to areas farther offshore where upwelling waters provided them with abundant food. Although the *Pakicetus* skull indicated this creature lacked the hearing organs needed for living underwater full time, later whales developed structures for hearing underwater.

Ocean desert or ocean prairie? Zoologists John M. Sieburth and Paul Davis of the University of Rhode Island in Kingston reported in August 1982 on their efforts to define the role microbes play in the biological productivity of deep ocean waters. Using screens with extremely fine meshes, high-speed centrifuges, and an electron microscope, Sieburth detected a class of microorganisms called picoplankton. These minute organisms are less than 2½ micrometers long. (A micrometer is one-millionth of a meter.) Davis measured accurately for the first time the concentration of microorganisms smaller than 25 micrometers (nanoplankton). This class of microorganisms is believed to form the base of the food chain.

Oceanographers had regarded the deep ocean as a biological desert compared with the richly productive nearshore waters that cover the continental shelves. However, Davis determined that the microorganisms keep the concentration of biological material in deep oceanic waters at a level about 17 per cent of that of the more productive waters over the continental shelves. This suggests that the clear blue waters of the deep ocean are far more productive than was believed.

Additional evidence of the productivity of ocean waters came in December from oceanographer Bruce H. Robison and marine biologist Alice L. Alldredge of the University of California, Santa Barbara. They each dived deep into the Pacific Ocean in a one-person motorized aluminum suit, called the Wasp, that let them study marine life at mid-ocean depths down to 600 meters (1,980 feet).

The Wasp divers saw unexpectedly dense concentrations of tiny crustaceans called copepods. The copepods, which are also a vital part of the ocean food chain, were stacked in a layer 15 to 25 meters (50 to 82 feet) thick at a depth of 450 meters (1,327 feet). The researchers estimated that there were from 2 million to 4 million copepods per cubic meter.

Robison and Alldredge also concluded from their Wasp observations that mid-water fish exist in greater numbers and variety than biologists had predicted. Earlier estimates set the mid-water fish population of the Santa Barbara Basin, off the California coast, at about 20 per cubic meter. The estimates were based on the number of fish brought up in trawl nets. But trawls often destroy such fragile fish as jellyfish. Robison and Alldredge, after observing the fish firsthand, determined that the population was about 10 times higher.

New breed of shrimp? While marine biologists explored the richness of life in the open ocean, other scientists were investigating ways to raise in captivity such desirable seafood species as clams, lobsters, salmon, and — especially — shrimp. Research on the controlled rearing of shrimp since about 1970 resulted in several commercial efforts. However, industry growth was hampered by lack of a reliable source of shrimp larvae and inability to reproduce and rear enough of them.

In August 1982, Addison L. Lawrence of Texas A&M University in College Station reported that he had successfully crossbred two species of shrimp. The ability to create hybrid shrimp may herald a major advance in the prospects for successful shrimp farming. Using artificial insemination techniques pioneered by biologist Paul Sandifer of the South Carolina Wildlife and Marine Resources Department, Lawrence and his colleagues produced a hybrid shrimp by crossing two species of white shrimp, *Penaeus setiferus* and *Penaeus stylirostris*. *P. setiferus* is native to the Gulf of Mexico and never comes in contact with *P. stylirostris*, which lives in the Pacific Ocean off the coast of Mexico. Even in the same tank, the two species do not mate.

When shrimp mate, the male squeezes out a sperm packet, or spermatophore, into an opening in the female's reproductive tract. The scientists were able to remove the fluid containing the sperm from the spermatophore, then use it to artificially inseminate the female. The scientists could tell which females were ready to reproduce by the color, size, and texture of the ovary, which can be seen through the shrimp's shell.

Geneticist James Lester of the University of Houston in Clear Lake City, Tex., confirmed the successful crossbreeding by analyzing the protein patterns of the offspring. Each of the two species of shrimp used in the experiment has its own distinct protein pattern, and Lester's examination showed that the hybrid shrimp displayed patterns of both parent species. This proved it is possible to manipulate genetic traits to improve cultured shrimp species for the seafood market. [Feenan D. Jennings and Lauriston R. King]

Ecology

The ability of an organism to escape environmental stresses by moving to a new home is an important survival adaptation. In a February 1982 report, ecologist Judith Smallwood of Northwestern University in Evanston, Ill., explained why ant colonies sometimes relocate their nests.

Smallwood studied *Aphaenogaster rudis*, an ant common to forests of the Eastern United States. These ants move often even when they are not under environmental pressures. *A. rudis* tends to build its nests in areas that are not completely overshadowed by forest vegetation. Smallwood wanted to see what effects competition with other ants and being shaded from the sun would have on the migration rates of *A. rudis* colonies.

Smallwood studied the ants in both their natural environment and the laboratory. In the Monongahela National Forest in West Virginia, she divided 64 nests into four groups — a group whose nests she shaded from the sun, a group that she provided with food, a group that she both shaded and fed, and a control group that she gave neither shade nor food. Smallwood used feeding as a means of decreasing competition between *A. rudis* and other species of ants to see if competition for food is a factor in making *A. rudis* colonies relocate their nests. Her purpose in shading nests was to simulate the effects of sunlight-blocking vegetation on *A. rudis* colonies.

After checking each of the nests twice a month during the spring and summer over a two-year period, Smallwood found that changes in the colonies' food supply had no effect on their likelihood to relocate. Shading, however, caused an increase in *A. rudis* migration. Smallwood concluded that shading lowered the interior temperature of the nests, making them less suitable for the proper development of the eggs and larvae of ants.

In her laboratory experiments, Smallwood put *A. rudis* into direct confrontations with another species of ant, *Formica subsericea*, to determine if interactions with more aggressive ants would cause the colony to move. She designed two experiments using artificial nests and foraging areas. Some sections of the artificial nests were connected by tubes that *A. rudis* could easily pass through but which the considerably larger *Formica* ants could not enter. The tubes provided refuges to which *A. rudis* could retreat to escape from *Formica*.

In one group of experiments, Smallwood tested the effect of confrontations between the two colonies within nests as well as in foraging areas. In a second set of experiments, Smallwood prevented *Formica* from directly invading the *A. rudis* nests. Instead, confrontations were allowed to occur only in the foraging area.

Smallwood found that *A. rudis* relocated its nests only when the nests were directly invaded by *Formica*. Encounters between the two species in the foraging area resulted in *A. rudis* simply avoiding the same food sites or retiring to its nests.

Crowding is another form of environmental stress. Ecologists have long been interested in the effects of crowding stress on frogs and toads, whose complex life cycle of egg to tadpole to adult is often complicated by the drying up of water at their breeding sites. As the amount of available water shrinks, the tadpoles must crowd closer together to survive. Ecologists Raymond D. Semlitsch and Jonalee P. Caldwell of the U.S. Department of Energy's Savannah River Ecology Laboratory in Aiken, S.C., studied the tadpoles of a variety of toad called the spadefoot. They reported in August 1982 that tadpoles in crowded water weigh less, take longer to mature, and are more likely to die than tadpoles in uncrowded water.

The spadefoot toad is a so-called explosive breeder. It has adapted to arid regions, where ponds often are short-lived, by growing rapidly out of the tadpole stage. It thus spends less time as a vulnerable tadpole than do other frogs and toads.

The ecologists collected 2-day-old tadpoles from an evaporating pool on the Savannah River and put them into aquariums in densities ranging from 3 to 30 tadpoles per aquarium.

The scientists found that tadpoles in the least crowded tank grew nearly four times faster than those in the most crowded tank. The average number of days required for tadpoles to reach

maturity ranged from 27 days in the least crowded tank to 86 days in the most crowded. More than 90 per cent of the tadpoles in the least crowded aquarium survived to adulthood, compared with less than 20 per cent of those in the most crowded tank.

In a second experiment, the researchers put spadefoot tadpoles hatched in the laboratory into four aquariums. The population densities ranged from 1 to 90 tadpoles per aquarium. At periodic intervals, the scientists removed 10 tadpoles from each of the more crowded aquariums and allowed those tadpoles to continue developing in isolation.

This experiment was designed to simulate the release of tadpoles from crowding stress, such as occurs when breeding pools are enlarged by rainfall. The sooner the experimental tadpoles were freed from crowding stress, the larger they grew and the quicker they reached adulthood.

These experiments showed that crowding has a pronounced adverse effect on the development of frogs and toads. The fact that the spadefoot toad spends less time as a tadpole and is smaller at the onset of maturity than other toads and frogs may be evolutionary adaptations that allow the spadefoot to escape quickly from breeding pools before evaporation increases crowding stress. But, as the study showed, once the spadefoot is under such stress, its mortality rate rises sharply.

Plants and insects often establish mutually beneficial relationships. The insects receive food and the plant is protected from other leaf-damaging insects. Such a relationship between the catalpa tree and several types of insects was reported in June 1982 by ecologist Andrew G. Stephenson of Pennsylvania State University in State College, Pa.

The catalpa grows in many forests in the central United States and is often used in landscaping. Stephenson was particularly interested in the role played by the catalpa's extrafloral nectaries — the nonflowering nectar-secreting organs of many higher plants. The catalpa's extrafloral nectaries consist of many closely crowded glands on the lower surface of the leaves.

Researchers from the University of Georgia in Athens lower a trap into the water of the Okefenokee Swamp, *top,* to collect samples of aquatic life. Another investigator collects samples with a huge tube, *above.* The scientists are taking part in a long-term ecological study of the swamp, which covers nearly 1,810 square kilometers (700 square miles) in southeastern Georgia.

Stephenson studied three catalpa trees in the Matthei Botanical Gardens at the University of Michigan in Ann Arbor. He first wanted to determine the effect of the catalpa sphinx moth, an insect pest, on the production of nectar. He marked 25 leaves on the same number of branches and circled each branch with a tarlike substance to keep ants from reaching the leaves. Once a week, Stephenson extracted nectar from the leaves and measured its sugar content. He found that leaves that were partially damaged by moths secreted more sugar than undamaged leaves. This indicated that the trees were trying to lure insect enemies of the moths to the damaged leaves.

To determine what sorts of insects feed at the nectaries, Stephenson observed the catalpa trees closely during three summers. He found that the most common visitors were five species of ants, two species of ladybird beetles, and a type of wasp.

Stephenson found that these nectar-feeding insects play an important role in protecting catalpa trees from leaf-feeding insects, primarily the sphinx moth. Ladybird beetles attack the moth's eggs and larvae. The wasp lays its eggs inside the young moth larvae, where they hatch. The wasp larvae then feed on the moth larvae. Ants remove moth eggs and larvae from leaves and carry them back to their nests to eat them. On his three study trees, Stephenson discovered that the unmarked leaves that were accessible to ants suffered less damage from moths than did the 25 leaves that ants could not reach because of the tarlike coating on the branches.

Finally, Stephenson examined the effect of ants on the production of the catalpa's beanlike fruit. He began by circling a number of flower-bearing branches with the same sticky substance used in the other experiment. One week after the trees flowered, he recorded the number of fruit pods produced by branches with ants and by branches that ants could not reach because of the coating. He found that the branches with ants — and thus fewer moth larvae — produced the most fruit.

Water snakes are among the most abundant reptiles in the Southeastern United States, but their ecological role is poorly understood. In December, ecologists Henry R. Mushinsky of the University of South Florida in Tampa; James J. Hebrard of the University of Nairobi, Kenya; and Darrell S. Vodopich of Baylor University in Waco, Tex., reported on their studies of the feeding behavior of four water snakes. They found that an ecological niche is not always filled by a single species. In this case, the four kinds of water snakes — diamondback, green, banded, and yellow-bellied — can be considered, from the standpoint of prey, as an ecological unit.

The scientists conducted their study southeast of Baton Rouge, La., in an area that includes a cypress swamp and a bottomland hardwood forest. To determine the snakes' prey, they examined the stomach contents of 340 snakes by forcing the snakes to regurgitate or by killing the snakes and cutting open their stomachs. The young of all four species fed on small fish.

The scientists wanted to learn how the snakes change their feeding habits as they grow and whether there are differences among the snake species in choice of prey. They found the most striking changes in prey preferences in the yellow-bellied and banded water snakes. These two species change their diet when they reach a length of 50 centimeters (20 inches). The banded snake switches from fish mainly to frogs and the yellow-bellied snake eats mostly toads. The diamondback and green water snakes eat mainly fish throughout their lives, although when they grow to a certain size — 80 centimeters (32 inches) for the diamondback and 70 centimeters (28 inches) for the green water snake — they switch from eating the same kinds of small fish to eating different varieties of large fish.

Thus, all four species can be considered a single predator until they attain a certain body size. Thereafter, each species functions separately. These shifts in diet also emphasize the importance of field investigations in learning the true feeding behavior of animals. In captivity, adult snakes of these four species willingly eat fish — even packaged filets. But in the wild, each snake seeks out the prey it prefers. [Stanley I. Auerbach]

Electronics

The compact disk (CD) digital phonograph was introduced to the United States consumer market in June 1982, stemming from a joint research program by Sony Corporation of Japan and N. V. Philips Gloeilampenfabrieken of Eindhoven, the Netherlands. The long-playing CD phonograph records are 12 centimeters (4¾ inches) in diameter and provide up to one hour's playing time. Instead of grooves, the record has a track of microscopic pits that are read by a laser beam instead of a phonograph needle. The polyvinyl chloride disk has a thin coating of aluminum and a protective layer of lacquer.

A low-powered laser in the phonograph scans the track as the record rotates. When the light strikes a pit, a device sends an electrical impulse — representing the digit "1" — to the phonograph's electronic circuits. Where there is no pit, the device sends no impulses to the circuits. No impulse represents a digital "0." The circuits convert these 1s and 0s to electrical waves that resemble the waves produced by a groove-type phonograph record. An ordinary amplifier strengthens the CD system's waves and sends them to speakers.

The CD system has several advantages over a groove-type phonograph. A phonograph needle picks up vibrations from the turntable motor, causing the speaker to emit a rumbling sound. However, the laser device picks up only light rays, so motor vibrations do not affect the CD's performance.

Furthermore, small changes in the speed of the turntable distort the pitch of the sound from a groove-type phonograph record. The faster the record rotates, the higher the pitch — and vice versa. Warps in an ordinary record also affect the rate at which the needle picks up information from the groove, distorting the sound. However, the CD system's pitch depends upon the sequence in which the laser device reads the digits and not on slight changes in the rate at which pits pass beneath the laser device. In addition, dirt can collect in ordinary phonograph record grooves and produce noise, but dirt

The Seiko TV-Watch, *below,* displays black-and-white pictures on a tiny screen that contains liquid crystals – substances that lighten and darken in response to electrical signals. The TV-Watch has a separate receiver and earphones, *below right.*

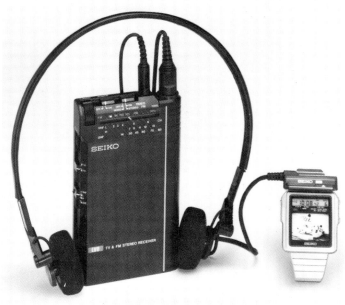

Electronics

Continued

The Yamaha MP-1 Portasound computerized musical keyboard stores music in its memory until the composer completes a tune. It then prints the score.

cannot get into the pits of a lacquer-sealed CD record.

CD players were expected to sell for $800 to $1,200 in the United States, with prices probably declining to $400 or $500 within a year. The disks were expected to cost $15 to $18.

Point and shoot. In October 1982, two companies introduced 35-millimeter single-lens reflex cameras that make abundant use of semiconductor chips to automatically take care of almost all aspects of picture-taking. The Vivitar TEC 35 made by West Electric Corporation of Japan has an integrated circuit that sets the exposure and focus, charges and fires the flash unit, winds and rewinds the film, and operates the frame counter. The camera focuses itself by transmitting an infrared pulse and then measuring the time it takes the pulse to strike the object being photographed and return to the camera.

Visitronic Division of Honeywell Incorporated in Denver announced an automatic focusing system that uses two arrays of 24 extremely sensitive

light detectors called charge-coupled devices (CCDs). Light from the object to be photographed passes through the main lens and then through 48 small lenses to the 2 sets of CCDs. When light strikes the CCDs, they send electrical signals to the camera's microprocessor — a tiny computer — which then uses the signals to compare the light from the two arrays. If the two patterns of light are different, the microprocessor operates a tiny motor to adjust the main lens, thus eliminating the difference and bringing the object into focus.

Computers play a key role at the $900-million Epcot (Experimental Prototype Community of Tomorrow) Center, a Walt Disney theme park that opened on Oct. 1, 1982, in Orlando, Fla. Computers monitor and control the rides and other amusements, the robot versions of Disney cartoon characters, and the park's security, water, and air-conditioning systems.

Visitors can view Sperry Corporation's Univac computer as it handles the major chores of environmental

Make Way for the Robots

A Genus robot patiently awaits its instructions.

Thanks to the ingenuity of semiconductor engineers, computer specialists, and mechanical designers, slavery is on the verge of returning to society. But these slaves will not be human. They are a new breed of machines that will work 24 hours a day without complaint, carry out their duties flawlessly, and require minimum supervision.

These marvelous machines—household robots—made their debut in 1983. Although the robots introduced by several companies in the United States were not capable of performing many useful duties, the future of home robots looks promising. Computer experts foresee the development of increasingly sophisticated robots that will prepare meals and serve guests, clean floors and windows, and load dishes and pots into the dishwasher.

Although mechanical servants have long been a fixture of grade-B science-fiction movies, it was not until the 1960s that the forerunners of household robots appeared. In 1968, the Stanford Research Institute in California unveiled Shakey, a robot that looked somewhat like an air conditioner on wheels. Equipped with a television camera and linked to a computer, Shakey could locate boxes and arrange them in a prescribed pattern. A decade later, researchers at Johns Hopkins Applied Physics Laboratory in Baltimore built a robot that could wheel around a large area, using a TV camera and touch sensors.

But it was the development of the microprocessor—the so-called computer on a chip—that made the household robot possible. Microprocessors are the brains of video games and desktop computers, and they are also an integral part of the new crop of home robots. These include HERO 1, introduced by the Heath Company of Benton Harbor, Mich.; Topo, from Androbot Incorporated in Sunnyvale, Calif.; Genus, built by Robotics International in Jackson, Mich.; and RB5X, named for the RB Robot Corporation in Golden, Colo. All these pioneer robots on wheels can talk, respond to various sounds, and maneuver around a room.

Topo costs $1,000 and can be controlled by a joy stick, similar to those used in video games, or by a computer keyboard. The robot can be programmed with the common computer language BASIC or with more complex languages called Topologo and Topoforth, which Androbot sells on computer diskettes for $125 each. A more intelligent "big brother" to Topo called BOB (Brains On Board) sells for $2,500. BOB comes from the factory already fully programmed. Its components include three microprocessors and an operating system that enables the robot to greet visitors and make its way about the house.

The squatty HERO 1—which stands for Heath Educational Robot—can be programmed to use its arm and clawlike gripper to pour drinks, walk the dog, or lift objects. HERO comes in kit form for $1,500 or fully assembled for $2,500.

Genus, the most expensive of the robots, ranges in price from $5,000 to $12,000. It already can be equipped with a vacuuming attachment. But while the roughly cylindrical robot can push a sweeper around a carpet, it cannot tell if it has done a good job.

RB5X—at $1,500—is a rolling cannister that looks a lot like R2D2 of the *Star Wars* movies. It learns by trial and error to navigate around a room.

Although these new devices may appear to be nothing more than expensive toys, their makers call them educational tools. Computer experts think the market for home robots will grow tremendously as more sophisticated programs become available. Future Computing Incorporated, a market research firm in Richardson, Tex., predicts the sale of personal robots may total a relatively insignificant 2,000 units in 1983. But it expects that sales will soar to more than 100,000 units by 1987 and may reach 1 million by 1990.

Psychologists predict that the robot may eventually become not only a taken-for-granted worker but also a loyal companion for the many lonely people in our society. These electronic friends will play a master-level game of chess, talk, sing, dance, and recite their owners' favorite poetry. Nolan Bushnell, founder of the Atari Company and now chairman of the board of Androbot, introduced BOB to newspaper reporters as "someone, not something." [Howard Bierman]

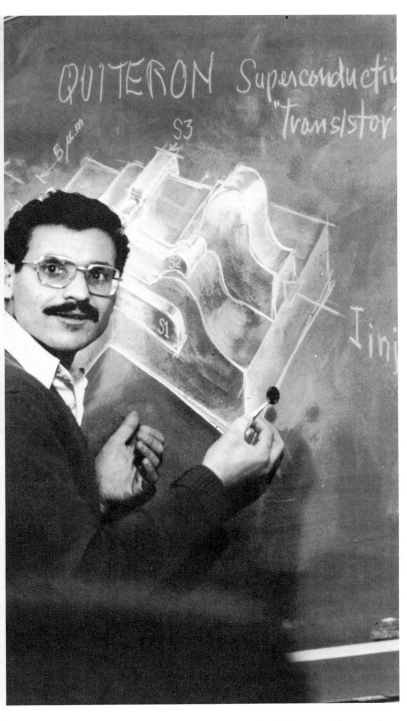

IBM electrical engineer Sadeg M. Faris holds a device containing samples of his invention, called a quiteron. It amplifies and switches electrical signals like a semiconductor transistor but, unlike a semiconductor, conducts current with no electrical resistance at extremely low temperatures. This enables the quiteron to do a semiconductor's job while consuming far less electrical power.

control, entertainment, and information retrieval. Eclipse S/140 computers, products of Data General Corporation, conduct the Astutor Computer Review show, an elaborate production that includes the projection of three-dimensional objects. The computers command animated figures, open huge doors, elevate stage lifts, and operate the lights and curtains. In addition, 29 computer terminals in various areas provide information to visitors.

Electronic weapons. The Falkland Islands conflict between Great Britain and Argentina demonstrated the awesome impact of electronics in battle. On May 4, 1982, an Argentine plane launched a $200,000 computer-controlled Exocet missile that sped over the ocean less than 2 meters (6½ feet) above the surface, thereby avoiding radar detection, and sank the $50-million British destroyer H.M.S. *Sheffield*. The British won the conflict, aided by superior electronic weapons. For example, British Harrier jets, with advanced navigation and tracking equipment, successfully deployed Sidewinder heat-seeking missiles against Argentina's air force.

Among the latest in U.S. electronic weapons is a cruise missile that can make decisions about its course based on information from its TERCOM (terrain contour matching) computerized navigation system. TERCOM has been undergoing field tests since early 1982. The missile's jet engine propels it over treetops and around hills at altitudes of less than 30 meters (100 feet), defying radar detection. It can deliver its armed payload within a square area 3 meters (10 feet) on a side from a range of 2,400 kilometers (1,500 miles).

The TERCOM system uses an electronic map of the missile's flight path. After launch, the missile's sensors scan the ground below and compare the terrain with the data stored in its computer. Deviations from the flight path alert the electronic system to put the missile back on course.

Computer-aided engineering. In 1982 and 1983, the semiconductor industry continued to outdo itself in the production of memory chips — pieces of silicon no larger than a fingernail, containing thousands of built-in electronic

Electronics

Continued

The Fox-Fone
Interceptor screens
incoming calls
electronically. Only
calls accompanied
by special code
numbers will pass its
scrutiny and allow
the telephone to ring.

components that store information. Chips became more complex, smaller, and more reliable. A major change involved the number of components built into a chip. In November 1982, Hewlett-Packard Company of Palo Alto, Calif., introduced computers that use semiconductor chips, each containing 450,000 transistors.

To make further improvements, semiconductor designers are turning to computer-aided engineering. This technique enables a designer to use an engineering database, which consists of information stored in a computer memory along with rules for using this information in design work. In the case of semiconductor design, the information consists of a description of the features and functions of semiconductor devices.

The designer uses the keyboard of a computer terminal to call up the information, which is displayed on a cathode-ray tube (CRT), a device similar to an ordinary television screen. As the designer types in computer-logic diagrams, chip layouts, and information about signal levels of the chip he or she is designing, the CRT display indicates how the chip would perform. Using a computer in this way not only shortens design time, but it also helps overcome a problem facing many companies that design semiconductors and electronic systems — an acute shortage of engineers skilled in chip design. With the aid of engineering databases, many large nonelectronic firms are able to engineer their own integrated circuits.

Fiber link. In February 1983, the American Telephone and Telegraph Company (A.T. & T.) began operating a 600-kilometer (372-mile) fiber optic link between New York City and Washington, D.C. This installation, the world's largest optical communications system, is part of a 1,250-kilometer (776-mile) project that will extend from Cambridge, Mass., to Moseley, Va. This system is expected to begin operating in January 1984.

Fiber optics is the technique of transmitting information on extremely short pulses of laser light along the inside of a thin, flexible glass or plastic fiber. A pair of glass fibers as thin as a human hair can handle 1,300 simul-

taneous telephone conversations. By contrast, a pair of copper wires used in ordinary telephone installations can carry only 24 conversations.

Fiber optics equipment first converts a vocal or other audio signal into an electrical signal. Next, the equipment converts this signal to a series of "on" and "off" pulses representing the digits 0 and 1.

These pulses then travel to a laser, which converts each 1 pulse into a sharp burst of light and each 0 pulse into a space between light bursts. The fiber carries the pulses to their final destination, where a decoder converts the sequence of light pulses back to nondigital electrical form. Finally, an amplifier and speaker convert the electrical signal to an audio signal.

Benefits of fiber optics include the potential for conveying considerably more information than the copper wires used in telephone installations or the coaxial cable used to carry television signals. Furthermore, the fiber is extremely thin and light. A bundle of fibers as thick as a thumb can carry as much information as a 7.5-centimeter (3-inch) bundle of copper wires.

The major drawback is cost — optical fiber costs more than copper wire. However, the cost of fiber optics is declining rapidly.

Other optical installations. In March 1983, A.T. & T. opened a 270-kilometer (168-mile) section of a proposed 1,020-kilometer (633-mile) optical-cable link between Sacramento, Calif., and San Diego. MCI Communications Corporation announced its plan in early 1983 to install a fiber optic system along the right of way of the National Railroad Passenger Corporation (Amtrak) from New York City to Washington, D.C.

Japan's government-operated Nippon Telephone and Telegraph Company (NTT) introduced a powerful optical amplifier in January 1983. Light pulses lose their intensity as they travel along the fiber from one point to another. Amplifiers spaced along the fiber make up for the loss by boosting the weakening signals. While previous optical amplifiers could increase the strength of a signal 200 times, the NTT amplifier can increase it 1,000 times. [Howard Bierman]

Energy

A major event in fusion power research occurred at 3:06 A.M. on Dec. 24, 1982, when scientists at Princeton University's Plasma Physics Laboratory in New Jersey produced their first test plasma — a hot gas made up of free electrons and free atomic nuclei — in the new Tokamak Fusion Test Reactor (TFTR). All the major parts of the $314-million machine worked according to plan. This event represented a major step in the development of a fusion nuclear reactor that will produce electrical power.

Nuclear power plants in operation today produce energy by fission, the splitting of an atomic nucleus into two parts. Fusion reactors will produce energy by combining two atomic nuclei to produce a more massive nucleus. In both types of reactions, subatomic particles called neutrons are emitted, producing heat energy. The first fusion reactors probably will obtain energy from the fusion of deuterium and tritium, two isotopes, or forms, of hydrogen. The device will heat a mixture of the isotopes to a temperature high

enough to make them fuse to form a helium nucleus and give off energy.

The Princeton researchers used ordinary hydrogen, rather than deuterium and tritium, as a test plasma to prevent fusion reactions during the test. Fusion reactions would make the interior of the TFTR radioactive and therefore difficult to use during the experimental period. The plasma lasted for 0.05 second and reached a temperature of 100,000°C. Scientists expect temperatures of more than 100,000,000°C when the TFTR is in full operation.

In October 1982, the Tritium Systems Test Assembly (TSTA) Facility at Los Alamos National Laboratory in New Mexico was dedicated. TFTS will develop technology for handling and processing deuterium and tritium fuel with a major emphasis on safety.

Breeder. On Sept. 22, 1982, workers began to prepare the site for the Clinch River Breeder Reactor Plant on the Clinch River in Oak Ridge, Tenn. The United States Department of Energy will build the reactor and operate

The Tokamak Fusion Test Reactor at the Princeton Plasma Physics Laboratory in New Jersey passed its first operational test on Dec. 24, 1982. It became the world's most advanced device for experiments on the controlled fusion of atomic nuclei – a potential source of vast amounts of cheap electrical power.

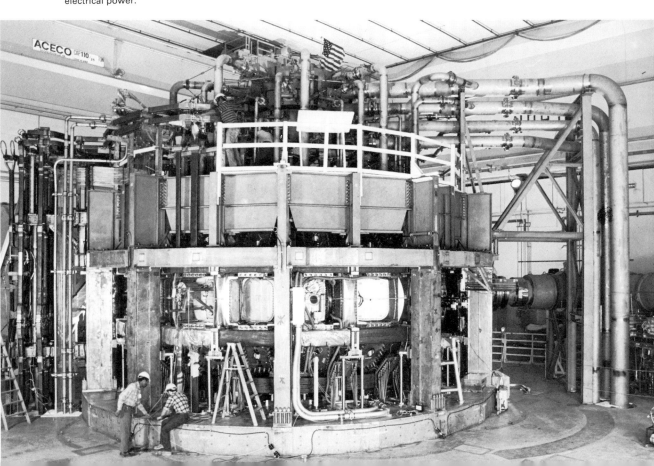

it for five years to demonstrate its safety and reliability, and to determine economic and environmental characteristics of a breeder reactor used as an energy source for electric companies.

A breeder reactor is a fission-type nuclear power plant that "breeds," or produces, more nuclear fuel than it uses. Ordinary nuclear fission power plants obtain energy from the fission of an isotope of uranium known as uranium 235. However, only about 0.71 per cent of the uranium in uranium ore is uranium 235. Most uranium is in the form of the isotope uranium 238, which is not fissionable. Separating the two isotopes is extremely costly, so the uranium used for reactor fuel consists mostly of uranium 238.

A breeder converts uranium 238 to another nuclear fuel, the isotope plutonium 239. Thus, breeders make more efficient use of the energy stored in natural uranium. Breeders can recover as much as 60 times more energy from natural uranium than can conventional nuclear reactors. In fact, processing all the waste uranium 238 stored at uranium enrichment facilities in the United States through a breeder reactor could supply enough energy to satisfy the demand for electricity in the United States for 500 years at present rates of consumption.

The Clinch River reactor will be a liquid metal fast breeder reactor (LMFBR). The reactor is called *fast* because fast neutrons cause the plutonium 239 nucleus to split, releasing energy. An ordinary reactor fueled by uranium 235 uses slow neutrons. A liquid metal—sodium—will transfer heat by circulating around the reactor core. Water does this job in ordinary reactors. Liquid sodium transfers heat more efficiently than does water, and does not slow down the fast neutrons that keep the fission process going.

Another advantage of liquid sodium is that it does not easily vaporize into a gas. It remains liquid at temperatures of 98° to 880°C (208° to 1616°F.) and therefore does not require pressurized piping in a reactor. By contrast, most nuclear power plants in the United States must pressurize the water used to transfer heat.

France, Great Britain, and Russia are already operating experimental

LMFBR plants, and Japan and West Germany plan to open demonstration plants by the mid-1980s. The first commercial-sized LMFBR power plant under construction is the 1,200-megawatt Super Phoenix in France, scheduled to open in 1984.

The Clinch River reactor's completion date was originally set for 1980, but has been rescheduled for 1989. The Clinch River plant will generate 375 megawatts of electrical power, enough for the residential needs of a city of 200,000 people.

Record reaction. Scientists experimented during the year with liquid sodium as a reactor coolant. In November 1982, the Fast Flux Test Facility (FFTF) at the Hanaford Engineering Development Laboratory in Richland, Wash., established a U.S. record of 53 consecutive days at full power for a sodium-cooled fast reactor. The FFTF, which was dedicated in April 1982, is the world's largest experimental sodium-cooled fast reactor. Researchers are using it to test fuels, materials, and components for fast breeder power plants. The reactor neither produces more fuel than it consumes nor generates electricity. The Clinch River reactor will be similar to the FFTF, but 2½ times as large.

The FFTF cooling system contains approximately 730 metric tons (800 short tons) of liquid sodium. The sodium enters the reactor core at 360°C (680°F.) and is heated to 540°C (1000°F.) as it flows past stainless steel tubes that contain the reactor fuel. The sodium is then piped out of the core and the heat is transferred to more sodium in another cooling system. Finally, an air-cooling system dissipates the heat.

Waste conversion. In September 1982, the New Waste Calcining Facility (NWCF) began operating at Idaho National Engineering Laboratory in Idaho Falls. NWCF is the first full-scale plant in the United States that converts into solids highly radioactive and corrosive liquid waste containing aluminum and nitrates from reactor fuel reprocessing plants. The capacity of the NWCF is 11,400 liters (3,000 gallons) per day.

The NWCF reduces the volume of the radioactive waste to one-eighth of

A Cool
Sound

Steam turbines power electrical generating plants. Gasoline engines drive automobiles. Compressors operate appliances such as household refrigerators. Now, a group of scientists at Los Alamos National Laboratory in New Mexico has developed a new type of engine that uses the energy stored in sound waves.

All these machines belong to a class of devices known as heat engines, because heat and energy play major roles in their operation. Heat engines have one of two functions — they produce heat to do mechanical work or they use mechanical work to transfer heat. The engine in your automobile burns a mixture of air and gasoline in the automobile's combustion chambers to create heat and then pressure that pushes pistons.

The cooling system in your electrical refrigerator uses mechanical work to transfer heat from one place to another. A compressor pushes a liquid refrigerant through a valve into a set of pipes or coils called an evaporator where the liquid absorbs heat and turns into a gas. Then the compressor drives the gas into an air-cooled condenser, where the gas turns back into a liquid and gives up heat. The evaporator becomes the coldest spot in the refrigerator; the condenser, the hottest. Thus, compressional work leads to a temperature difference.

The sound engine that physicists Gregory W. Swift, Albert Migliori, Thomas Hofler, and I developed also uses mechanical work to transfer heat and produces temperature differences as high as 100°C (180°F.). However, instead of a compressor, our engine uses a loudspeaker to drive a refrigerant. Because the device uses sound and heat, scientists call it an acoustic heat engine.

We found that sound from the loudspeaker creates a temperature difference between the ends of rectangular fiberglass plates that are stacked like a deck of cards. In a typical experiment, we used a stack of plates that are 10 centimeters (3.9 inches) long, set inside a helium-filled fiberglass tube that is 50 centimeters (20 inches) long and 2.5 centimeters (1 inch) in diameter. Spacers kept the plates 1 millimeter (0.04 inch) apart. One end of the tube

has a permanent cap. Closing the other end is the diaphragm of a loudspeaker, which serves as a piston.

At the beginning of an experiment, the plates are all the same temperature. When we turn on the loudspeaker, the piston vibrates toward and away from the plates at a frequency, or rate of vibration, of 500 cycles per second. This is approximately the frequency of B above middle C on the piano. But the sound waves are about 100,000 times as loud as a voice speaking at a conversational level.

When the piston moves toward the plates, it compresses the helium atoms inside the tube, causing the pressure of the helium gas to rise. The helium atoms simultaneously increase in temperature by a small amount and move a short distance toward the capped end of the tube. Magnetic forces inside the loudspeaker make the piston slow down, stop, then reverse direction. The atoms do the same. At this time, atoms near a plate are hotter than the plate, and so transfer heat to the plate. The atoms then move rapidly away from the direction of the capped end of the tube, as their pressure and temperature drop. As the gas expands, the piston again slows, stops, and reverses direction. The helium atoms again follow suit. However, this time the atoms are colder than the plate, and so the plate transfers heat to them.

Thus, in one oscillation, or back-and-forth cycle of the piston, atoms give heat to the plate when they are nearest to the capped end of the tube and take heat from the plate when they are nearest to the loudspeaker. All the gas atoms act alike, so their effects add up, establishing a temperature difference along the plates. The ends near the loudspeaker become colder than the ends near the cap.

Other experiments suggest that principles of this engine could be applied to make an acoustic engine that would generate electrical power.

The acoustic heat engine is so new that we have not tried to use it in such devices as refrigerators or electrical generators. However, the acoustic heat engine may one day serve not only to provide refrigeration simply and easily, but also to generate electrical power efficiently.   [John Wheatley]

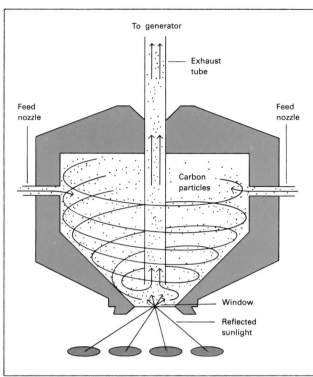

To generator

Exhaust tube

Feed nozzle

Feed nozzle

Carbon particles

Window

Reflected sunlight

Energy

Continued

Energy Converter
Sunlight reflects off mirrors, *above,* into a window at the bottom of the Small Particle Heat Exchange Receiver, (SPHER), *above right,* a solar energy device developed at Lawrence Berkeley Laboratory in California. Carbon particles fed into the SPHER collect heat at the window and transfer it immediately to the surrounding air, forcing the air to rise rapidly through a tube to an air-driven electrical generator.

its initial volume through a process called fluidized-bed calcination. First, the radioactive liquid is sprayed as a fine mist onto a bed of hot granules about the size of coarse sand. The temperature of the granules is 500°C (930°F.). Jets of air lift and agitate the granules so that the liquid waste is distributed evenly. The heat vaporizes the liquid, leaving behind aluminum and nitrates that have combined with oxygen to form oxide coatings on the granules. The coated granules, approximately 0.5 millimeter (0.02 inch) in diameter, are called calcine.

Fans blow the radioactive calcined waste into cylindrical stainless steel tanks encased in reinforced concrete vaults. The storage tanks and concrete vaults have an expected life of 500 years and are designed to withstand natural disasters, such as earthquakes and tornadoes. The gases from the calciner vessel pass through cleaning, scrubbing, and filtering equipment before being vented into the atmosphere.

Cooler cycle. In November 1982, construction started on a new type of

geothermal electrical power plant in Heber, Calif. Geothermal plants harness the energy in hot, pressurized water trapped in underground rocks. Geothermal wells are drilled into areas where such water is trapped and the water is pumped out.

Most geothermal plants now operating in the United States use the flash cycle, in which the water passes into a tank where it boils, or flashes, into steam. The steam then drives a turbine generator, producing electricity. A major disadvantage of the flash cycle is that the water must be extremely hot. Four out of five geothermal reservoirs in the United States have temperatures below 200°C (400°F.), which is too low for the flash cycle.

The Heber plant will use water that comes from the ground at a temperature of 180°C (360°F.) to heat and vaporize chemicals that vaporize at a much lower temperature than water. The mixture will consist of 90 per cent isobutane and 10 per cent isopentane. This vapor will then drive a turbine to produce electricity. Finally, pumps

Energy

will inject the water back into the ground at about 70°C (160°F.).

The turbine generator can produce 70 megawatts of electrical power. San Diego Gas and Electric will operate the plant at full capacity for a two-year demonstration period beginning in January 1986.

The geothermal reservoir near the plant covers an area of 3,000 hectares (7,400 acres). The maximum temperature of the water is about 190°C (375°F.). Experts estimate that the reservoir contains enough heat to provide more than 500 megawatts of power for 30 years.

Better exchange. During the fall of 1982, the U.S. Department of Energy successfully tested the prototype of a new kind of solar energy device at its Advanced Component Test Facility at Georgia Institute of Technology in Atlanta. The device, developed by physicist Arlon J. Hunt of Lawrence Berkeley Laboratory in California and called the Small Particle Heat Exchange Receiver (SPHER), uses solar energy to heat air. It operates on the same principle as solar boilers.

Sunlight reflects off 550 mirrors, each 1 meter (3 feet) in diameter, beneath the cylindrical SPHER container. The mirrors focus the light so that it enters the SPHER through a window that is 20 centimeters (8 inches) in diameter. Flowing past the window inside the container is a rapid stream of air containing black particles of carbon, each less than one-thousandth of a millimeter in diameter.

The black particles are heated by the sunlight and in turn heat the air. The heat exchange is highly efficient because the particles have a large total surface area. For example, 1 gram of particles has a surface area of 50 square meters, equivalent to 15,000 square feet per ounce. The maximum air temperature recorded during the experimental program was 750°C (1380°F.) and the output of electrical energy exceeded 30 kilowatts.

According to Hunt, a SPHER that supplied enough hot air to generate electricity for 10,000 homes would use only about 5 kilograms (11 pounds) of carbon particles per hour.

Solar storage. In November 1982, the Research Center of Gould, Incorporated, in Rolling Meadows, Ill., announced the development of a sealed, maintenance-free lead-acid battery that stores energy collected by solar cells. One of the limitations of solar cells has been the lack of an efficient energy-storage system that could release the stored electrical energy at night or during cloudy days.

Ordinary sealed lead-acid batteries wear out too quickly. However, tests of a prototype of the new battery at Sandia National Laboratories in Albuquerque, N. Mex., indicated that the battery will last from 5 to 7 years when 80 per cent of its stored energy is discharged daily.

Super cables. Researchers experimented with flexible superconducting power transmission cables at Brookhaven National Laboratory (BNL) on Long Island, N.Y., during the winter of 1982-1983. Because superconducting cables lose their electrical resistance at extremely low temperatures, a superconductor of a given size can carry five times as much current as an ordinary cable.

The BNL researchers built their flexible cable by winding niobium-tin tape around a bronze core, then wrapping plastic electrical insulation around the tape. They then placed two 130-meter (430-foot) lengths of superconducting cable side by side in a chamber that was 40 centimeters (16 inches) in diameter. The experimenters cooled the cables to about 8°C (14°F.) above absolute zero (-273.15°C or -459.67°F.) by pumping cold helium gas through the chamber.

They tested the cables with a current of 4,100 amperes and a voltage of 80 kilovolts, which matches the output of a nuclear power station, and found the system to be extremely efficient in transporting electrical energy. The operation of the cooling system required only about 1 to 2 per cent of the amount of power transmitted through the cable for every 161 kilometers (100 miles) of cable.

The cable is flexible enough to wind on a standard reel used for ordinary power transmission cable, so a power company would not need to use completely new equipment and techniques to install this type of superconducting cable.   [Marian Visich, Jr.]

Environment

Toxic substances that take decades to show their deadly effects caused increasing environmental concern in the United States during 1982 and 1983. As a result of their long latency periods, a number of hazardous substances came into wide use before their dangers were fully recognized. A growing number of people found themselves faced with major health problems resulting from exposure to toxic materials decades ago. See LAYING WASTE IN AMERICA.

Asbestos is one example of a substance whose full dangers were belatedly recognized. Victims of asbestos-caused disease increasingly sought court settlements during 1982.

The Manville Corporation, the largest U.S. asbestos producer, faced more than 15,000 health-damage suits at an average settlement cost of $40,000. Threatened with this potential financial loss, the company filed for bankruptcy on Aug. 26, 1982, thus suspending payments to all victims. Another asbestos firm, UNR Industries, Incorporated, took similar action on July 29, 1982, to obtain relief from approximately 12,000 lawsuits.

Asbestos is a naturally occurring mineral fiber used in many products for its heat-resistant properties. It is used in asbestos-cement sheets for roofing and walls and in fire-retardant textiles and paint. In addition, the fibers are employed in brake linings for cars and trucks, in hulls of ships, and in power plants.

Wherever asbestos is used, tiny wirelike fragments of the mineral break off through friction and become airborne. These airborne particles may be inhaled and lodge deep in the lungs. Over a period of 10 to 40 years, the embedded fragments damage lung tissue and cause scarring that clogs the lungs, producing a disease called asbestosis. Over a similar period, people exposed to asbestos may also develop a deadly form of cancer known as mesothelioma, which affects the linings of the chest and abdomen.

Researchers have also linked asbestos with cancers of the digestive system, larynx, and kidneys. About

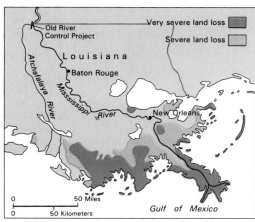

Louisiana's Vanishing Marshlands
Eroded by the Gulf of Mexico, the marshes on Louisiana's southern coast are rapidly disappearing, *above*. Environmental damage is aggravated by canals cut across the wetlands to facilitate oil drilling, *left*. The canals allow salt water from the Gulf to seep into the freshwater marshes and kill many plants and animals.

Clouds of toxic smoke billow from tank cars in Livingston, La., where a freight train carrying hazardous chemicals derailed on Sept. 28, 1982. The accident caused fires and explosions that lasted for days and forced the evacuation of about 3,000 people.

Environment

Continued

250,000 Americans will die of asbestos-related diseases in the next 20 years.

The problems caused by asbestos are particularly evident in workers who mine asbestos, manufacture asbestos products, or install asbestos insulation. The thousands of workers that have sued asbestos producers for health damages claim that industry officials knew about the dangers of asbestos as long ago as the 1930s but withheld this information.

A new source of airborne asbestos was revealed in June 1982 by French scientists at the Department of Sanitary and Social Affairs of Paris. The scientists reported that hazardous levels of asbestos fibers can come from floors covered with vinyl asbestos tile. The researchers found that normal foot traffic on such floors can release enough asbestos fibers into the air to equal the dangerous levels in buildings with sprayed-on asbestos insulation.

2,4,5-T. Another toxic compound in the environment linked to widespread health problems in 1982 and 1983 was the herbicide 2,4,5-trichlorophenoxy-acetic acid (2,4,5-T). The weedkiller contains traces of dioxin, perhaps the most poisonous chemical known to science. Studies have demonstrated that extremely small quantities of dioxin may cause cancer or birth defects in animals.

The United States used 2,4,5-T as part of a mixture called Agent Orange during the Vietnam War. Between the early 1960s and the early 1970s, U.S. planes sprayed millions of acres of Vietnamese farms and forests with Agent Orange to destroy enemy food crops and cover. Thousands of U.S. veterans of the Vietnam War have since suffered health problems ranging from skin disorders and tremors to cancer and genetic defects. Approximately 15,000 of them have filed claims with the Veterans Administration (VA) for service-connected disabilities attributed to Agent Orange. Until 1982, when a new law made veterans exposed to herbicides eligible for treatment, the VA refused to honor those claims because there are few scientific studies of the effects of dioxin

EPA: Can We Protect the Protector?

In early 1983, the Administration of U.S. President Ronald Reagan was rocked by a scandal within the Environmental Protection Agency (EPA). At issue was whether top officials of the agency were protecting industrial polluters instead of the environment.

The EPA had been created by the Congress of the United States in December 1970 in response to a growing public demand for a cleaner environment. The new agency was given the task of curbing poisons and pollutants released into the air and water by establishing and enforcing environmental protection rules and conducting research on the effects of pollutants. The EPA was also given the task of aiding the cleanup of the worst toxic-waste dump sites in the United States. Toward this end, Congress set up a $1.6-billion Superfund in December 1980. See LAYING WASTE IN AMERICA.

By March 1983, six congressional committees were investigating charges that EPA officials had mismanaged the Superfund. As the scandal widened, half a dozen key EPA officials, notably EPA Administrator Anne Gorsuch Burford, had resigned or been fired. In an effort to undo some of the damage to the EPA's image, Reagan announced in March that William D. Ruckelshaus, who had been the EPA's first administrator, was again taking command of the agency.

Many environmental groups advocate removing the EPA from the executive branch of the government. One group has started a national petition drive asking Congress to reorganize the EPA as a truly independent agency. Environmentalists hope such a move would solve a basic question that has underlain the entire EPA controversy: How can an agency that should be making decisions solely on the basis of scientific data avoid being influenced by politicians and special-interest groups? [David L. Dreier]

Environment

Continued

on human beings and a cause-and-effect relationship is difficult to trace.

Contaminated town. In December 1982, large quantities of dioxin were discovered in the soil of Times Beach, Mo., where it had been sprayed in 1971 in an oil mixture used to control dust on unpaved roads. Levels of dioxin occur in the soil there at concentrations 100 times greater than federal standards for safe levels.

On Feb. 22, 1983, the United States Environmental Protection Agency (EPA) announced it would spend about $35 million to buy the entire town of Times Beach so that families and businesses could relocate. Between 25 and 100 other Missouri sites were also being investigated for contamination.

Waste-eating bacteria may aid in cleaning up toxic substances that are now widely dispersed in the environment. During 1983, microbiologist Ananda M. Chakrabarty and his colleagues at the University of Illinois Medical Center in Chicago continued efforts to create a new strain of bacteria able to break down dioxin into harmless waste products.

Chakrabarty and his co-workers built upon genetic-engineering techniques they had used in 1981 to develop a strain of bacteria that consumes 2,4,5-T. They gathered bacteria from Love Canal, N.Y., and other toxic-waste dump sites, then combined the dump-site bacteria with bacteria that could break down complex hydrocarbons and chlorine compounds.

Bacteria contain rings of genetic material called plasmids that exchange genes fairly easily, allowing new strains of bacteria to evolve. The scientists reasoned that if they slowly starved the microbes and added increasingly higher concentrations of 2,4,5-T, this would in effect speed up evolution by forcing the bacteria to incorporate new genes and evolve into a strain that could use 2,4,5-T as food. Experiments confirmed their theory. Chakrabarty believes that bacteria might be developed to attack the insecticide dichloro-diphenyl-trichloroethane (DDT); industrial wastes such

Environment

Continued

as polychlorinated biphenyls (PCBs); and other toxic compounds.

Eagles regain fertility. In December 1982, zoologist James W. Grier of North Dakota State University in Fargo reported encouraging results from a 16-year study of the effects of DDT on the bald eagle population in northwestern Ontario, Canada. In the United States, the EPA banned the use of DDT in 1972, because the insecticide harms wildlife and remains in the environment for decades.

One of the species most threatened by DDT was the bald eagle. DDT contaminated the fish and other prey eaten by the eagles. An accumulation of DDT in the eagles' bodies caused them to lay eggs with such thin shells that the eggs cracked under the weight of the parent birds, killing the eaglets before they hatched. Grier found that the eagles in Ontario were recovering from DDT contamination and regaining their former levels of fertility much faster than predicted.

The monitoring of toxic-waste dumps to detect leakage of pollutants into ground water will be made cheaper and easier by a new technique employing fiber optics, according to a November 1982 report by chemist Tomas B. Hirschfeld of Lawrence Livermore National Laboratory in Livermore, Calif. Fiber-optic cables — bundles of thin, flexible glass strands that carry light beams — were first developed for communication signals.

Hirschfeld's technique uses a fiber-optic cable to carry a laser beam down to the level of ground water under a toxic-waste dump. Chemically contaminated water fluoresces — gives off light — when it absorbs energy from the laser beam, whereas clean water does not. The same cable that delivered the laser energy detects any light emitted by polluted water.

Fiber-optic technology could save as much as $500,000 per year in monitoring costs at an average toxic-waste dump site. Other pollution-control applications are now being developed for fiber optics, including the detection of uranium and plutonium leaks at nuclear plants.   [Walt Westman]

Genetics

The first convincing example of genetic engineering in mammals was reported in December 1982. A group of scientists in the United States, using gene-transfer techniques, bred rat-sized mice from normal mice by inserting a rat growth-hormone gene into fertilized mouse egg cells.

The group included researchers from the University of Washington in Seattle, the University of Pennsylvania in Philadelphia, the University of California in San Diego, and the Salk Institute in La Jolla, Calif. The scientists began by fusing part of a mouse gene with a rat gene, then producing copies of the combined gene in bacteria. The rat gene coded for a growth hormone; the mouse gene coded for a protein called metallothionein, whose function is to rid the body of heavy metals.

The metallothionein gene has two parts — a production segment that codes for the manufacture of the protein and a control segment that responds to elevated levels of metal in the mouse by ordering more of the protein to be produced. The researchers reasoned that by splicing the control segment of the metallothionein gene to the rat growth-hormone gene, they would obtain a growth-hormone gene that could be turned on by metal. A mouse with the hybrid gene in its cells would then produce more growth hormone if the metal in its diet were increased.

The scientists used an enzyme to cut the metallothionein gene into its two segments. They used a different enzyme to attach the control segment to a rat growth-hormone gene whose own control region had been removed. The researchers then injected the spliced gene into the nuclei of newly fertilized mouse eggs and implanted the eggs into mouse foster mothers.

Twenty-one baby mice developed from the eggs; only seven of these mice carried the spliced gene. To the researchers' surprise, four of the mice had more than one copy of the spliced gene. One mouse had 8 copies; one had 10; one, 20; and one, 35.

The mouse with 35 copies of the growth-hormone gene died seven

Two mice from the same litter show the effect of a growth-rate hormone gene that was injected into fertilized mouse eggs. The smaller mouse did not acquire the gene. The larger mouse did.

Genetics

Continued

weeks after birth. The others grew to adulthood and, by the time they were 74 days old, two of them were almost twice normal size. As expected, the mice had very high levels of growth hormone in their bodies. About 50 per cent of the giant mice's offspring inherited the special gene, and those mice also grew to be about twice the size of normal mice.

To see whether the spliced gene would cause the mice to grow faster than normal, the scientists had fed them a special diet containing a large amount of zinc. Six of the seven mice with the spliced gene grew faster than their normal litter mates. But they had begun to grow faster even before getting the zinc-laced diet, so the metal's role in the experiment is uncertain.

The scientists then created a spliced gene using a human growth-hormone gene. Mice receiving that gene also grew to be about twice normal size. If a similar gene technique can be used in farm animals, farmers could look forward to producing lines of oversized, rapidly growing livestock.

Jumping genes. Another important gene-transfer experiment was carried out in 1982 by scientists at the Carnegie Institution of Washington's Department of Embryology in Baltimore. Geneticists Allan C. Spradling and Gerald M. Rubin announced in October that they had changed the eye color of a strain of fruit flies as part of a study of so-called jumping genes.

Genes are made of deoxyribonucleic acid (DNA) and are located on chromosomes, threadlike objects in the nucleus of a cell. Some strains of fruit flies carry DNA segments called transposons. These are also called jumping genes because they can change their position from one place to another on the chromosomes.

Spradling and Rubin chose to work with a transposon called the P element, which changes position frequently. They reasoned that if newly fertilized fruit fly eggs could be injected with DNA carrying the P element, then the P element might jump from the injected DNA into the chromosomes. The fly that subsequently

Genetics

Continued

developed would have the P element in all of its cells.

The P element has no visible effect on a fly, so Spradling and Rubin used a gene that produces red eyes in fruit flies as a marker to test their hypothesis. They spliced the eye-color gene into the P element, then injected the spliced gene into fertilized eggs from a strain of flies with brown eyes. Flies that had incorporated the spliced P element gene into their chromosomes would therefore have red eyes instead of brown eyes. From 45 injected eggs, the scientists got 19 flies with red eyes. Those flies produced offspring that also had red eyes, showing that the gene was being passed on.

Cattle sexing. Researchers at Genetic Engineering in Denver announced in January 1983 that they had developed a method for determining the sex of week-old cattle embryos. The procedure is based on the work of molecular biologist Thomas E. Wagner of Ohio University in Athens.

American cattle breeders usually remove the embryo from a valuable female a week after conception so that the cow can quickly become pregnant again. The removed embryo is inserted into the uterus of a less valuable cow called a foster mother, where it completes its development in about nine months. But farmers had no way of knowing the sex of an embryo.

The Genetic Engineering method provides an easy test of an embryo's sex by using a particular antibody. Antibodies are protein molecules that seek out and attach to anything foreign to the body.

Wagner isolated the antibody used in this method. It only attaches to a protein called HY, which is produced by male embryos. To determine the sex of a cattle embryo, the embryo is immersed in a solution containing the antibody. If the antibody attaches, the embryo is male; if it does not attach, the embryo is female. This will allow farmers to decide which embryos to inject into foster mothers and which to destroy. Generally, dairy farmers want female calves, while beef farmers want male calves.   [Daniel L. Hartl]

Geology
See Earth Sciences

Immunology

In 1982 and 1983, immunologists made rapid progress in understanding the mechanisms of the body's defense against disease. These investigations, however, were overshadowed by the appearance of an unusual array of infectious diseases and cancers in previously healthy persons. These conditions have been given the collective name of acquired immune deficiency syndrome (AIDS).

Under normal circumstances, the human immune system easily and routinely destroys a wide array of invading bacteria, fungi, and viruses. Therefore, these organisms usually do not cause disease. But persons who are born with a less effective immune system, or whose immunity is impaired by disease or drugs, are susceptible to ravaging infections by many ordinarily harmless organisms.

In June 1981, the Centers for Disease Control (CDC) in Atlanta, Ga., began to document reports of such infections that had appeared in previously healthy persons in late 1979 and early 1980. CDC officials also learned that a rare type of skin cancer called Kaposi's sarcoma, which most often afflicts older people, was occurring with unprecedented frequency in young adults. The CDC soon discovered that AIDS was affecting four distinct groups: male homosexuals, intravenous drug users, Haitian refugees, and hemophiliacs — persons whose blood lacks clotting ability.

By May 1983, more than 1,400 Americans in 35 states had contracted AIDS, and more than 500 had died. The disease also had been detected in 16 other countries.

Studies of AIDS victims' blood revealed a harmful imbalance in the amounts of two varieties of T lymphocytes, a type of white blood cell. The two types of T cells perform opposite functions. Helper T cells, which normally make up 40 to 60 per cent of all T cells in the blood, boost immune activity. Another 15 to 30 per cent are suppressor T cells, which dampen immune activity. In AIDS patients, the situation is reversed, with suppressor T cells predominating.

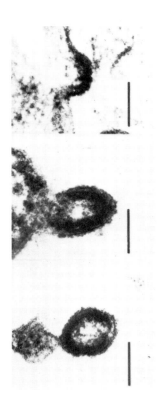

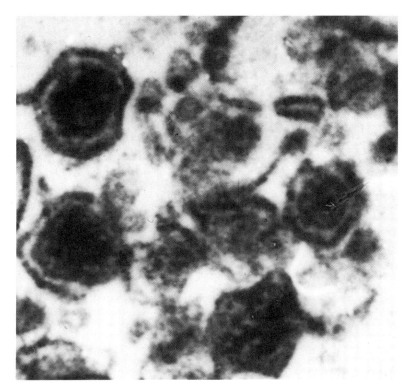

Immunology

Continued

Human T-cell leukemia virus (HTLV), *above right* (magnified 35,000 times), isolated from a cancerous white blood cell, is the first virus to be directly implicated in a human cancer. A newly created HTLV (magnified 75,000 times) "buds" through the membrane of a white blood cell, *above left*.

The cause of AIDS remains a mystery, although most investigators believe that an infectious agent, such as a virus, may be responsible. Why the disease has been mostly restricted to such clearly defined groups is also unclear. Researchers suspect that promiscuous male homosexuals could transmit the infectious agent through multiple sexual contacts, much like a venereal disease. Hemophiliacs, who often require blood-clotting factors and transfusions, apparently can pick up AIDS from donor blood. Intravenous drug users, who often share needles and syringes, may be transmitting the organism in that manner. The fact that many Haitians have contracted AIDS may mean that the disease originated in Haiti and was contracted by vacationing American homosexuals.

In April 1983, medical researcher Jane Teas of Harvard University's School of Public Health in Boston theorized that AIDS is caused by a new strain of a virus that has been infecting Haitian pigs for several years. Teas said a number of Haitians could

have picked up the virus by eating sausage encased in infected (uncooked) pig intestines. A few of those Haitians might have been homosexuals who then transmitted the virus to American homosexuals visiting Haiti.

In May, several scientists reported finding evidence that AIDS might be caused by a virus that also causes a form of leukemia. Others suspect that cytomegalovirus, a herpesvirus, may be involved (see HERPES IS FOREVER).

Hepatitis vaccine. In July 1982, the U.S. Food and Drug Administration approved a new vaccine for the prevention of hepatitis B. This disease, which is caused by a virus, affects the liver and can sometimes be fatal. Persons who have had hepatitis B may carry the virus in their blood for years, during which time they can transmit the disease to other people.

The vaccine is derived from the blood plasma of hepatitis B carriers. More than 19,000 persons have received the hepatitis B vaccine.

Monoclonal antibodies. In 1982 and 1983, physicians began using mono-

Getting Over the Measles

Oct. 1, 1982, was the target date for the elimination of measles within the United States, set four years earlier by the secretary of health, education, and welfare (HEW). Public health officials were greatly encouraged at the start of 1982, when the week of January 8 to 15 was the first in 70 years of record keeping in which no U.S. measles cases were reported. However, despite the fact that progress continued to be made in fighting the disease, the measles-free record was spotted by outbreaks later in 1982 and in 1983.

Measles, or rubeola, is caused by a virus. In most cases, the symptoms are mild, last about 10 days, and include a rash and fever. But measles can lead to such serious complications as pneumonia; middle ear infections; encephalitis, or inflammation of the brain; and central nervous system disorders. According to the Centers for Disease Control in Atlanta, Ga., 1 out of every 2,000 measles cases in the United States leads to mental retardation or permanent brain damage, and 1 in 3,000 cases results in death.

A serious central nervous system disease called subacute sclerosing panencephalitis may be related to measles. This devastating disorder may show up several years after a person has recovered from measles, first causing muscle spasms and later, convulsions, insanity, coma, and death.

Pregnant women who catch measles may suffer spontaneous abortion, or miscarriage. The disease can also cause premature labor and result in newborns of below-average weight.

Measles is responsible for an estimated 500,000 deaths per year worldwide. In some countries, it is the leading cause of death in children under 5 years old.

For all these reasons, physicians applauded the development of a killed-virus measles vaccine in 1963 and of the more effective weakened-virus vaccine developed two years later. After vaccination of children began in 1963, the number of measles cases in the United States dropped dramatically from about 500,000 per year to 22,000 cases in 1974 and 1,697 cases in 1982. But there was a rise in measles from 1974 to 1976 — when money for vaccination was diverted to other diseases.

A special antimeasles strategy was then introduced as part of HEW's highly successful Childhood Immunization Initiative begun in 1977. The program proposed to achieve and maintain high levels of immunity, to know who was susceptible, to know where the disease was, and to respond promptly to all occurrences.

For the most part, that strategy succeeded. Today all 50 states require children to show proof of immunization against measles and other childhood diseases before entering school. Forty states require such proof through grade 12. State and local health departments maintain active surveillance programs, calling physicians and clinics to inquire about patients complaining of "fever and rash."

Much success has rewarded these efforts. From 1963 to 1983, there was a 99.7 per cent reduction in the number of U.S. measles cases.

But even now, not everyone is protected. Young adults in their late teens to early 20s who entered kindergarten before the mandatory school immunization laws were enacted have become the most likely measles victims. The 15- to 19-year-old age group is more likely than others to suffer serious complications, and older measles victims are more likely to die from it.

Consequently, what used to be a common illness in kindergarten has become a worrisome threat in college dormitories. In 1982, HEW's goal of a measles-free nation suffered a setback when large outbreaks of measles occurred at colleges in Texas and Arkansas. Early in 1983, outbreaks occurred among college students in Indiana.

Such outbreaks tend to result from measles virus brought into the United States by visitors from other countries or by Americans returning from trips abroad. For this reason, measles will not be totally eradicated in the United States until it is conquered in other countries as well. Measles can be highly controlled, but " . . . only a continued aggressive program will keep up our defenses," warned Richard S. Schweiker, former U.S. secretary of health and human services. "Immunization maintenance must be a cornerstone of our health plans for the future." [Elizabeth Pennisi]

Immunology

Continued

clonal antibodies to treat certain diseases, including some forms of leukemia, a cancer of white blood cells. Antibodies are proteins that recognize and bind to foreign antigens, such as bacteria or viruses.

Monoclonal antibodies are great quantities of a particular antibody mass-produced in laboratories by genetic engineering techniques. A monoclonal antibody is tailor-made to recognize one particular antigen. Monoclonal antibodies are thus able to seek out and destroy one kind of cell while leaving all other cells unharmed.

In early 1982, a team of physicians led by immunologist Fred Rosen of Harvard University in Cambridge, Mass., used monoclonal antibodies to treat a child born without a normal immune system. The child had accidentally been given a blood transfusion, and some of the white cells in the donated blood attacked the child's own cells. A normal immune system would have destroyed the foreign white cells. Since the child lacked normal immunity, the Harvard team prepared monoclonal antibodies that would do the job. They injected the child with these antibodies, which attached to and eliminated the white cells in the transfused blood.

Researchers experimenting with monoclonal antibodies in the treatment of leukemia found that the antibodies are able to eliminate cancerous cells but leave normal cells alone. However, they still cannot predict the long-term outlook for leukemia patients receiving this therapy.

Researchers are also using monoclonal antibodies to prevent the immune systems of organ-transplant patients from rejecting the foreign tissue.

Cyclosporin A. Researchers at medical centers throughout the United States in 1982 and 1983 were involved in testing a new drug that may be able to prevent the body from rejecting a transplanted organ without completely shutting down the immune system. The drug, cyclosporin A, seems to be able to eliminate the T cells that attack foreign tissue while leaving other immune cells intact.   [Paul Katz]

Medicine

Dentistry. Swedish researchers reported in March 1983 that reducing the concentration of the *Streptococcus mutans* bacteria in the saliva of parents may help prevent tooth decay in their children. *S. mutans* is the chief cause of tooth decay.

Because these bacteria are not present in infants' mouths before their first teeth begin to come in, some researchers had theorized that the mother or father may be the source of the infection. Studies supporting this theory showed that the concentration of *S. mutans* in young children's saliva closely matched the concentration of the bacteria in their parents' saliva. It was presumed that the mother or father transmits the infection to their children by kissing or by sharing food or eating utensils.

The researchers at the University of Göteborg in Sweden attempted to determine if reducing the concentration of *S. mutans* in highly infected adults would prevent the infection in their children. They divided 87 highly infected mothers into two groups. Mothers in the experimental group had their teeth professionally cleaned and treated with fluoride and their cavities filled. These mothers were also counseled about avoiding foods that aid the growth of the bacteria and received instructions on oral hygiene. Mothers in the control group received no professional treatment and followed no set program of oral hygiene.

Only 35 per cent of the infants of mothers in the experimental group became infected with *S. mutans*, compared with 65 per cent of the infants of mothers in the control group. The researchers attributed infections of children in the experimental group to the mothers' poor cooperation in the oral hygiene program or to high bacterial concentrations in the saliva of the infants' fathers. The researchers concluded that reducing or eliminating *S. mutans* in parents may be an important method of preventing tooth decay in children. They also speculated that such action could slow the spread of the infection through the entire population.   [Paul Goldhaber]

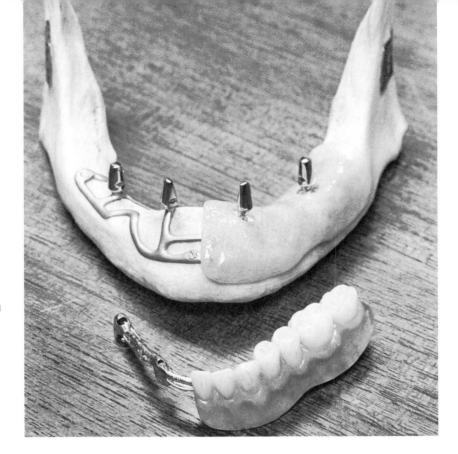

A metal frame implanted under the gums of a jawbone weakened by disease provides a base for pegs onto which artificial teeth are fixed.

Medicine

Continued

Internal Medicine. In March 1983, Jose M. Belizan and co-workers at the Institute of Nutrition of Central America and Panama and the Johns Hopkins University School of Hygiene and Public Health in Baltimore reported that increased calcium intake can lower blood pressure in young adults.

High blood pressure, or hypertension, the most common medical problem among adult Americans, is the leading cause of stroke and heart attack. Antihypertensive drugs can both lower blood pressure and reduce cardiovascular disease, which affects the heart and blood vessels. However, these drugs can produce unpleasant side effects. So researchers are interested in new forms of treatment.

The idea that more calcium in the diet might control blood pressure grew from studies showing that residents in areas with hard water, which contains high levels of calcium, have less cardiovascular disease than do people living in areas with soft water.

Some researchers have theorized that this might be due to a lower inci-

dence of hypertension. However, their studies never established a firm relationship between hard water and blood pressure levels. Belizan and his colleagues speculated that since water accounts for no more than 10 to 15 per cent of total daily calcium intake, significantly higher calcium intakes were needed to demonstrate the possible relationship between calcium and blood pressure.

To test this hypothesis, the researchers divided healthy volunteers, aged 18 to 35, into two groups. The members of both groups had similar medical histories, blood pressure, and blood chemistry. One group received 1 gram of calcium daily for 22 weeks; the other group received a placebo, or inert substance. The volunteers' calcium intake from food was also measured to estimate total calcium consumption for the two groups.

By the end of the study, blood pressure had declined by 5 to 9 per cent in both males and females taking the calcium tablets. Although the researchers were unable to explain this effect, they speculated that the increased amount of calcium may suppress the amount of parathyroid hormone secreted in the body. This hormone, which regulates the removal of calcium from the bones and its release into the bloodstream, can also cause the arteries to constrict. Thus, reducing parathyroid levels may lead to a relaxation of the arteries and a drop in blood pressure.

If this is true, the normal adult diet may be deficient in calcium and thus contribute to high blood pressure.

Good news about oral contraceptives. Oral contraceptives do not increase a woman's chances of developing breast and ovarian cancer, according to three long-term studies reported in March 1983 by the Centers for Disease Control (CDC) in Atlanta, Ga.

The first study investigated the association between the pill and breast cancer, the most common form of cancer in U.S. women. Among the factors known to increase the chances of developing breast cancer are early menstruation, first pregnancy at an older age, and late menopause. Because

these are all related to hormonal changes, researchers suspected that oral contraceptives, which contain the female sex hormones estrogen and progesterone, might increase the likelihood of developing breast cancer. The use of oral contraceptives has been widespread for about 20 years, so researchers believed sufficient time had passed for them to obtain reliable results in their investigations.

The CDC study compared a group of 689 women who had breast cancer with 1,077 who did not. The percentage of women using oral contraceptives was the same in both groups. The study revealed that women who had taken oral contraceptives over a long period of time were no more likely to develop breast cancer than were women who did not take the pill.

A similar CDC study focused on ovarian cancer. This type of cancer is far less common than breast cancer, but there are still 18,000 new cases and 11,000 deaths in the United States each year. Ovarian cancer seems to be more common in childless women or

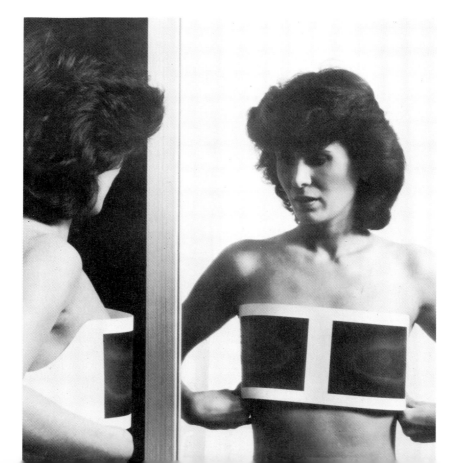

A new breast examination method called Thermascan uses heat-sensitive foil to detect the presence of disease. When wrapped around the breasts, the device produces colored patterns corresponding to the temperature of various parts of the breast. Abnormal temperatures may reveal the presence of such abnormalities as tumors or cysts.

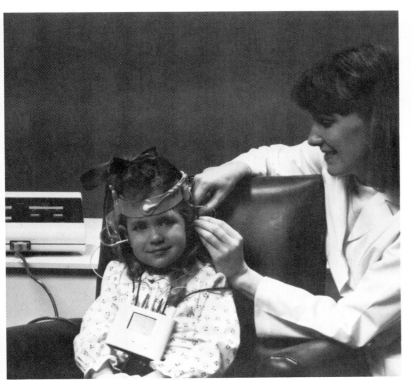

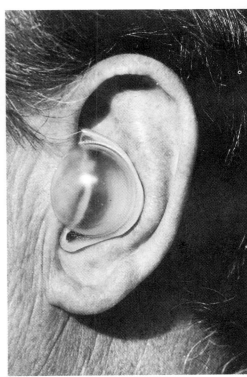

Medicine

Continued

Electrodes placed in the ear canal of a child, *above,* can detect hearing loss in children too young to describe what they hear. The electrodes transmit sounds and the brain responds with electrical signals that appear on a display unit suspended around the child's neck. A new device to improve hearing in patients with mild hearing loss fits into the ear canal, *above right.* It amplifies high-frequency sounds.

women with few children, suggesting that pregnancy has a protective effect.

When 179 women aged 20 to 54 suffering from ovarian cancer were compared with 1,642 women who had no history of the disease, researchers found that rates of ovarian cancer among oral contraceptive users were about 50 per cent lower. Based on these data, researchers calculated that oral contraceptive use prevents 1,700 cases of ovarian cancer in the United States each year.

A third CDC study revealed that oral contraceptives also seem to provide some protection against endometrial, or uterine, cancer, which attacks 39,000 American women each year and causes about 3,000 deaths. Oral contraceptive users were 50 per cent less likely to develop this type of cancer than were nonusers. However, the benefit was limited to women who had taken the pill for at least one year. Childless users benefited the most.

Another report in October 1982 by a team led by epidemiologist J. P. Banderbroucke of Erasmus University

in Rotterdam, the Netherlands, suggested an additional benefit of oral contraceptives. The researchers found, in a study of women in the Netherlands, that oral contraceptive use seems to reduce by 50 per cent the risk of developing rheumatoid arthritis.

Other new evidence shows that earlier reports of cardiovascular disease in oral contraceptive users may have been greatly exaggerated. Users under age 35 rarely develop blood clots in the veins, high blood pressure, or heart disease. Users over age 35 run a slightly higher risk.

Alzheimer's disease. In January 1983, researchers at Johns Hopkins University in Baltimore announced that a chemical defect in the brain may be the cause of Alzheimer's disease, a progressive brain disorder characterized by loss of memory, learning ability, and judgment. The disease affects 10 to 15 per cent of Americans over age 65, or about 4 million people. About half of all patients in nursing homes are victims of this disabling senility. In part because of

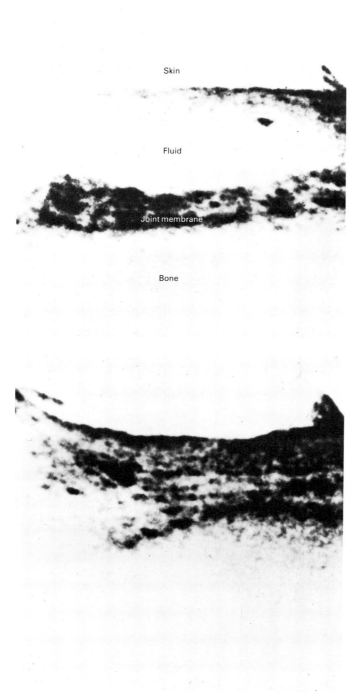

Skin

Fluid

Joint membrane

Bone

Ultrasound pictures of a knee inflamed by arthritis before treatment, *top,* and after, *above,* can provide an objective way for physicians to determine the amount of inflammation in a joint and the effectiveness of the medication.

the Johns Hopkins discovery, scientists believe that an effective treatment will be found for Alzheimer's disease.

Neurophysiologist Mahlon DeLong and co-workers at Johns Hopkins found the defect in a small group of nerve cells called the substantia innominata, located deep under the front part of the brain. In the 1970s, researchers discovered that the cells play a role in memory.

The Johns Hopkins scientists found that some of these nerves, which extend into the cerebral cortex, degenerate in patients with Alzheimer's disease. As a result, the level of choline acetyltransferase, an enzyme produced in the nerve cells, falls.

Choline acetyltransferase stimulates production of acetylcholine, a substance involved in the transmission of nerve impulses. Low levels of acetylcholine in the brain impair memory and learning ability, and this seems to be the cause of Alzheimer's disease.

Researchers tried unsuccessfully to increase acetylcholine levels in the brain by simply administering it intravenously. However, a new approach to the problem was reported in November 1982 by psychiatrist Kenneth L. Davis and psychologist Richard C. Mohs of the Veterans Administration Medical Center in the Bronx, N.Y. They administered physostigmine, a chemical that inhibits the production of an enzyme that breaks down acetylcholine. The scientists found this at least slowed the decline in acetylcholine levels. Of the 16 Alzheimer's disease patients treated with physostigmine, 13 showed measurable improvement in their recall of general knowledge.

Although Davis and Mohs administered the physostigmine intravenously, other researchers have achieved some success with an oral form of the drug. But nerve cells must still be producing acetylcholine for this drug to work. Therefore, the researchers have assumed it would be most effective in the early stages of Alzheimer's disease.

Healing wounds. Rapid healing of wounds caused by burns, injuries, and bedsores is often critically important to the recovery of a patient. Until now, however, there have been no practical methods to accelerate wound healing.

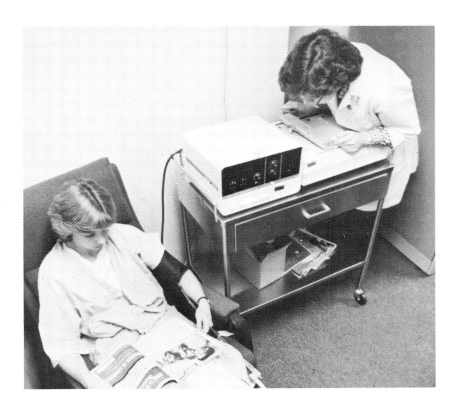

A computerized system that monitors blood pressure automatically every 2 to 10 minutes for 30 minutes can identify patients whose blood pressure is only slightly above normal.

Medicine

Continued

In March 1983, Michael B. Sporn and his colleagues at the National Cancer Institute and National Institute of Dental Research in Bethesda, Md., reported that they had found a substance that made wounds in rats heal faster. The experiments centered on peptides called transforming growth factors (TGFs), which stimulate cells to mature and reproduce.

The researchers began their study by determining what effect the TGFs would have on indicator cells. Indicator cells are animal cells that normally do not multiply in an artificial environment, such as a test tube. But when the researchers added TGFs to a test tube containing indicator cells, the cells multiplied.

Next the researchers tested the ability of TGFs to speed wound healing. They surgically inserted three pairs of tiny wire mesh chambers under the skin in the backs of laboratory rats. The animals' body-repair systems responded to these chambers as if they were wounds, and the hollow chambers allowed the scientists to examine the types and amounts of cells that accumulated at the wound sites.

After four days, the researchers found that the healing process had begun. The chambers were encased in connective tissue. However, they contained few fibroblasts — cells that aid in repairing damaged tissue. Fibroblasts migrate into a wound from surrounding tissue and lay down collagen — the most common substance found in soft connective tissue.

Once a day for five days, the scientists then injected TGFs into one of each pair of chambers on the rats' backs. They injected albumin, a type of protein, into the other chambers, which served as a control.

At the end of that period, the researchers found that the chambers injected with TGFs contained significantly more fibroblasts and collagen and were more firmly attached to the surrounding tissue than were the chambers injected with albumin. The scientists concluded that the TGFs greatly increased the speed at which wounds heal. [Michael H. Alderman]

Medicine

Continued

Unlike a human skin graft, *below left,* a new artificial skin made of collagen, *below right,* speeds healing of burns and reduces scarring and shrinkage of the burned area.

Surgery. The most dramatic surgical event of 1982 and 1983 was the artificial heart implant performed on Barney B. Clark, a 61-year-old retired dentist from the Seattle area. The 7½-hour operation, which took place on Dec. 2, 1982, at the University of Utah Medical Center in Salt Lake City, was performed by a team headed by William C. DeVries, chief of thoracic and cardiovascular surgery at the center. It was the first time that a permanent artificial heart had been implanted in a human being as a replacement for a permanently damaged or dying heart. See Rebuilding Bodies.

Clark died on March 23, 1983, 112 days after the surgery, as a result of the massive failure of all the organs in his body, except the artificial heart. It continued to pump blood even after Clark was declared dead.

The artificial heart implanted in Clark was the Jarvik-7 heart, named after bioengineer Robert K. Jarvik of the University of Utah, its principal designer. Made largely of molded polyurethane, the heart is slightly larger than a human heart but weighs about the same. It had been tested extensively in animals and had kept calves alive for up to nine months and sheep up to six months. Studies done on human cadavers before Clark's surgery showed that the heart would fit comfortably into a large or possibly medium-sized man, but would not fit into most women.

A natural heart has four chambers — two atria and two ventricles. The atria, the upper chambers, collect the blood from the body through a major blood vessel called the vena cava and pass it to the ventricles, or lower chambers, which pump the blood to the body through the aorta, the main artery from the heart.

The Jarvik-7 heart has only two ventricles. It is powered by a 13.5-kilogram (30-pound) air compressor outside the body. The compressor is linked to the ventricles by two 1.8-meter (6-foot) air hoses. Compressed air causes a rubber diaphragm in each ventricle to expand, which forces the blood from the chamber. Special in-

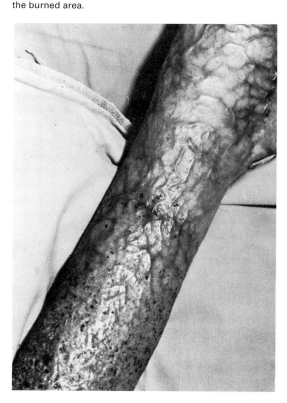
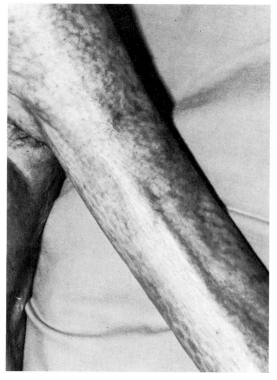

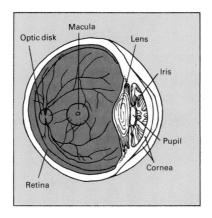

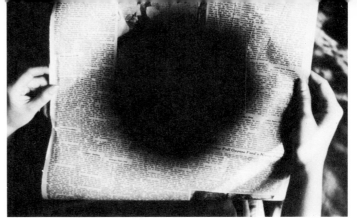

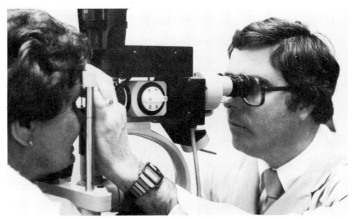

Breakthrough in Treating SMD
Senile macular degeneration
(SMD) results when tiny
blood vessels grow into the
macula, *above*. Blood and
fluid leaking from the
vessels damage the macula's
light-sensing cells and destroy
central vision, *above right*.
The first effective treatment
for SMD involves using a
laser to seal off
the leaking vessels.

Medicine

Continued

flow and outflow valves ensure that the blood flows in the correct direction.

The Jarvik-7 heart is made of a biologically inert material so that the recipient's immune system will not reject it. However, the danger of infection is great because the air hoses connect with tubes from the heart through an opening in the abdomen.

Clark was chosen to receive the heart because conventional medical treatment for his heart disease was no longer effective. He suffered from idiopathic cardiomyopathy, a heart muscle disease of unknown cause. It results in a condition known as congestive heart failure, in which the heart is unable to maintain the normal circulation of blood through the body.

DeVries and his team performed the artificial heart transplant on Clark the evening before it was originally scheduled because they feared he would die before morning. At that time, his diseased heart could pump only about 1 liter (1 quart) of blood per minute. A normal heart pumps about 4.7 liters (5 quarts) per minute.

During the operation, the surgeons removed Clark's ventricles, but left the atria as an anchor for the artificial heart. Once they had inserted the artificial heart, the surgeons discovered that its left ventricle was defective and so they had to replace it.

After the surgery, Clark experienced a stormy convalescence. One week later, he suffered seizures, which doctors speculated may have been caused by the increased flow of blood to his brain. On December 4, Clark underwent additional surgery to correct a lung condition. In another operation on December 14, surgeons replaced part of the artificial heart because a valve had cracked.

For a time, Clark's condition improved sufficiently to allow him to leave the intensive care unit and begin to rebuild his muscle strength by using a walker and pedaling an exercise bicycle. Then his condition began to deteriorate, and he died on March 23.

The surgical team determined that Clark's death was not caused by the mechanical failure of the artificial

Medicine

heart. However, they are not certain whether his death from multiple organ failure resulted from damage that existed before the heart was implanted or from the failure of the heart to pump a sufficient amount of blood to the organs. Clark's organs may also have been damaged by the rapid increase in blood flow that occurred after the artificial heart was implanted. DeVries stated that he would not perform another artificial heart implant until all information obtained from the first attempt had been analyzed.

Attacking cancer cells. An innovative new technique for destroying cancer cells, pioneered in Japan, was being evaluated at several medical centers in the United States during the year. Stephen A. Rosenberg, chief of surgery at the National Cancer Institute in Bethesda, Md., reported in October 1982 on clinical studies of the technique, called intraoperative radiation therapy (IRT). It involves directing a single dose of radiation into a tumor exposed during surgery. According to Rosenberg, IRT can be used to destroy tumors that can be completely removed by surgery as well as tumors that can be only partially removed because they have invaded nearby organs.

Like other forms of radiation therapy, IRT destroys both normal and cancer cells. However, IRT may provide a more effective way to protect normal tissue. When a cancer patient undergoes ordinary external radiation therapy, lead shields, which act as a barrier to radiation, are laid over the patient's body to protect normal tissue. However, such shields may be only partly effective because internal organs often overlap and an organ near the one being irradiated may also be affected. IRT allows the surgeon to move other organs out of the way of the radiation or to place a shield over those that cannot be moved.

In Japan, this technique has been used successfully on more than 700 patients. Surgeons in the United States hope IRT will enable them to more effectively destroy tumors whose size or location prevents their effective removal by surgery.

A silicon implant can relieve jaw pain caused when disks that separate the upper and lower jaws are damaged or dislocated and no longer act as a cushion.

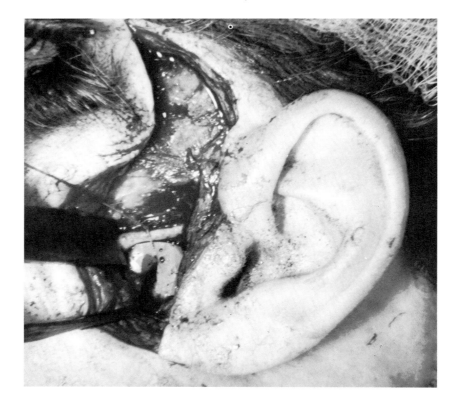

Medicine

Continued

Meteorology
See Earth Sciences

Microbiology
See Molecular Biology

Laser therapy for eyes. A new laser treatment can prevent the leading cause of blindness among the elderly, according to a report issued in May 1982 by the National Eye Institute (NEI) in Bethesda, Md. The procedure, which takes only 10 to 15 minutes, is the first effective treatment for blindness caused by senile macular degeneration (SMD), a disorder that afflicts more than 10 million Americans. However, to be effective, the condition should be treated within a few days after symptoms of the disease appear.

Generally, SMD is a relatively harmless condition in which lumps develop under the macula, a yellowish dot in the center of the retina that allows people to see detail. Usually, SMD does not destroy sight. However, 5 to 20 per cent of SMD victims develop neovascularity, a condition in which membranes in the retina break down and tiny blood vessels grow into the macula. These vessels leak blood and fluid, damaging light-sensing cells in the macula and destroying central vision. Symptoms of the disease include blurred or distorted vision and blank spots in the line of sight.

The NEI study was conducted at 12 medical centers across the United States. Patients were divided into two groups. One group was given no treatment. The other group was treated with a laser beam that sealed off the leaking vessels or destroyed them before they caused serious, permanent loss of vision. The study, which began in 1979, was supposed to last for five years. However, the benefits of the treatment became so obvious that the NEI halted the study in 1982 and endorsed laser therapy for SMD.

The study also demonstrated the need for early treatment. The NEI found that in 83 per cent of the cases diagnosed within two weeks of the onset of symptoms, laser treatment could prevent serious vision loss. However, the treatment was successful in only 10 per cent of SMD patients treated five or six months after symptoms first appeared. Beyond that time, the disease had progressed too far for effective treatment. [Frank E. Gump]

Molecular Biology

Molecular biologists at the University of Colorado announced in November 1982 that they had discovered a ribonucleic acid (RNA) molecule that can alter itself. It can snip out a section called an intron and then splice itself back together.

Introns, or intervening sequences, are sections of deoxyribonucleic acid (DNA) — the master molecule of heredity — that have no apparent function. When DNA is copied into RNA for the manufacture of a protein, the introns are also copied. Enzymes then remove the introns and join the remaining RNA segments. The newly discovered RNA molecule, which was found in a protozoan, or one-celled animal, is able to remove its single intron without the aid of enzymes.

The researchers, led by molecular biologist Thomas R. Cech, discovered the unusual properties of the RNA while studying the process by which a molecule of the RNA loses its intron. The RNA molecule they were investigating is used by the protozoan *Tetrahymena thermophila* as part of a ribosome, a particle in the cell on which protein molecules are assembled. The scientists separated a number of unspliced RNA molecules from *Tetrahymena* and prepared to carry out the splicing reaction in a test tube.

They had expected that the removal of the intron and the rejoining of the RNA segments would occur only if they added the correct enzymes to the reaction. However, they found that in a salt solution supplemented only with guanosine — a simple compound that is one of the building blocks of RNA — the RNA molecule appeared to splice itself. This result was so unexpected that the investigators theorized that the RNA must still have contained tiny amounts of protozoan enzymes.

The scientists then conducted a genetic-engineering experiment that provided convincing evidence that the RNA molecules were indeed splicing themselves. Using special enzymes, they cut the gene that codes for the ribosomal RNA out of the protozoan's DNA. Next, they inserted the gene into the bacterium *Escherichia coli,* thereby creating a strain of bacteria that produced a protozoan RNA molecule. The RNA molecules were able to remove their introns in exactly the same way as the RNA taken directly from the protozoan had done.

Because this RNA is completely foreign to *E. coli* and because *E. coli* has no known RNA-splicing enzymes, it did not seem possible that the experimental results were due to undetected splicing enzymes. The scientists speculated that the RNA molecule can fold itself into a structure that enables it to carry out the splicing operation.

The University of Colorado discovery suggests that, early in their evolution, cells relied on RNA to carry out biochemical reactions. Eventually, the cells evolved the specialized enzymes. Because enzymes are more efficient than RNA at controlling reactions, they finally took over that function.

Speedy evolution. During 1982 and 1983, molecular biologists at several institutions made great progress toward understanding a genetic phenomenon known as hybrid dysgenesis.

At the same time, they learned that a kind of rapid evolution occurs in the fruit fly *Drosophila melanogaster*.

Hybrid dysgenesis is the opposite of another phenomenon called hybrid vigor, on which much plant and animal breeding is based. Hybrid vigor is a set of beneficial characteristics brought about by a cross between two organisms that differ substantially from each other to produce hybrid offspring that are superior to either parent. Hybrid dysgenesis, on the other hand, is a set of harmful characteristics arising in offspring that have inherited an unfavorable combination of genes. Fruit flies showing hybrid dysgenesis have abnormal eggs and sperm. As a result, they have poor fertility and a high rate of genetic alterations among their offspring.

After carefully studying this phenomenon, geneticist Margaret G. Kidwell of Brown University in Providence, R.I., was able to define the circumstances under which it occurs. She found that genetically pure strains of fruit flies fall into one of two cate-

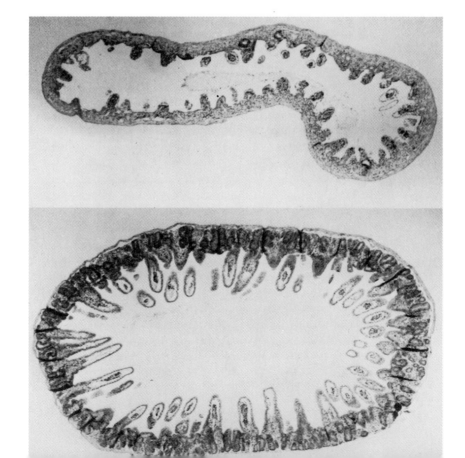

A cross section of the intestine of a mouse shows severe damage by gamma radiation, *right,* top. The intestine of a mouse that received WR-2721, a chemical that protects against radiation, was not as badly damaged, *right,* bottom. The chemical works by eliminating free radicals – atoms or molecules with unpaired electrons.

Several *Agrobacterium tumefaciens,* a common plant-infecting microorganism, attach themselves to a carrot cell and prepare to insert some of their DNA into the plant's cell. *A. tumefaciens* is being used in experiments to transfer genes from one plant to another to create new varieties of plants.

Molecular Biology

Continued

gories, P-type and M-type flies. Kidwell discovered that only crosses between P males and M females produce dysgenic offspring.

Further studies by Kidwell and geneticist William R. Engels of the University of Wisconsin in Madison led to the hypothesis that P-type flies have a transposon, or jumping gene, in their chromosomes. A transposon is a block of genes that can break free of its usual location on a chromosome and move to a different location. Apparently, these jumping genes are usually kept in place by special proteins. However, when the egg of an M-type fly is fertilized by the sperm of a P-type fly, the transposon is delivered into the fertilized egg unaccompanied by the suppressing proteins. The jumping genes then insert themselves at many sites in the chromosomes. They can cause mutations by interfering with other genes.

Molecular biologists Paul M. Bingham of the National Institute of Environmental Health Sciences in North Carolina and Gerald M. Rubin of the Carnegie Institution of Wash-

ington's Department of Embryology in Baltimore provided further experimental evidence that hybrid dysgenesis is caused by transposons.

In their work, the researchers used a technique called DNA hybridization. This procedure uses DNA strands split lengthwise as an analytical tool. Such splitting separates the bases that make up the rungs of the ladderlike molecule. Separate DNA strands from different animals or cells will rejoin at places where their bases match, thus creating hybrid DNA.

The researchers put DNA from fruit fly chromosomes into a solution that caused the double-stranded molecule to separate into single strands. The scientists then added radioactive fruit fly DNA that they knew were transposons. This DNA also split into separate strands. They next altered the chemical conditions in a way that allowed the DNA strands to link again, by joining at matching base pairs.

Some of the new DNA molecules contained one strand from a fruit fly chromosome and the other from a ra-

"You'll find that when you're seen on a million-volt electron microscope, you really want to look your best."

Molecular Biology

Continued

dio-tagged transposon. Using photographic film to detect small amounts of radioactivity, the researchers easily located these hybrid molecules. By noting where the radioactive transposons had attached to the chromosome DNA, they were able to determine the locations of transposons within the fruit fly chromosomes.

The researchers found that P-type flies contain transposons at many sites in their chromosomes while M-type flies, with rare exceptions, usually have none. Furthermore, the investigators discovered that the frequent mutations in the reproductive cells of dysgenic hybrids are indeed due to transposons jumping into the fruit fly chromosomes. See GENETICS.

Finally, this research clarified a highly unusual observation about P-M hybrid dysgenesis. Other scientists had learned that all fly strains currently collected in the wild have the genetic characteristics of P-type parents in crossbreeding experiments, while all old laboratory strains have the characteristics of M-type parents. The old laboratory strains were derived from various male-female pairs of flies caught early in the 1900s, when *Drosophila* genetics was first studied.

A particular strain is maintained by continually inbreeding the offspring of the original flies. Either the process of continual inbreeding of flies caused transposons to be eliminated from the chromosomes of laboratory fruit flies or there has been a 20th-century "epidemic" of transposons in the wild, from which laboratory strains were inadvertently quarantined.

Therapeutic gene switching. While much research in molecular biology continues to focus on such basic processes as RNA splicing and gene jumping, scientists are also making progress in developing improved methods of diagnosing and treating human genetic diseases. For example, there have been dramatic advances in understanding the role of genes in human cancer (see CANCER'S GENETIC CONNECTION). Two other developments during the year emphasized the extent to which molecular biology and medicine are

Molecular Biology

Continued

An ameba of the kind that causes amebic dysentery gives a "kiss of death" to a red blood cell, *below*. This releases a toxin into the blood cell's membrane that causes the cell to cease functioning, thus enabling the ameba to ingest it, *below right*.

beginning to interact. Both lines of research involved the set of human genes that code for the production of the oxygen-carrying blood protein hemoglobin.

In January 1983, physicians at the City of Hope Medical Center in Duarte, Calif., and the Pasteur Institute in Paris announced that they had developed a prenatal genetic test for sickle cell anemia—an inherited disease that produces misshapen red blood cells. Sickle cell anemia is caused by a single mutation in the gene that codes for one of the parts of hemoglobin, known as the beta chain or beta-globin. If a child inherits mutant genes from both parents, the child will develop sickle cell anemia.

Although the disease is easily diagnosed from blood samples, it is difficult to diagnose prenatally because withdrawing fetal blood endangers the fetus. Fetal DNA, however, is easy to obtain through the low-risk procedure of amniocentesis—the withdrawal of fluid from the mother's womb. The fluid contains many cells that are ge-

netically identical to the fetus rather than to the mother.

Until recently, diagnosing sickle cell anemia by testing fetal DNA seemed almost impossible. In a sample of DNA weighing only a few millionths of a gram, the test must be sensitive enough to detect one abnormal base pair—a single rung in the "twisted ladder" DNA molecule—out of the 3 billion base pairs present in human chromosomes. Nonetheless, using hybridization techniques, researchers have devised several such tests.

The sickle cell test developed by the California and French researchers is the most effective one yet devised. The scientists created two artificial DNA segments to serve as probe molecules that match up with human DNA. One of these synthetic probe molecules has bases that match the normal beta-chain gene, while the other matches genes with the sickle cell mutation.

Usually, DNA strands will hybridize even if they differ at a few points. But the scientists were able to create experimental conditions under which

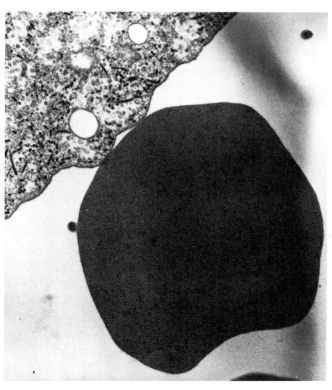

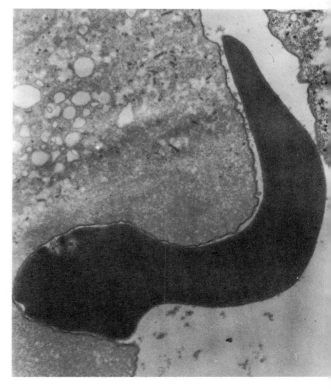

Molecular Biology

Continued

Hexagonal crystals of rhinovirus 14, one cause of the common cold, were created for use in X-ray studies to determine the structure of the viruses. Each crystal contains more than 10 billion individual virus particles.

two strands will hybridize only if they match perfectly. Thus, if a fetus's DNA hybridizes with the sickle cell probe, physicians can make a reliable diagnosis of sickle cell anemia.

Fetal hemoglobin. Another serious inherited blood disease is beta thalassemia. Like sickle cell disease, it is a form of anemia caused by a mutation in the hemoglobin beta-chain gene. Although patients can be kept alive into adulthood with frequent blood transfusions, most severe cases of beta thalassemia are ultimately fatal. In December 1982, researchers at the University of Illinois College of Medicine in Chicago and the National Institutes of Health (NIH) in Bethesda, Md., reported that they had developed a treatment for the disease. The therapy uses a drug that causes the body to produce a form of hemoglobin ordinarily produced only before birth.

Scientists had long proposed that beta thalassemia could be treated effectively if a way could be found to reactivate the genes for this fetal hemoglobin, which is known as gamma-globin. By some not-yet-understood genetic mechanism, gamma-globin genes are turned off at about the time of birth. Gamma-globin is then replaced by beta-globin. From their studies of a rare genetic trait in which the body continues to manufacture fetal hemoglobin, scientists knew that gamma-globin functions satisfactorily in adults. But they did not know how to make the genes of beta thalassemia victims produce gamma-globin.

The Illinois and NIH researchers decided to test a drug called 5-azacytidine (5-azaC) with beta thalassemia patients. The drug had shown promising results in experiments with baboons and tests in cell cultures. The investigators found that 5-azaC is extremely effective in both stimulating genes to produce gamma-globin and relieving the severe symptoms produced by the abnormal beta-globin in thalassemia patients. This procedure remains highly experimental, but it may point the way toward a new approach to the treatment of hereditary diseases.　　[Maynard V. Olson]

Neuroscience

A promising new treatment for multiple sclerosis (MS), a progressive crippling disease that attacks the central nervous system, was announced in January 1983 by medical researchers at Boston's Brigham and Women's Hospital. The therapy consists of injections of ACTH, a hormone that is used to treat most MS patients, in combination with an anticancer drug, cyclophosphamide.

MS afflicts some 250,000 Americans. Its cause is unknown, but the research team, led by physicians Howard L. Weiner and Stephen L. Hauser, followed up earlier findings suggesting that MS is an autoimmune disease — one in which the body's immune system attacks its own tissues. MS destroys the myelin, or protective sheathing, of the nerve fibers in the brain and spinal cord.

The investigators selected 58 patients, from 20 to 52 years of age, for the study. All had a severe and progressive form of the disease, and their conditions had worsened in the preceding nine months. Every patient received injections of ACTH, and 20 were also given cyclophosphamide, which suppresses the immune system.

Patients receiving both ACTH and cyclophosphamide did significantly better than those given only ACTH. One year later, 16 of the 20 had either improved or had not worsened.

Isolated brain. Neuroscientists at New York University Medical Center in New York City announced in November 1982 that they had developed a procedure to remove, and maintain in a functioning condition, the complete brain of a guinea pig. The researchers, Rodolfo Llinás and Kerry Walton, said the brains were kept alive for up to 10 hours by immersing them in a solution containing nutrients and oxygen. The solution was also circulated through the brains.

In their procedure, the scientists anesthetized a guinea pig and removed its brain. They then circulated the solution through one of the major cerebral arteries. When they stimulated areas of the brain with electrical probes, neurons elsewhere in the brain

Neuroscience

Continued

The brain of a cat in a coma, *below,* shows two small areas of high metabolic activity (arrows) that are absent in the brain of a normal cat, *below right*. This indicates that coma is the result of a specific brain system that produces unconsciousness for a particular reason, perhaps to conserve oxygen for brain cells.

fired in response. Also, electroencephalograph readings of the brain were similar to those of an intact brain. This technique will enable neuroscientists to study the communication of neurons within complete brains.

Memory proteins. Researchers in the Boston area reported experimental results in 1982 and 1983 that supported the theory that specific proteins are involved in memory and learning. Working with mice and goldfish, the scientists found that certain proteins in the animals' brains were altered after they mastered a task. The proteins may function as building blocks for learning and memory.

The research was conducted at Harvard University Medical School in Boston and McLean Hospital in Belmont, Mass., under the direction of neuroscientist Victor E. Shashoua. He and his colleagues had discovered the proteins in earlier studies and named them ependymins, after the ependymal zone, the brain area where they are produced. They had found that an animal's ependymins undergo certain

changes after the animal has learned a new skill.

In their later experiments, the researchers discovered that the altered brain proteins of both goldfish and mice are released from the ependymal zone into the brain's extracellular fluid—a watery fluid that surrounds cells in the brain. The scientists speculated that one of the functions of extracellular fluid in the brain may be to distribute ependymins to brain cells and circuits involved with learning and memory. The proteins would then, presumably, help to make more permanent the newly formed electrochemical connections produced during the learning process, thereby helping to establish the new skills or memories.

Growth chemical. Two teams of scientists at the Salk Institute in La Jolla, Calif., announced in the summer of 1982 that they had isolated a substance from human pancreatic tumors that appears to be the same as a brain protein called growth hormone releasing factor (GRF). GRF is normally present in extremely small amounts—

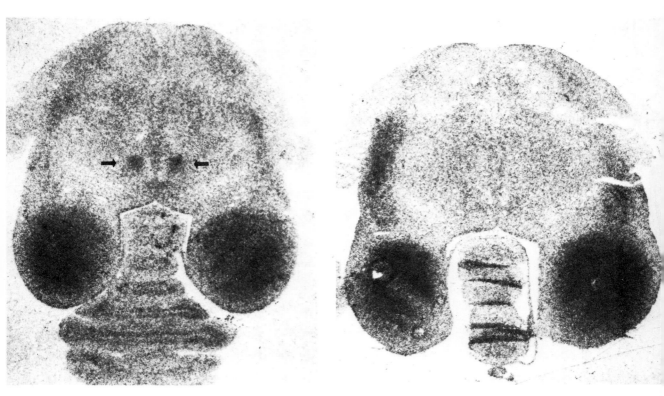

An extremely fine electrode, about 5 one-thousandths of a millimeter in diameter at the tip, detects impulses from individual human nerve fibers. It can also stimulate single nerve fibers to produce various sensations.

billionths of a gram—in the hypothalamus, the part of the brain that controls the release of hormones from the pituitary gland. One of these is growth hormone, which produces normal growth and plays an important part in body metabolism.

Scientists previously had not been able to determine the molecular structure of GRF because they could not collect enough of the substance to analyze it. Then the Salk researchers learned of two patients—one in France, the other in Virginia—who were suffering from cancers of the pancreas, causing acromegaly, a disorder characterized by abnormal growth of bones in the face and limbs. The scientists reasoned that the malignant pancreases might be producing GRF.

The research groups, led by neuroscientists Roger Guillemin and Wylie Vale, studied tissue taken from the tumors of the two patients. Both groups found large amounts of a GRF-like substance. After working out the structure of the protein, the scientists were able to synthesize it in the laboratory.

In tests with dogs and rats, the synthesized GRF caused the animals' pituitaries to produce larger amounts of growth hormone.

Human trials of the substance began in January 1983. Vale's group, collaborating with researchers at the University of Virginia School of Medicine, reported tests of the effects of synthetic GRF on six normal adult male volunteers. Each volunteer showed elevated levels of growth hormone in his blood shortly after receiving an injection of the protein. The hormone was quickly broken down in the men's bodies and so caused no growth effects. Clinical trials with growth-retarded children began in early 1983 at several medical centers, including the University of Virginia. The children were given regular doses of GRF to maintain the production of growth hormone.

The Salk Institute scientists speculated that synthetic GRF might also be of benefit to some adult patients. They said the most likely application would be in helping burn victims to regenerate lost skin. [George Adelman]

Nutrition

"Diet, Nutrition, and Cancer," a report issued on June 16, 1982, by a special committee of the National Research Council (NRC), recommended that the typical American diet be modified to reduce the risk of cancer. The committee studied and summarized evidence about links between diet and cancer from many sources, including epidemiological data, laboratory experiments, and clinical observations of cancer patients.

The committee recommended that Americans decrease fat intake from the present average of about 40 per cent to 30 per cent or less of total calories in the diet. People can reduce fat consumption by eating less fatty meat and high-fat dairy products and by using less fat and oil in cooking. The guidelines also urged that more fruits, vegetables, and whole-grain products be included in the daily diet and less salt-cured, smoked, and pickled foods, such as smoked fish, bacon, and sausage.

The committee warned about the risks of excessive alcohol drinking and cigarette smoking, which have been

associated with cancer of the mouth, throat, and respiratory tract. The group's report also called for special efforts to identify cancer-causing substances and keep them out of foods, and urged more testing of foods for links with cancer and birth defects.

Calcium and osteoporosis. In December 1982, a group of researchers headed by physician Robert P. Heaney of Creighton University in Omaha, Nebr., reported that early childhood nutrition, especially calcium intake, may be important in determining a person's peak bone mass as an adult. Loss of bone mass can result in bone fractures due to osteoporosis—a condition in which the bones become porous and fragile. Osteoporosis is a major health problem for the elderly, particularly women.

Early food habits may help determine lifelong food consumption patterns, including those leading to calcium deficiency. Dietary surveys show that more than half of the women in the United States above the age of 15 have calcium intakes below the Rec-

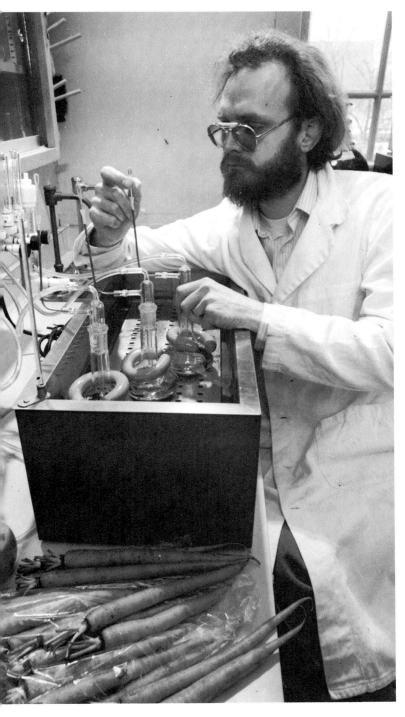

Philipp W. Simon, a plant geneticist in the U.S. Agricultural Research Service, analyzes the chemicals that give carrots flavor as part of a project to develop better-tasting, more nutritious varieties of carrots.

ommended Dietary Allowance (RDA) established by the NRC. Nutritionists suggest that adequate calcium be given a high nutritional priority, especially for females. To meet the RDA of calcium, an adult would have to drink approximately three 8-ounce (200-milliliter) glasses of milk daily or eat such calcium-rich foods as sardines, oysters, salmon, collard greens, spinach, mustard greens, cheese, or yogurt. People who do not get enough calcium from their food should take a calcium supplement.

Diet and tooth decay. Scientists have long known that diet plays an important role in the formation of tooth decay. In December 1982, dentistry professor Charles F. Schachtele of the University of Minnesota in Minneapolis reported a new method that may help determine which foods contribute to tooth decay, whether some foods help prevent cavities, and if foods can be made less harmful to teeth.

The first step in cavity formation involves the accumulation on tooth surfaces of a complex material known as dental plaque. It consists of saliva, food particles, and bacteria. The bacteria digest carbohydrates in food and change them into acids that can dissolve tooth enamel.

To investigate the relationship between diet and cavities, Schachtele placed small electrodes in the mouths of volunteers. Wires linked the electrodes to laboratory equipment that could monitor the acid-producing process. Then Schachtele had the volunteers eat a variety of foods.

Schachtele found that foods in the typical U.S. diet produce more acid and therefore more tooth decay than was previously thought. In addition, the acid-producing process may continue for 2 to 4 hours after eating—much longer than the 20 to 30 minutes formerly believed to be the limit. So brushing and flossing after eating are important. On the other hand, certain foods, including cheese, reduce acid formation.

Rare deficiencies. During 1983, scientists learned more about two nutrients that had been little known because no one had ever become deficient in them while consuming ordinary foods. Deficiencies in the two

Nutrition

Continued

nutrients, the mineral selenium and the vitamin biotin, showed up in patients being fed intravenously. Intravenous feeding provides a patient who cannot eat with nutritional needs by injecting a liquid diet directly into the blood. The solutions used for such feeding contain nearly all the nutrients known to be essential for human health, but not biotin or selenium.

In February 1983, pediatricians C. Lawrence Kien and Howard E. Ganther of the Medical College of Wisconsin in Milwaukee documented selenium deficiency in a child receiving intravenous feeding. Biotin deficiencies in other patients being fed intravenously were reported at the same time by Sheila M. Innis and Duncan B. Allardyce of the University of British Columbia in Vancouver, Canada.

Selenium is a component of glutathione peroxidase, an important enzyme with many functions in the body. Scientists have not yet learned all the signs of selenium deficiency, but one known symptom is muscle weakness. Biotin plays a role in the metabolism of carbohydrates and fats. A biotin deficiency causes dry skin, loss of appetite, vomiting, and depression.

Vitamin pill use. Healthy individuals whose diets contain a wide variety of foods should obtain adequate amounts of all essential nutrients and have no need of vitamin pills or other food supplements. Nevertheless, the food-supplement industry continues to flourish. In November 1982, a research team led by Howard G. Schutz, professor of consumer sciences at the University of California at Davis, reported perhaps the largest, most sophisticated study ever conducted to determine the extent of food-supplement use in the United States. Schutz and his colleagues collected data by questionnaire from 2,451 adults living in seven states.

The researchers found that 66.6 per cent of the people in the study used some form of food supplement. Food-supplement users were actively interested in nutrition, but the reasons they gave for taking supplements revealed a lack of accurate information about nutrition.   [Eleanor A. Young]

Oceanography
See Earth Sciences

Paleontology
See Earth Sciences

Physics

Atoms and Nuclei. One more element was added to the periodic table in August 1982, when a team of researchers in Darmstadt, West Germany, succeeded in producing a single nucleus of element 109. The nucleus had 109 protons and 157 neutrons. The team, led by physicists Peter Armbruster and Gottfried Münzenberg, produced the nucleus by bombarding a foil of bismuth with a beam of iron atoms from the Heavy Ion Society accelerator.

A nucleus of iron 58, which has 26 protons and 32 neutrons, struck a nucleus of bismuth 209 containing 83 protons and 126 neutrons. As a result, the nuclei fused to form the nucleus of element 109. One neutron carried away the collision energy so that the fused nucleus could hold together.

Joining two heavy nuclei to make a heavier one is a delicate operation. One of the nuclei must be accelerated to a high speed, so that it can overcome the force of repulsion that drives nuclei apart whenever they approach one another. But if the accelerated nucleus moves too rapidly, the impact of the collision will shatter the fragile combined nucleus before it can fully form. The two nuclei must gently "touch bumpers."

The Darmstadt team calculated that this would be possible if they accelerated the iron 58 nuclei to an energy of 299 million electron volts. Even then, it took 10 days to produce a single nucleus of element 109. And at each step up the periodic table, it will get more difficult to coax nuclei into joining.

The new nucleus was, as expected, extremely unstable. The mutual repulsion of its 109 positively charged protons broke it apart after a few milliseconds. This is much too short a time to enable scientists to identify the element by chemical tests. Instead, they estimated its mass and charge by deflecting it in electrical and magnetic fields and measuring its velocity.

It broke up just as theorists had predicted. First, it quickly emitted two alpha particles, each made up of two protons and two neutrons. Then, it fissioned into two smaller nuclei.

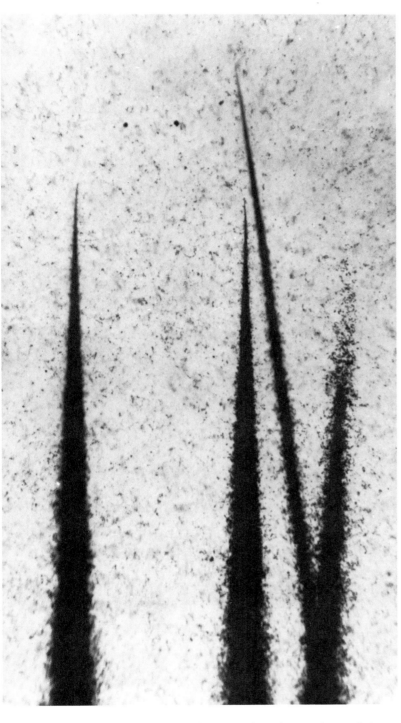

Three of the first uranium nuclei ever accelerated to near the speed of light left dark streaks as they came to rest in a special photographic emulsion in experiments at Lawrence Berkeley Laboratory in California. The right track divided when a nucleus split into two lighter nuclei.

Producing a nucleus that is so unstable is of little practical significance. However, it is a step toward the so-called island of stability expected to be found on the periodic table in the vicinity of element 114.

The island of stability is predicted by the theory that describes how protons and neutrons arrange themselves in orbital shells in the nucleus. According to the theory, protons and neutrons occupy separate groups of shells. Each shell holds only a limited number of protons or neutrons; and the stability of a nucleus depends upon how its shells are filled.

Nature fills each of the two sets of shells one shell at a time. Thus, for example, as the number of protons increases, they go into one shell until it is filled. The next proton shell then fills up and so on.

Nuclei with exactly filled shells of both protons and neutrons are much more stable than neighboring nuclei. A nucleus with 114 protons and 184 neutrons, for example, would have all shells filled and therefore would be extremely stable.

Fast pulses. During 1982 and 1983, physicists at Bell Laboratories and International Business Machines Corporation (IBM) continued to experiment with methods that can produce pulses of laser light as short as 30 femtoseconds (fs). (One fs is one-quadrillionth of a second.) Using lasers to generate very short flashes of light is one of the most rapidly advancing techniques in physics, and potentially one of the most useful.

Scientists have studied molecules since the mid-1970s by injecting them with pulses of light energy from lasers. The way in which a molecule, or an atom within a molecule, absorbs and re-emits such energy provides information about how energy moves in molecules and how it affects the structure of molecules. Similar experiments can map the flow of energy in liquids and solids.

However, the technique has been limited to the study of molecules and atoms that change energy levels relatively slowly. These changes must last longer than the duration of the laser pulse. Energy in some large molecules moves too rapidly for most lasers.

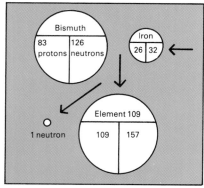

Element 109 Created
The Heavy Ion Society
accelerator in Darmstadt,
West Germany, *left,* made
the first atomic nucleus
containing 109 protons on Aug.
29, 1982. An iron nucleus with
26 protons struck a bismuth
nucleus, *above,* containing 83
protons, emitting a neutron and
fusing to form the new nucleus.

Physics

Continued

One major example of rapid energy motion involves light and rhodopsins, the visual pigment molecules in the retina of the eye. When a rhodopsin molecule absorbs a bundle of light energy, called a photon, the energy level of the molecule is boosted within a few trillionths of a second. Just as quickly, the molecule reverts to its original form. The energy it gives up in doing so generates a nerve impulse to the brain. Before the development of fast laser pulses, scientists could not study the altered form of rhodopsin.

Physicist Charles V. Shank and his colleagues at Bell Laboratories in Holmdel, N.J., produced the 30 fs light pulses. In 1981, this group had produced a pulse only 90 fs long, using a ring dye laser that they had perfected. In an ordinary laser, light reflects back and forth between parallel mirrors at its ends. In a ring dye laser, however, the light follows a closed path, passing through the laser in one direction.

To shorten the ring dye laser pulse, the Bell team used a technique called chirping, developed by physicist Dan-

iel Grischkowski and his colleagues at IBM's Watson Research Center in Yorktown, N.Y. A pulse is chirped by passing it through a substance that alters the lengths of its light waves. Chirping makes the waves at the end of the pulse shorter than those at the beginning. When the pulse is then sent through a glass fiber, the short waves travel slightly faster than longer ones. The back of the pulse catches up with the front, so the pulse emerges from the fiber shorter than it went in.

New machine. In September 1982, Michigan State University in East Lansing dedicated a new superconducting cyclotron, one of the most versatile machines yet constructed for accelerating heavy nuclei. The most powerful of all such accelerators is the Bevalac, at Lawrence Berkeley Laboratory (LBL) in Berkeley, Calif. In May 1982, LBL physicists announced that in the Bevalac they had accelerated uranium nuclei to 90 per cent of the speed of light. These were the heaviest nuclei ever accelerated to such a high speed. [Robert H. March]

Physics

Continued

W Particle Discovered
A proton and an antiproton in colliding beams annihilated each other in a flash of energy that condensed into a shower of particles, including an electron, in an experiment at the CERN research center in Switzerland in late 1982. Calculations showed that an invisible particle called a neutrino emerged opposite the electron, signaling the first artificial formation of a subatomic object called a W particle.

Particles and Forces. In January 1983, physicists at the laboratory of the European Organization for Nuclear Research (CERN) near Geneva, Switzerland, announced the long-awaited discovery of the W particle. The team was led by Carlo Rubbia of the CERN staff and Harvard University in Cambridge, Mass., and Simon Van der Meer of the CERN staff. It included 126 physicists from 13 laboratories in 7 European nations and the United States.

The W particle is one of a member of a small group of particles that serve as "go-betweens" within atoms, transmitting the forces that hold atoms, nuclei, and the particles inside nuclei together. But the W particle is the only such object that transforms one kind of subatomic particle into another. When the W transmits its force — called the weak force — heavy, unstable particles change into lighter, more stable ones. In one such process, known as nuclear beta-decay, a neutron turns into a proton by emitting a negatively charged W particle. The W does not itself ap-

pear among the final products because it is also heavy and unstable. Instead, it breaks down into a negatively charged electron and an electrically neutral neutrino.

Scientists had suspected the existence of the W particle since they began studying the weak force more than 40 years ago. And in 1967, physicists Sheldon L. Glashow and Steven Weinberg of Harvard and Abdus Salam of Imperial College in London and the International Center for Theoretical Physics in Trieste, Italy, proposed a theory that predicted the mass and other properties of the W particle. They theorized that the W particle is 90 times as heavy as a proton. The three physicists received the 1979 Nobel Prize in physics for their theory of the weak force.

The CERN discovery is very important, because the theory's predictions rest on the assumption that the weak force is a form of the electromagnetic force. The discovery of the W particle represents the best evidence that this assumption is correct. Scientists once

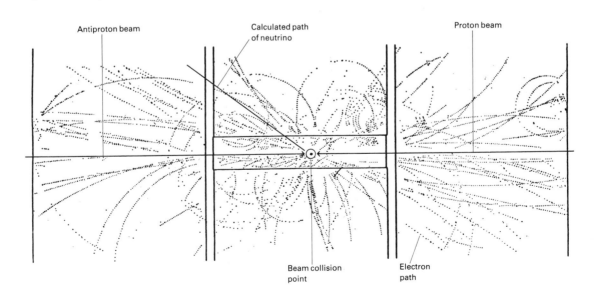

Antiproton beam

Calculated path of neutrino

Proton beam

Beam collision point

Electron path

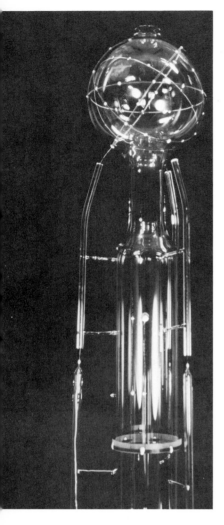

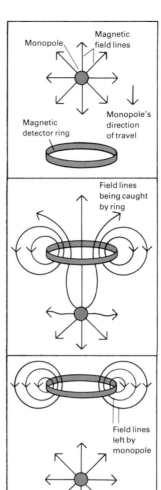

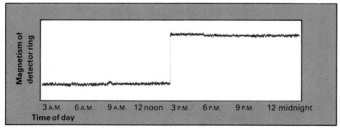

thought these two forces were separate and belonged to a group of four fundamental forces in the universe that also included gravity and the so-called strong force that holds nuclei together. One of the fondest dreams of physicists has been to prove that all the fundamental forces are variations of a single "master force."

The CERN team produced the W particle in a particle accelerator—a machine that accelerates a beam of particles to a high speed and then collides the beam with a target, which may be a solid object or another particle beam. The collision produces a flash of energy, which then turns into particles. In order to produce a given particle, an accelerator must supply an amount of energy equivalent to the particle's mass. Until recently, no accelerator could provide enough energy to produce a W particle.

The machine that finally did the job was CERN's Super Proton Synchrotron (SPS) accelerator. The SPS can simultaneously accelerate a beam of protons and a beam of their antimatter opposites, antiprotons, around a circular path 2 kilometers (1.2 miles) in diameter. Protons carry positive electrical charge and antiprotons carry negative charge, so the beams travel around the accelerator's ring in opposite directions.

At certain points, the beams cross paths. Each time they cross, a few particles collide and annihilate one another, producing a microscopic fireball containing 540 billion electron volts (GeV) of energy. (One eV is the amount of energy that an electron gains when it moves across an electrical field of one volt.) The theory predicts that a W particle will emerge once in about 10 million collisions.

Finding the W was like looking for a needle in a haystack. Not only is W particle production rare, but the fireball contains so much energy that it usually produces 50 or more other particles. The fact that the W particle quickly breaks up into combinations of lighter particles further complicated the search for the particle.

To detect the W particle, Rubbia's team surrounded one point at which the beams would cross with many layers of particle detectors. The inner-

A Monopole, Maybe

The first detection of a magnetic monopole – an isolated north or south magnetic pole – may have occurred on Feb. 14, 1982, when a printout showed the amount of magnetism in a magnetic detector ring at Stanford University in California increased sharply, *above*. A monopole, *top right,* may have passed through the ring, leaving enough magnetic field lines behind to cause the increase. An improved detector with three rings, *top left,* went into operation at Stanford in January 1983 in an effort to obtain a similar result and confirm that monopoles do exist.

most layers were grids of fine wires that produced electrical signals revealing the paths of the particles as they emerged after a proton-antiproton collision. The outer detectors helped identify the particles and measure their energy. The detectors fed signals to a network of small computers, which recorded the collisions that showed some promise of W particle production. A large computer later reconstructed a picture of what happened during these collisions.

In 30 days of operation in November and December 1982, the detectors sampled 1 billion collisions. Of these, 100,000 were promising enough to record. The team focused its initial attention on searching for W particles that break up into an electron and a neutrino, each moving in opposite directions. The electron flies out of the collision with at least 15 GeV of energy and at a large angle to the beam path. The neutrino passes through the apparatus undetected. Physicists infer its existence by adding up the energies of all the particles emitted in all directions from the collision point. If energy is missing in the direction opposite an electron's path, this indicates the presence of a neutrino.

The experimenters found five examples of missing energy. By adding the energy of each electron to that of the missing neutrino, they estimated the mass of the W particle to be 88 times that of a proton, remarkably close to the 90 predicted by the theory.

The discovery was confirmed later in January by another team of CERN experimenters, headed by Pierre Darriault, using a less elaborate detector system at another beam collision point. They found four events that seemed to be the same as those observed by Rubbia's team.

In May 1983, the Rubbia team reported that the SPS may have produced a neutral version of the W particle, the Z^0 particle, in April.

European leadership. The discovery of the W particle marked the passage of leadership in subatomic physics from the United States to Europe. CERN and other European laboratories boast accelerators and particle detectors unmatched by any in the United States.   [Robert H. March]

Condensed Matter Physics. In December 1982, physicist Robert Burnham and co-workers at Xerox Corporation's Palo Alto Research Center in California and Nick Holonyak, Jr., of the University of Illinois at Urbana-Champaign announced the development of a solid-state laser that has about the same area and thickness as a period on a printed page. Yet the tiny laser can produce 1 watt of deep red light continuously. By contrast, typical gas lasers of this power are considerably larger than a standard hard-cover book.

The device, a quantum well diode laser, is made of a layered alloy of gallium-aluminum-arsenide. The middle layer, which is the active layer, is made of nearly pure gallium arsenide, and is only six-millionths of a millimeter thick. The two layers on either side of it are 10 times as thick and contain about 30 atoms of aluminum for every 70 atoms of gallium. These layers are in turn sandwiched between two still thicker outer layers, containing 25 atoms of aluminum for every 75 atoms of gallium. The entire device is about 0.25 millimeter (0.01 inch) square and one-thousandth of a millimeter thick.

Electrical current travels through the layers in the form of moving negatively charged electrons and positively charged holes — spaces left behind when electrons are removed. The middle layer acts as a pit, called a quantum well, which the electrons either overshoot or fall into.

When an electron falls into a hole, the electron gives up energy in the form of a photon — a bundle, or quantum, of light. A photon vibrates with a frequency equal to its energy divided by a number called Planck's constant.

According to the laws of quantum mechanics that govern the emission of photons, electrons in an object can emit photons that have only certain special amounts of energy. Furthermore the number of possible amounts of energy, and the amounts themselves, given up by electrons as they fall into holes in an object depend upon the size of the object. The smaller the object, the smaller the number of possible energies. Because the laser's middle layer is extremely

Angle on
the Outfield

Good judgment.

Scientific curiosity often extends to subjects that are not usually associated with science. Sports is an example. A scientist watching or participating in a sport may wonder about the scientific principles behind some aspect of the athletic activity.

When I started coaching Little League baseball a few years ago, I became interested in the problem of judging a fly ball. I knew that an experienced outfielder determines almost immediately where a fly ball is going and runs at just the right speed to reach the ball as it is about to land. The information that the player uses to judge how far and how fast the ball will fly must therefore be contained in the very first part of the ball's flight, as the ball rises up and away from the batter. I began to wonder exactly what that information was.

Some of my Little Leaguers, who were just learning the game, had no idea how to judge a fly ball. The typical boy would react to a fly ball by taking one or two uncertain steps, sticking his glove into the air in the general direction of the ball, and hoping that the ball somehow would find the glove.

When I tried to teach my players how to react to a fly ball, I soon discovered that there is no useful coaching technique. I found that the skill of judging a fly ball must be completely self-taught, and that players acquire it only through constant practice. By trial and error, the player learns to "read" the initial flight of the ball and develops the reflexes that send his or her body to the right place. However, I discovered that an outfielder is not consciously aware of the details of this learning process. My question therefore became: What information does the fielder's subconscious mind use in learning to judge a fly ball?

I soon discovered that I was not the first scientist to ask this question. In 1968, physicist Seville Chapman of Cornell Aeronautical Laboratory in Buffalo, N.Y., proposed that an outfielder unknowingly uses geometry and trigonometry to direct body movements. According to Chapman, the fielder is guided by the angle that his or her line of sight to the ball makes with the ground. By running so that

this angle changes at a specific rate as the ball is in flight, the player arrives at the landing point just as the ball comes down.

However, Chapman did not take into account the effect of air resistance on the flight of the ball. It turns out that air resistance reduces the distance that a typical fly ball travels by about 40 per cent, changing the shape of its trajectory enough so that a player could not possibly use the geometric and trigonometric factors suggested by Chapman to determine the landing point of the ball.

After thoroughly studying the effects of air resistance on baseball flight, I concluded that an outfielder must use more than just visual information to judge the flight of the ball. Not only do the eyes of the fielder follow the flight of the ball, the head usually moves as well. The motions of the head and eyes must be precisely coordinated to keep the eyes fixed on the ball.

The coordination of movements of the eyes and head is controlled by the vestibular system—the three fluid-filled semicircular canals located in the inner ear. When your head moves, the motion of the fluid triggers rapid nerve impulses that cause the rest of your body to react to the motion. Your vestibular system enables you to maintain your balance and to tell up from down.

I believe that the sudden, rapid motion of an outfielder's head upon looking upward to follow the flight of a fly ball provides the vestibular system with the necessary sensory information to accurately predict the path of the ball. The bodily reflexes that an outfielder develops in learning through practice how to judge a fly ball are coordinated by the vestibular system. The vestibular system sends signals relating the movements of the head, as the player watches the ball, to the body movements required to get to the place where the ball comes down.

Unfortunately, this theory does not suggest any new and better way to teach a beginner how to judge a fly ball. Nevertheless, what I have learned has given me a much deeper appreciation of the complex process that must take place when an experienced outfielder makes an easy catch of a "routine" fly ball.   [Peter J. Brancazio]

© 1983 The New Yorker Magazine, Inc.

"Oh, for heaven's sake, Jackson, stop blubbering.
You knew this job was dangerous when you took it."

Physics

Continued

small, when an electrical current flows across the laser, the middle layer emits photons, each of which has the same energy and frequency, corresponding to light of a deep red color.

The basic principle of the laser is that photons of this frequency encourage electrons in the gallium arsenide to fall into holes, emitting still more photons of the same frequency. As a result, it is possible for a weak current to cause the middle layer to emit tremendous numbers of photons with a single frequency. When the current rises above about 0.3 ampere, the device begins to emit laser light. The light output increases with further increases in the current. Only 1.5 amperes will produce ½ watt of light.

Quantized Hall effect. In 1982 and 1983, physicists made major advances in the study of the Hall effect—a relationship among currents and fields in metals. The effect is named for physicist Edwin H. Hall, who discovered it in 1879. Hall found that when an electrical current travels through a metal in a magnetic field that is at right an-

gles to the current, an electrical field builds up at right angles to both the current flow and the magnetic field. The strength of this electrical field is proportional to the strengths of the current and the magnetic field.

Then in 1980, West German and British physicists discovered a variation called the quantized Hall effect. They imposed a strong magnetic field perpendicular to a very thin conducting layer in an electronic device known as a semiconductor-insulator junction. This caused a current to flow through the layer. Surprisingly, they found that the strength of the resulting electrical field was no longer simply proportional to the magnetic field and current, but increased by quanta, or steps, as the magnetic field increased. Furthermore, the interval between successive steps did not depend on the nature of the specific conducting material. Rather, the steps were always at an exact or whole-number multiple of the current times the square of the charge of the electron divided by Planck's constant.

303

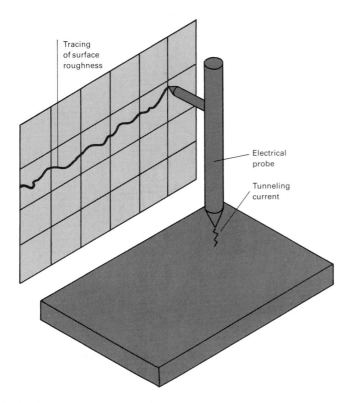

Tracing
of surface
roughness

Electrical
probe

Tunneling
current

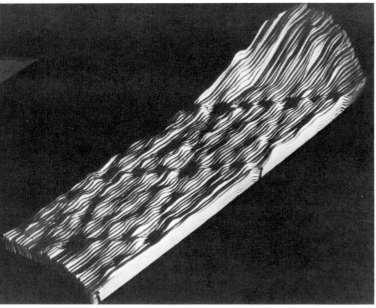

Tunneling Microscope
An electrical probe developed by IBM scans the surface of a silicon chip,
top, at such close range that electrons flow as a so-called tunneling
current between probe and surface. Recordings of the current from
a series of scans are combined to form a model of the surface's features,
above, that are separated vertically by up to 0.28-millionth of a millimeter.

Early in 1982, physicists Daniel C. Tsui of Princeton University in New Jersey and Horst L. Stormer and Arthur C. Gossard of Bell Laboratories in Murray Hill, N.J., discovered a variation on the quantized Hall effect. At extremely low temperatures, less than 5°C (9°F.) above absolute zero (−273.15°C or −459.67°F.) and in extremely strong magnetic fields, the steps are no longer only at integral multiples, but are also at fractions of integral multiples. The physicists discovered steps that were precisely one-third and two-thirds of integral multiples. And, by the summer of 1983, there was some evidence of steps at other fractions such as two-fifths, in which the denominator is odd.

In early 1983, physicist Robert Laughlin of Lawrence Livermore National Laboratory in California pointed out that these odd values are a consequence of repulsive electrical, or Coulomb, interactions among the electrons. At low temperatures and in a high magnetic field, the electrons in the conducting layer behave like a liquid. The motions of the individual electrons are no longer independent of one another. Rather, the electrons have highly coordinated motions that produce the fractional steps.

Charge density waves. In 1983, physicists discovered another striking example of the quantized behavior of large numbers of electrons at low temperatures. Such movements occur in compounds known as transition metal trichalcogenides. Normally, electrons in these compounds are spread out uniformly in one direction, and so current flows much more easily in that direction than in the two directions perpendicular to it.

As these materials are cooled below certain critical temperatures — the highest, −129°C (−200°F.) for the trichalcogenide niobium triselenide — the crystal structure of the substance rearranges itself slightly. The electrons no longer remain spread out uniformly. Rather, they assume a wave-like structure like that of air molecules in a sound wave, with alternating regions of high charge and density and zones of low charge and density. This structure of electrons is called a charge density wave.

Physics

Continued

Experiments on low-temperature trichalcogenides showed that when a small, steady voltage is applied across the direction in which current easily flows, a steady, or direct, current is set up in accordance with Ohm's law: The current equals the voltage divided by the material's electrical resistance. However, as the voltage increases, the current increases above the level predicted by Ohm's law. Furthermore, the current takes on the characteristics of a direct current combined with a small, random alternating current that has a broad band of frequencies.

The added direct current arises from the motion of the entire charge density wave as a unit along the crystal. The waves are usually "pinned" to the crystal at locations where the waves have low energy. The difficult problem was to understand how the wave of electrons frees itself from the pinning forces so that it can slide along the crystal as a unit.

Several groups of scientists, including John Bardeen and his colleagues at the University of Illinois at Urbana-Champaign and George Grüner and co-workers at the University of California at Los Angeles, determined the nature of the pinning force and the mechanism by which the wave moves.

The motion of the wave that the physicists discovered can be compared to the movement of a marble on a washboard. When the washboard is horizontal or only slightly tilted, the marble is trapped in a well between rills. This is similar to the situation in the crystal under low or no voltage. When the washboard is tilted enough—corresponding to a high voltage—the marble hops from one rill to the next. However, the charge density wave begins to move long before such a voltage is reached. Its motion at high voltage is actually more like a marble that could bore a tunnel through a rill rather than hop over it.

This tunneling stems from the wave-like nature of the electrons themselves. In some respects, electrons act as if they are particles like tiny marbles, while in other ways they behave as if they are waves.

The voltage applied in the trichalcogenide experiments would not provide the electrons with enough energy to overcome the pinning force if the electrons acted like tiny marbles. However, with the electrons behaving as waves, the higher the voltage, the greater the probability of tunneling.

It is remarkable for large numbers of electrons to coordinate their tunneling as they do when charge density waves move. This coordination extends over a region nearly 0.1 millimeter (0.004 inch) long. The physicists believe that the random alternating part of the current arises from oscillations of the charge density waves.

Chaotic circuits. In 1982, physicists Carson D. Jeffries, José Perez, and James Testa of the University of California in Berkeley carried out a series of experiments that showed random behavior of semiconductor diodes—electronic devices that have two electrical terminals and conduct electricity more easily in one direction. Physicists are interested in when and why an object or a group of objects stops behaving according to an apparent pattern and starts to act randomly. They hope to develop theories that account for complex phenomena of this type.

The Berkeley physicists installed a diode in an electrical circuit and applied to this circuit a steady alternating voltage, called the driving voltage, which caused the diode voltage to alternate as well. For each peak of the driving voltage, there was one peak value of the diode voltage. However, when the experimenters increased the driving voltage beyond 0.64 volt, the relationship of the peaks suddenly changed. The diode voltage peaks then began to alternate between two values. And, with further increases of driving voltage, the relationship changed further. At successive driving voltage peaks, 4, 8, 16, and 32 values of diode voltage appeared in sequence.

However, when the experimenters raised the driving voltage above 1.86 volts, the values of the diode voltage at its peaks appeared to vary at random from peak to peak. Around certain higher voltages, however, the system appeared to have some regularity again. Several other groups of scientists found comparable behavior in vastly different simple physical systems, showing that this type of chaos is very general.　　[Gordon Baym]

305

Psychology

Several studies in 1982 and 1983 related intelligence to how fast a person thinks. Psychologists used such data as well as other research to explore long-standing questions about a possible biological basis of intelligence.

Quick thinking. At the annual meeting of the British Psychological Society in April 1982, British psychologist Hans Eysenck described experiments by two teams of British researchers that indicate persons with high intelligence quotient (IQ) scores make judgments more quickly than those with low IQ scores. The idea that mental "quickness" may be the main factor in determining intelligence was suggested in the late 1800s by British scientist Sir Francis Galton. The research teams tested Galton's idea experimentally.

Psychologists Chris Brand and Ian Deary of the University of Edinburgh in Scotland asked volunteers to perform simple tasks, such as comparing the lengths of two lines flashed on a screen. The volunteers, ranging from 4-year-olds to adults, recorded their responses by pressing a button. The researchers compared response times with IQ scores and found that both adults and children who made faster decisions in those simple tasks also scored higher on IQ tests. No other factor—such as race, sex, age, or economic background—was so strongly related to IQ.

The psychological research team of Alan and Elaine Hendrickson at the Institute of Psychiatry in London performed similar experiments using an electroencephalograph (EEG) to record "brain wave" reactions to simple tones. They attached electrodes to the heads of volunteers and then played a series of identical tones through earphones. Subjects with higher IQs showed a quicker EEG response to the tones, and the resulting brain wave patterns were more complex.

Eysenck used these results to argue that IQ scores measure a real quality and that there is a biological basis for intelligence. Recognizing tones or simple lines does not depend on culture or learning opportunities, he said. Also, the correlation of IQ and fast thinking in 4-year-olds shows that this is not a trait acquired with age. Therefore, Eysenck believes that heredity plays some role in intelligence. But this does not contradict the idea that experience and opportunity shape intelligence.

Quality thinking. Psychologist Earl Hunt of the University of Washington reported in January 1983 that intellectual differences are due to the quality of mental information processing, not just speed. Hunt and his co-workers tested a group of volunteers to determine how they represent a problem to themselves. The volunteers watched a screen while a sentence, such as: "The plus sign is over the star" flashed on. A picture followed the sentence. The subjects had to indicate as quickly as possible whether the picture showed the same thing that had been described by the sentence.

Then the researchers asked what mental processes the volunteers used to make their decision. Some said they imagined the scene described in the sentence, then compared their mental image with the actual image shown on the screen a few seconds later. These "imagers" were very quick to make their decisions, and they were very accurate. Others said they waited for the picture, described it to themselves, then compared this description with the sentence they saw earlier. These "verbalizers" were slow to make decisions, and they were less accurate than the imagers.

Imagers and verbalizers were consistent. They stayed with their preferred strategies when tested on different tasks. But Hunt found that many volunteers could switch information-processing strategy if asked to do so. All those in their late teens and early 20s, even habitual verbalizers, were able to adopt the visual imagery approach. Many increased the speed of their answers by doing so. But the ability to switch to visual imagery declined with age, reaching a low in the 56- to 67-year age group, the oldest Hunt tested.

Born talkers? A husband-wife psychology team, Dennis and Victoria Malfese of Southern Illinois University in Carbondale, reported in March 1983 that babies vary in early sensitivity to spoken language.

The Malfeses measured the EEG responses of 60 children to simple spoken sounds such as "baa" and "gaa."

Psychology

Continued

Elaine Hendrickson, a brain researcher at London's Institute of Psychiatry, uses an electroencephalograph to monitor brain waves of a schoolgirl listening to a series of tones. The test is part of a study linking complexity of brain waves to intelligence.

All were healthy, normal-weight children from middle-class homes. According to analysis of brain waves, some babies responded differently to each of these sounds shortly after birth; others did not. The children were tested every six months for three years. Then the researchers gave each child a standardized test of language development and vocabulary. The Malfeses found a strong relationship between a child's response to differing sounds as an infant and the verbal ability test scores of the same child at age 3. These results suggest that children are born with different abilities to learn language.

However, the Malfeses point out that there are two limitations to their study. First, the differences predicted by the early tests might disappear as the children grow older. This can be found by testing the same individuals for many years. Second, the results might not apply to a more culturally and economically varied group of children. But if the same relationship between infant responses and verbal ability tests are found in children from different backgrounds, it will be strong evidence that heredity, and not just culture, plays a role in determining a person's verbal ability.

Computer techniques for extracting subtle patterns from the often confusing jumble of peaks and valleys in EEG graphs are allowing psychologists to get more useful information out of the EEG than ever before. A breakthrough in computer analysis of the EEG was reported in December 1982 by Alan S. Gevins and five other researchers at the EEG Systems Laboratory in San Francisco. Gevins and his team studied simple perceptual and motor activities similar to those used in playing video games.

Volunteers with electrodes attached to their heads had to predict the path of an arrow on a TV screen, then quickly push a button to move a dot into the path of the arrow. The activities are performed in quick sequence—first the perceptual, then the motor. Each involves different brain areas. The perceptual task of plotting the

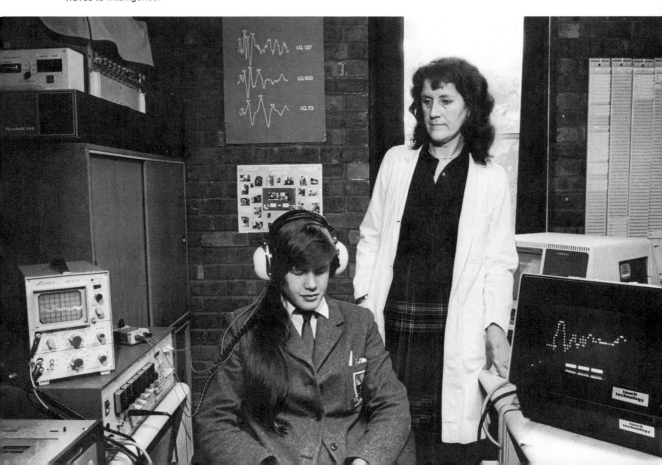

path of the arrow takes place in the right midbrain, which is used for spatial tasks. The task of pushing the button is controlled by the left midbrain, which is used for control of simple movement.

The computer-enhanced EEG revealed rapidly shifting, very precise patterns of brain activity, which the researchers called the "shadows of thought." They were able to see activity move within a half second from the right midbrain area where the course of the arrow was plotted to the left midbrain area as the volunteer pressed the button.

This was the first time EEG activity had been analyzed in such a detailed way, revealing split-second shifts in the location of thought processes within the brain.

Bonding debunked. Psychologists decided during the year that a theory about bonding between mothers and infants is probably not true. Based on observations of various animal species, pediatricians Marshall H. Klaus and John H. Kennell claimed in their 1976 book *Maternal-Infant Bonding* that the first few minutes after birth were critically important for establishing biological and emotional ties between a human mother and child.

Now it appears that the early data has flaws and the bonding theory does not hold true for humans. In a new book, *Parent-Infant Bonding* (1982), Klaus and Kennell report that later studies did not support their previous claims. The new studies on human mother-infant relationships by developmental psychologist Marilyn J. Svedja at the University of Michigan School of Medicine and other researchers show that "the effects of early contact, if any, are extremely subtle and short-lived."

The demise of the bonding theory, as applied to humans, is good news to mothers who must be separated from their babies due to medical complications after birth. Parents need not worry about the early separation; other factors are more important in the relationship between parents and a baby. [Russell A. Dewey]

Public Health

During 1982 and 1983, a devastating new disease called acquired immune deficiency syndrome (AIDS) became a full-blown epidemic in the United States. By the spring of 1983, physicians had diagnosed about 1,400 cases of AIDS. One new case per day had appeared in 1981. By May 1983, the incidence of new cases rose to between 4 and 5 per day. More ominously, among AIDS patients whose condition was diagnosed in mid-1982 or earlier, 60 per cent had died.

Apparently, the condition involves a failure of the immune system, which leaves the body defenseless against infection. The defect appears to occur in T lymphocytes, white blood cells that play a major role in immunity.

AIDS victims develop a rare cancer called Kaposi's sarcoma and severe infections from microorganisms that are no threat to an individual with normal immunity.

The disease itself seems to be spread through intimate bodily contact or blood. Most cases occur among male homosexuals who have had frequent, multiple sexual contacts. Intravenous drug users who share needles form another high-risk group. Still other victims have been hemophiliacs who received blood-clotting agents produced by pooling blood from many donors. Some children of AIDS patients, the patients' heterosexual partners, and — for unknown reasons — Haitians have also been infected.

Because AIDS seems to be an infectious disease, the United States Public Health Service (PHS) has recommended several steps to stop its spread. PHS recommends that high-risk groups refrain from donating blood; that sexual contact with known AIDS patients be avoided; and, in general, that sexual encounters with unknown partners be minimized. See HERPES IS FOREVER; IMMUNOLOGY.

Starch blockers. The quest for a simple, effortless way to control weight led thousands of dieters in the United States to take tablets called starch blockers before the Food and Drug Administration (FDA) banned their sale in July 1982. The manufacturers

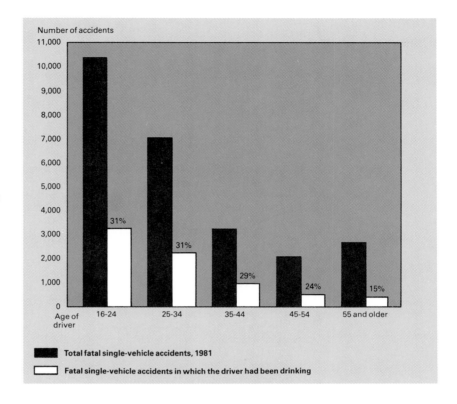

Number of accidents

Alcohol and Autos: The Fatal Mix
A study of single-vehicle accidents in the United States in 1981 showed that nearly 30 per cent of all drivers killed in such accidents had been drinking. The rate of alcohol-related deaths was highest among the youngest drivers and fell with increasing age.

Age of driver: 16-24 (31%), 25-34 (31%), 35-44 (29%), 45-54 (24%), 55 and older (15%)

■ Total fatal single-vehicle accidents, 1981
□ Fatal single-vehicle accidents in which the driver had been drinking

Public Health

Continued

of starch blockers claimed that the pills inhibited the action of the intestinal enzyme alpha-amylase. Alpha-amylase splits complex starch molecules, which cannot be absorbed by the body, into smaller molecules of glucose, a form of sugar that is easily absorbed. By inhibiting the action of alpha-amylase, starch blockers supposedly prevented digestion of such starchy foods as bread and potatoes.

In 1975, biochemists J. John Marshall and Carmen M. Lauda of the University of Miami in Florida extracted the alpha-amylase inhibitor from kidney beans. Experiments showed that rats fed the inhibitor gained less weight and excreted more starch than did rats in a control group receiving the same diet without the inhibitor. Human beings given the starch blocker had a smaller than normal rise in the level of glucose in their blood after eating.

On the basis of this modest evidence, more than 100 different companies marketed starch blockers. During early 1982, U.S. dieters consumed more than 1 million tablets of starch

blockers each day. To avoid stringent control by the Bureau of Drugs of the FDA, manufacturers sold the pills—which were made from beans—as food supplements rather than as drugs.

Internist George W. Bo-Linn and his co-workers at Baylor University Medical Center in Dallas in December 1982 reported on a study designed to test the impact of starch blockers on starch absorption. Using a special solution, the researchers cleaned all food matter from the stomachs and bowels of five volunteers. Then the volunteers consumed a high-starch meal, mainly spaghetti and bread. The meal provided more than 100 grams of carbohydrates, about 400 calories. On alternate days, both before and during the meal, the volunteers took either starch-blocker tablets or placebos—look-alike tablets that had no effect.

The Baylor team reasoned that if the starch blockers were effective, they would have caused starch levels in the subjects' feces to rise by up to 400 calories. Instead, whether the volunteers took a starch blocker or a placebo, they excreted the same amount of carbohydrates, about 80 calories.

The researchers were not certain why starch blockers, which inhibit alpha-amylase in the test tube, were ineffective in the Baylor study. The scientists suggested that the human pancreas secretes much more alpha-amylase than the body needs. Thus, even after a person takes the commercially recommended dose of starch blockers, there is enough enzyme left to digest the starch in food.

Cigarettes and heart attack. Switching to a cigarette low in nicotine will not reduce the risk of heart attack, according to a study reported in February 1983 by epidemiologist David W. Kaufman and a team of investigators at the Boston University School of Medicine in Cambridge, Mass.

The Boston University study evaluated the correlation between the number of cigarettes smoked and the amounts of carbon monoxide and nicotine inhaled and the occurrence of heart attacks. The researchers surveyed the smoking habits of 502 male heart attack patients under the age of 55 at 78 hospitals in Connecticut, Massachusetts, New York, and Rhode Island. The 502 men were compared with a control group of 835 male patients in the same age group admitted to the hospitals for other reasons.

The researchers found that 71 per cent of the heart attack patients smoked, compared with only 51 per cent of the patients in the control group. Even more significant, an increasing risk of heart attack was associated with increasing numbers of cigarettes smoked. The heaviest smokers were twice as likely to have suffered a heart attack as the lightest smokers.

The researchers then categorized the smokers according to the amount of nicotine and carbon monoxide in their brands of cigarettes. Surprisingly, the scientists found no correlation between the levels of these elements and the incidence of heart attacks. These data give little comfort to smokers who hope that use of low tar and nicotine cigarettes will lower their risk of heart disease.   [Michael H. Alderman]

Science Awards

Five scientists—two British, two Swedish, and one American—were awarded Nobel Prizes for chemistry, physics, and physiology or medicine in 1982. The awards were presented at formal ceremonies in Stockholm, Sweden, in December. The cash value of each prize was approximately $157,000.

Chemistry. The Nobel Prize for chemistry was awarded to physicist Aaron Klug of the Medical Research Council's Laboratory of Molecular Biology at Cambridge University in England. Klug combined the analytical power of X-ray crystallography and electron microscopy to create a technique that he used to reveal detailed structures of viruses and important genetic components within cells.

His technique, called image reconstruction, involves exposing an electron micrograph of a crystallized substance to laser light. The light diffracts, or scatters, when it strikes an image on the film. Klug then uses the resulting pattern of dots to create a more detailed version of the electron micrograph image. He uses a series of such two-dimensional pictures of various "slices" of the crystal to form a three-dimensional image of a biological structure. His technique is used on structures that are too large to be studied by X-ray crystallography, in which X rays are scattered by atoms in a crystal.

Klug used his technique to determine that the rod-shaped tobacco mosaic virus is a series of more than 100 disks stacked around a core of ribonucleic acid (RNA). He also showed that such "spherical" viruses as the ones that cause polio and warts are actually 20-sided structures. Klug and his Cambridge colleagues have studied the structure of transfer RNA, a key element in forming proteins from the cell's blueprints. He is currently helping investigate the detailed structure of nucleosome core particles, perhaps the smallest components of chromosomes, strands of genetic material in the nucleus of the cell.

Born in Lithuania in 1926, Klug lived in South Africa from 1929 to

Major Awards and Prizes

Winners of the Nobel Prizes and their work are treated more fully in the first portion of this section.

AAAS Socio-Psychological Prize: Richard A. Schweder

ACEMB-University of Pennsylvania First Gold Medal (biochemical engineering): Allan C. Cormack

AIBS Distinguished Service Award (biology): Karl Maramorosch

Amateur Achievement Award (astronomy): Jay Gunter

American Heart Association-CIBA Award: Kozo Okamoto, Kyuzo Aoki, Yukio Yamori

APS High Polymer Prize: Hiroyuki Tadokoro; Motowo Takayanagi

Arthur L. Day Medal (geology): Eugene M. Shoemaker

Becton-Dickinson Award (clinical microbiology): G. D. Hsiung

Bonner Price (nuclear physics): Charles D. Goodman

Bowie Medal (geophysics): Syun-iti Akimoto

Bruce Medal (astronomy): Yakov Borisovich Zel'dovich

Bucher Medal (geophysics): John W. Handin

Buckley Solid State Physics Prize: Alan J. Heeger

Carski Award (distinguished teaching): M. John Pickett

Collier Trophy (astronautics): T. A. Wilson, The Boeing Company

Comstock Prize (physics): Theodore W. Hansch, Peter P. Sorokin, Thomas J. Watson

Dannie Heineman Prize (physics): Martin D. Kruskal

Davisson-Germer Prize (physics): Earl Ward Plummer

Delmer S. Fahrney Medal (telecommunications): Bernard A. Schriever

Edward Longstreth Medal (physics): Erich P. Ippen, Peter V. Shank

Elliott Cresson Medal (chemistry): E. Bright Wilson

Ewing Medal (geophysics): Fred N. Spiess

Fermi Award: Herbert L. Anderson, Seth H. Neddermeyer

Fisher Award (microbiology): John Hanna Brewer

Fleming Medal (geophysics): S. Keith Runcorn

Frank G. Brewer Trophy (aerospace education): Edward W. Stimpson

Franklin Medal: physics, Kenneth G. Wilson; medicine, Cesar Milstein

Gairdner Awards (medicine): Gilbert Ashwell, Günter Blobel, Arvid Carlsson, Paul Janssen, Manfred Mayer

Garvan Medal (chemistry): Ines Mandl

General Motors Cancer Research Foundation Award: Denis P. Burkitt, Howard E. Skipper, Stanley N. Cohen

Goddard Award (astronautics): George Mueller

Hazen Award (medicine): Michael S. Brown, Joseph L. Goldstein

Horace N. Potts Medal (chemistry): Charles G. Overberger

Horwitz Prize (biology): Barbara McClintock, Sussmu Tonegawa

I-R 100 Award (industrial research): Kenneth Yee, Donald Blomquist, Roald Schrack

Klumpke-Roberts Award (contributions to public understanding of astronomy): Helen Sawyer Hogg

Langmuir Prize (physics): Dudley R. Herschbach

Lasker Awards: basic research, Harold E. Varmus, Raymond L. Erikson, Robert C. Gallo, Hidesaburo Hanafusa, J. Michael Bishop; clinical research, Roscoe O. Brady, Elizabeth F. Neufeld

Lilly Award (microbiology): Ira Herskowitz

Lounsbery Award (biology, medicine): Günter Blobel

Luck Award (scientific reviewing): Michael E. Fisher

Macelwane Award (geophysics): William L. Chameides, Donald S. DePaolo

Michelson Medal (optics): R. Hanbury Brown, Richard Q. Twiss

Muhlmann Award (astronomy): François and Monique Spite

NAS Award for Applied Mathematics and Numerical Analysis: Peter D. Lax

NAS Award for Initiatives in Research: Steven M. Kosslyn

NAS Award in Chemical Sciences: Henry Taube

NAS Public Welfare Medal: Mina Rees

Nobel Prize: chemistry, Aaron Klug; physics, Kenneth G. Wilson; physiology or medicine, Sune K. Bergstrom, Bengt I. Samuelsson, John R. Vane

Oersted Medal (physics teaching): John A. Wheeler

Oppenheimer Memorial Prize (chemistry): Victor F. Weisskopf

Passano Foundation Young Scientists Award: Allan Spradling, Gerald Rubin

Penrose Medal (geology): Aaron C. Waters

Perkin Medal (chemistry): Bruce Hanna

Peter Debye Award (physical chemistry): George C. Timentel

Priestley Medal (chemistry): Robert S. Mulliken

Pupin Medal (engineering): Kenneth A. Roe

Reed Award (aeronautics): Robert Widner

Roger Adams Award (chemistry): A. R. Battersby

Royal Astronomical Society Gold Medal: Fred L. Whipple

Russell Award (astronomy): Bart J. Bok

3M Life Sciences Award (biology): Hector F. DeLuca

Trumpler Prize (astronomy): Donald Winget, Nicholas Suntzeff

U.S. Steel Foundation Award for Molecular Biology: James C. Wang

Wadsworth Award (health sciences): James V. Neel

Warner Prize (astronomy): Scott Tremaine

Wetherill Medal (physics): Lawrence A. Harris

Wilson S. Stone Memorial Award (biomedical sciences): Ethan A. Lerner

Wolf Prize (physics): Martin Perl, Leon Lederman

Wright Trophy (aeronautics): Willis M. Hawkins, Jr.

1949. He earned a master's degree in crystallography in Cape Town before his search for wider intellectual horizons took him to Trinity College, Cambridge, where he earned a Ph.D. He has worked at the Medical Research Council in Cambridge since the early 1960s.

Physics. The Nobel Prize for physics was awarded to theoretical physicist Kenneth G. Wilson of Cornell University in Ithaca, N.Y., for his work in developing a mathematical theory to explain the critical point at which matter changes from one phase to another, such as solid to liquid or liquid to gas. The citation recognized that "Wilson's theory . . . implies that many systems, different and completely unrelated, can show identical behavior near the critical point." Wilson's work has aided scientists in solving many of the most difficult problems in physics involving magnetism, turbulence, and subatomic particles.

Wilson's analysis is based on the use of a mathematical approach called renormalization group method—a way of reducing an infinity of possible calculations to a manageable number. He developed his theory while working on describing a critical point at which iron can no longer become magnetic.

Wilson is now applying his technique to an examination of the strong nuclear force that holds the atomic nucleus together and which seems to grow stronger at greater subatomic distances.

Wilson is one of the youngest winners of a Nobel Prize. He was born in Waltham, Mass., in 1936 and showed an interest in science when he was in second grade. Wilson has been a professor of physics at Cornell University since 1971.

Physiology or Medicine. The Nobel Prize for physiology or medicine was shared by three scientists—Swedish chemists Sune K. Bergstrom and Bengt I. Samuelsson of the Karolinska Institute in Stockholm and British pharmacologist John R. Vane of Wellcome Research Foundation in Beckenham, England.

The scientists were honored for their research on hormonelike substances called prostaglandins. Prostaglandins often work in antagonistic pairs. For example, one prostaglandin promotes the inflammatory process while another inhibits it, and one lowers blood pressure while another raises it.

Prostaglandins were discovered in the 1930s by Sweden's Ulf S. von Euler, who shared the 1970 Nobel Prize for physiology or medicine. Von Euler had encouraged Bergstrom to work on the chemical analysis of prostaglandin. Bergstrom purified several prostaglandins in the 1960s, determined their chemical structure, and showed that they were manufactured in the body from unsaturated fatty acids.

Samuelsson's work provided a detailed picture of arachidonic acid from which all prostaglandins are created. He also clarified other processes involved in the body's manufacture and use of prostaglandins.

Vane was recognized for his discovery of another type of prostaglandin called prostacyclin. This substance inhibits the clumping together of platelets in the blood. Such clumps form the kind of clots responsible for heart attacks and strokes. The discovery of prostacyclin provided the basis for new areas of study in the cause and prevention of cardiovascular disease (see DRUGS). Vane also discovered that aspirin almost completely blocks the formation of prostaglandin from arachidonic acid.

Scientists expect that future research on prostaglandins will lead to treatments for a variety of human ills.

Sune K. Bergstrom was born in Stockholm in 1916 and earned a doctorate in both medicine and biochemistry at the Karolinska Institute. He joined the faculty there in 1958 and served as rector from 1969 to 1977. He is chairman of the Nobel Foundation.

Bengt I. Samuelsson, born in 1934 in Halmstad, Sweden, was a student of Bergstrom's and followed in his footsteps, earning doctorates in both medicine and biochemistry at Karolinska Institute. He joined the staff there in 1960 and is now dean of the medical faculty.

John R. Vane was born in 1927 in Worcestershire, England. He earned his Ph.D. at Oxford University in chemistry and pharmacology. He became director of Wellcome Research Laboratories in 1973. [Irene B. Keller]

Space Exploration

After 10 years of development and four test flights, the National Aeronautics and Space Administration's (NASA) $10-billion reusable space shuttle began commercial operations in November 1982 with the fifth flight and first commercial venture of *Columbia*. That mission, from November 11 to 16, was followed five months later by the inaugural voyage of NASA's second winged spaceship, *Challenger*, from April 4 to 9, 1983.

***Columbia's* fifth flight** proved that America's space transportation system was ready to go to work. It was the first mission to carry four astronauts; the first to use mission specialists, or nonpilot astronauts; and the first to deploy a satellite. Commander Vance D. Brand, 51, and Pilot Robert F. Overmyer, 46, were at the controls. Meanwhile, mission specialists Joseph P. Allen, 45, and William B. Lenoir, 43, deployed Satellite Business Systems Number 3 and Telesat Canada's Anik 3.

***Challenger* spacewalk.** The first U.S. spacewalk in nine years was performed from *Challenger* on April 7, 1983, by mission specialists Donald H. Peterson, 49, and Story Musgrave, 47. Wearing 112.5-kilogram (250-pound) space suits and attached to the shuttle by 45-meter (50-foot) tethers, they practiced satellite repair tasks in the open cargo bay for nearly four hours while Commander Paul J. Weitz, 50, and Pilot Karol J. Bobko, 45, flew the spaceship.

Challenger also launched the $100-million Tracking and Data Relay Satellite (TDRS). Weighing 2,268 kilograms (5,000 pounds), it was the largest and most complex privately owned communications satellite ever built. Powerful springs pushed the satellite out of *Challenger*'s cargo bay. Then a rocket boosted the satellite from the shuttle's 298-kilometer (185-mile) altitude toward geosynchronous orbit 35,680 kilometers (22,300 miles) over northeast Brazil. The satellite was the first of three satellites in a data-relay system that would link future shuttle flights as well as other satellites to a central terminal at White Sands, N.

Mission specialists Story Musgrave, left, and Donald Peterson float tethered to slide wires in *Challenger*'s cargo bay on April 7, during the first U.S. spacewalk in nine years.

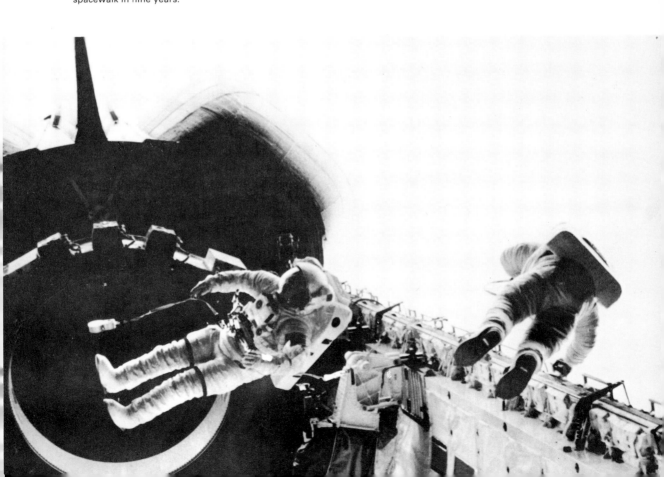

Mex., eliminating the need for most NASA ground stations.

Although a rocket malfunction left the TDRS in a lower orbit than planned, technicians were later able to jockey the satellite to a higher altitude by firing its attitude-control thrusters.

The crew was named for *Challenger*'s second mission, planned for mid-June. It included physicist Sally K. Ride, 32 — the youngest astronaut mission specialist and the first American woman to fly in space.

An orbit endurance record was set by two Russian spacemen who ascended to orbit in a *Soyuz T-5* spacecraft on May 13, 1982. After a record-breaking 211 days in orbit aboard the *Salyut 7* space station, cosmonauts Anatoly Berezovoy and Valentin Lebedev returned to earth in a *Soyuz T-7* on December 10.

During their extended stay in space, the cosmonauts lost weight, suffered fatigue, became increasingly irritable, and suffered a drop in the number of their red blood cells.

From June 24 to July 2, French Air Force Lieutenant Colonel Jean-Loup Chrétien and two cosmonauts, Colonel Vladimir A. Dzhanibekov and engineer Aleksandr S. Ivanchenkov, dropped in on Berezovoy and Lebedev for a visit. Then in late August, Svetlana Y. Savitskaya, a 34-year-old test pilot and the first woman cosmonaut to reach orbit in 20 years, was launched to the station in a *Soyuz T-7* along with two other cosmonauts, Lieutenant Colonel Leonid I. Popov and Aleksandr A. Serebrov, on August 20. All three returned to earth on August 27.

Salyut 6, the predecessor of *Salyut 7*, met its end on July 30, 1982, after nearly five years in orbit. It re-entered the earth's atmosphere and plunged into the Pacific Ocean. Launched on Sept. 29, 1977, it was occupied for 676 days of its lengthy stay in space. Crew members came primarily from the Soviet Union. But Russian-trained cosmonauts from Bulgaria, Cuba, Czechoslovakia, East Germany, Hungary, Mongolia, Poland, Romania, and Vietnam also spent time in the most-lived-in space station.

International aid satellites. The Soviet Union launched *Cosmos 1383*, the first spacecraft in a new international search and rescue system, on June 30, 1982. The United States, Canada, and France will cooperate in the program.

The Russian spacecraft carries special receivers — as will others in the group — tuned to standard international radio frequencies for distress signals. The satellites will be able to locate aircraft and ships in trouble almost anywhere on earth and relay their position to rescuers. By February 1983, *Cosmos 1383* had picked up and relayed distress signals leading to the rescue of 19 persons. Among them were three Canadian survivors of an airplane crash in British Columbia, and two Americans whose small boat capsized in the North Atlantic Ocean off Cape Cod.

NASA launched the system's second satellite on March 28 from Vandenberg Air Force Base in California.

Two misses. A nuclear-powered Soviet reconnaissance satellite, *Cosmos 1402*, launched on Aug. 30, 1982, began to fall from orbit prematurely in December. The 3,636-kilogram (8,000-pound) main stage re-entered the earth's atmosphere over the Indian Ocean and disintegrated on Jan. 23, 1983. But worldwide concern centered on the craft's nuclear reactor, which was still aloft and filled with 50 kilograms (110 pounds) of radioactive enriched uranium. The reactor finally plunged into the South Atlantic Ocean on February 7. Scientists were unable to determine whether the reactor contaminated the earth's atmosphere during its descent.

Ariane, the European Space Agency's (ESA) heavy launch rocket, regarded by NASA as the shuttle's competitor for satellite payloads, crashed after launch on Sept. 10, 1982. Its cargo, including a maritime communications satellite and a weather data relay satellite for Africa, was lost in the Atlantic Ocean. *Ariane*'s failure required ESA to find a new launch vehicle for *Exosat*, the first European astronomical X-ray observatory. *Exosat* was launched on May 26, 1983, using a NASA Delta 3914 rocket.

Other launches. NASA launched the first Infrared Astronomical Satellite (IRAS) into a 900-kilometer (560-mile) near-polar orbit on January 25.

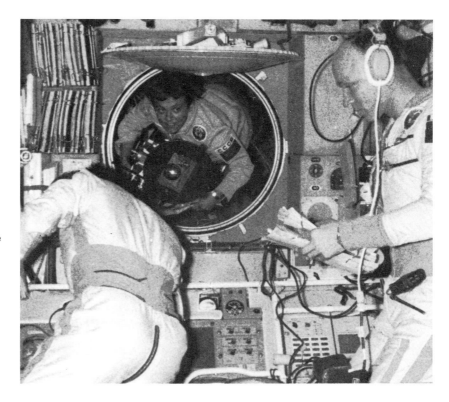

During their record 211-day stay aboard the *Salyut 7* space station, Soviet cosmonauts Anatoly Berezovoy and Valentin Lebedev greet Svetlana Y. Savitskaya, the second woman in 20 years to make a journey into space.

Space Exploration

Continued

A joint project of NASA, Great Britain, and the Netherlands, the satellite carries a 57-centimeter (22.4-inch) telescope that is specially cooled to prevent it from producing its own interfering radiation. IRAS can detect objects emitting infrared radiation, which does not penetrate earth's atmosphere, with 1,000 times more sensitivity than instruments flown on balloons, planes, and sounding rockets. Immediately after reaching orbit, IRAS returned infrared images from a nearby galaxy called the Large Magellanic Cloud. See ASTRONOMY.

Conestoga 1, the first privately launched spacecraft, lifted off from a cattle ranch on Matagorda Island, Texas, on Sept. 9, 1982. The "bargain-priced" craft was made of surplus solid-fuel rocket parts, and the entire launch operation cost about $2.5-million. It was the first successful project of Space Services Incorporated of America, a Houston-based firm. For this test flight, its payload consisted of 152 liters (40 gallons) of water. The rocket soared 320 kilometers (200

miles) high and traveled 480 kilometers (300 miles) from the launch site on its 10½-minute flight before splashing down in the Gulf of Mexico. Encouraged by the success, mission director Donald K. Slayton, a former NASA astronaut, announced that Space Services Incorporated would launch a satellite in 1984.

Pioneer 10, launched from Cape Canaveral, Fla., on March 2, 1972, crossed the orbit of Pluto on April 25, 1983, and the orbit of Neptune on June 13. Thus it became the first spacecraft to leave the solar system and enter interstellar space. The spacecraft carries a plaque intended to communicate the time and place of its launch and something about its builders to members of any scientifically advanced civilization it may encounter. When *Pioneer 10* crossed Neptune's orbit, it was 4.5 billion kilometers (2.8 billion miles) from earth and traveling at 49,167 kilometers (30,588 miles) per hour. It will not enter the planetary system of any other star for at least 10 billion years. [Marsha F. Goldsmith]

Surgery
See Medicine

Zoology

Scripps Institution of Oceanography scientists studying the behavior of Weddell seals in Antarctica prepare to "bag" a seal's head, *below,* so it will stay calm when they attach a time depth recorder (TDR) to its flipper. Back in the laboratory, the men take readings from a retrieved TDR, *below right,* and obtain a graph, *bottom,* showing how often and how deep the seal dived in its search for food.

Two spider web mysteries were unraveled in 1983. Both involved ways in which the silk threads that spiders spin are used to direct animal traffic.

Stop signs. Entomologists Thomas Eisner and Stephen Nowicki of the Division of Biological Sciences at Cornell University in Ithaca, N.Y., reported in January 1983 that they had determined the function of stabiliments, thickened areas of silk laid out across the center of webs made by orb weaver spiders. The stabiliments have shapes as varied as a cross, a vertical strand, or a round patch. Scientists had thought that these stabiliments might stabilize or strengthen the webs, or aid the spider in locating or capturing insect prey. However, spiders seemed to secure prey even without them.

Eisner and Nowicki observed that only spiders that leave their webs up throughout the day add stabiliments. Spiders that spin in the evening and take their webs down the following morning do not add stabiliments. The researchers theorized that stabiliments act as stop signs that deter birds from accidentally flying into and destroying webs during the day.

The researchers tested their hypothesis on Barro Colorado Island in Panama and on Islamorada in the Florida Keys. They used 60 webs produced by spiders that do not add stabiliments to their webs. Allowing the webs to remain on the bushes where they were spun, Eisner and Nowicki left 30 untouched and added artificial stabiliments, made from white paper, to the other 30. The scientists checked the test webs at two-hour intervals between 6 A.M. and noon, the time when most birds were flying. Then they rated the webs as "intact," "damaged," or "destroyed."

The artificial stabiliments definitely helped prevent web damage. Only 10 per cent of the webs without artificial stabiliments remained intact by noon, but 62 per cent of the webs with stabiliments survived. The researchers suggested that small ground mammals, such as mice and rabbits, and large insects, such as butterflies, may also avoid webs with stabiliments.

Zoology

Continued

Stabiliments – noticeably thickened silk parts of orb weaver spider webs – serve as "stop signs" to deter other animals from blundering into webs and destroying them.

A few prey may also see the stabiliments and be warned away. But the spiders eat the webs in the process of taking them down, and if the webs were torn away, the spiders would lose an important source of protein. Apparently, the trade-off of losing a few insect prey that can also see the stabiliments is an economical one, compared with losing the whole web.

Spiderways. Spiders also use their silk for constructing "highways," according to a report in April by entomologists Yael D. Lubin of the Charles Darwin Research Station in Guayaquil, Ecuador, and Michael H. Robinson of the Smithsonian Tropical Research Institute in Panama. They discovered the silk highway system while investigating the behavior of *Achaearanea wau* spiders in forests of Papua New Guinea.

The spiders live in colonies, or communal webs, containing up to several hundred individuals. Web-building is usually done at night.

After observing several colonies of spiders for several months, Lubin and Robinson noticed a sudden increase in building activity. Females worked one night to extend the web in one direction until they had constructed a broad highway 1 meter (39.37 inches) wide and several meters long. The next night, many impregnated female spiders, capable of laying eggs, migrated from the old colony. Very few males made the move. The spiders kept together in small clusters and inched along the highway to a new site, where they built a new communal web. No further movement occurred between the old and new colonies.

Not all of the females migrated from the old colony, so it continued to exist. The researchers found that the spiders moved only when colonies had more than 100 members, suggesting that migration is due to lack of space.

Lubin and Robinson deduced that the mass moves probably have several advantages over migration by individuals. The communally built silk highway may protect the females from predators. The relatively large number of transplanted spiders may form a

E.P., the first emperor penguin to be successfully reared by humans, still needs the security of nestling against a large, soft motherlike object – a role filled at San Diego's Sea World by a large stuffed dog.

colony with a good chance of success. And the fact that large numbers of migrating females are capable of laying fertilized eggs ensures the continuation of the new colony.

Chemical warfare. People have waged war against termites for centuries with little success. Termites live in large colonies where new members seem constantly to replace those that are poisoned. However, Ralph W. Howard, a researcher with the Department of Agriculture's Forest Service in Gulfport, Miss., reported in June 1982 that the insecticide methoprene, a chemical that mimics a natural termite hormone, seems to disrupt the social structure of termite colonies.

Young termites molt, or physically change form, to become workers, egg layers, or soldiers. In a colony feeding on normal wood, only a few termites molt into soldiers — colony sentinels that use their hardened pincerlike mouthparts to attack such intruders as raiding ants. However, when termites eat wood impregnated with methoprene, about half of them molt into soldiers. Soldiers are unable to feed themselves because of their specialized mouthparts, so worker termites must feed them digested wood. With so many soldiers in a methoprene-treated colony, the workers cannot care for them all. The result is mass starvation of soldiers and a colony vulnerable to destruction by enemies.

Unfortunately, scientists also discovered that termites are waging chemical warfare against us. An international team of researchers led by atmospheric scientists Patrick R. Zimmerman and James P. Greenberg of the National Center for Atmospheric Research (NCAR) in Boulder, Colo., reported in November that termites may produce significantly large quantities of methane and carbon dioxide. The researchers found that bacteria in the guts of termites produce these gaseous compounds as by-products of *anaerobic* (oxygenless) decomposition of the wood they eat.

The scientists created experimental colonies of as many as 2,000 termites in specially equipped glass jars. They fed the termites carefully measured amounts of wood, then analyzed and measured the gaseous emissions from

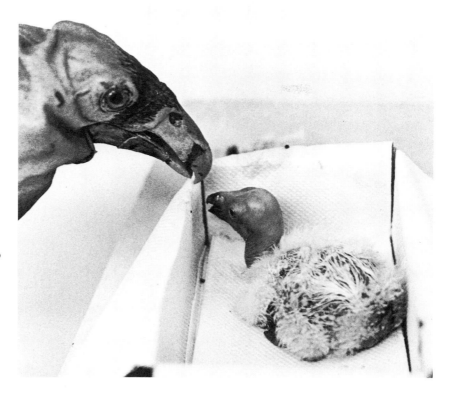

Sisquoc, the first California condor ever born in captivity, was hatched at the San Diego Zoo on March 31, 1983. The baby is fed by a hand puppet resembling an adult condor so that it will grow up familiar with its own species.

Zoology

Continued

the colonies to determine the quantity of methane and carbon dioxide produced in a given time period. The scientists wanted to determine the efficiency of gas production — the ratio of the amount of gas produced to the amount of wood eaten. The NCAR team also made field tests of termite nests in the Arizona desert and in forests in Guatemala and Kenya. From all these data, the researchers estimated how much methane and carbon dioxide would be produced by all the termites on earth.

The amount of methane and carbon dioxide in the earth's atmosphere is significant because both gases are involved in the so-called greenhouse effect by which some of the heat from the sun is trapped rather than reflected away from earth. Since scientists began measuring in 1958, the carbon dioxide concentration in the atmosphere has been rising. Some fear the level may go high enough to raise the earth's average surface temperature by 2° to 3°C. This could melt the polar icecaps and cause changes in climate.

An increase in methane concentration would complicate the situation.

Scientists had thought that the major sources of carbon dioxide were decaying organic matter, burning fossil fuels, and plant respiration. The major sources of methane gas were thought to be rice paddies, natural wetlands, burning forests, gas-reservoir leakage, and the belching of cattle digesting grass. No one had considered termite colonies an important source of the two gases. However, the NCAR team estimated that the amount of carbon dioxide termites produce is twice as much as the worldwide production from burning fossil fuels. And termite-produced methane may account for as much as half of the methane on earth.

Scientists are not as worried about termite production of carbon dioxide as they are about fossil fuel production of the gas. Termites just speed up the natural plant-use cycle while fossil fuels add an entirely new source of carbon dioxide. Termite production of methane, however, is a serious problem because there is no natural recy-

"Go to your room!"

Zoology

Continued

cling of that gas—it just accumulates in the atmosphere.

Because such currently stepped-up activities as clearing tropical forests and converting them to pasture and farmland tend to increase the numbers of termites, the NCAR team's report contributed to scientific concern about earth's future climate.

Meat-eating bees. David W. Roubik of the Smithsonian Tropical Research Institute reported in September 1982 that *Trigona hypogea*, a species of stingless bees that live in tropical forests, relies on dead animal flesh, rather than plant pollen, for protein.

People who live in the tropics are careful to avoid the foul-tasting honey of certain stingless bees. These bees collect fluids from dead animals as well as pollen and nectar from flowers. Sometimes these fluids, including snake venom, end up in the honey. But *T. hypogea* is the first species discovered that does not pursue flowers at all. The bees have no pollen baskets on their hind legs. Instead, they have five large pointed teeth on each mandi-ble—their jawlike seizing and biting organ. They use these to feed on the carcasses of monkeys, birds, lizards, fish, snakes, and large insects. Roubik watched groups of 60 to 80 bees in Panama clean a large lizard down to its skeleton in only three days.

The foragers chew the flesh off the animal and carry some of the partially digested food back to the nest where they regurgitate it. Worker bees in the nest use a glandular secretion to convert the regurgitated matter into preserved food for newly emerging bees. Unlike pollen, which can be kept in hive chambers with developing eggs, the decaying flesh must be biochemically preserved or it would rot.

Although these meat-eating bees compete with ants, the main foragers of tropical forests, the two insects seem to coexist. During his investigation, Roubik found that ants left the meat-eating bees alone. The ants confined their scavenging to the night hours, giving the bees a free hand to gather all they could during the day.
[William J. Bell and Elizabeth Pennisi]

Science You Can Use

In areas selected for their current interest, *Science Year* presents information that the reader as a consumer can use in making decisions—from buying products to caring for personal health and well-being.

Shielding Your Eyes

If you stay out in the sun for long periods without wearing sunglasses, your eyes may receive harmful amounts of solar radiation. Sunglasses protect your eyes by filtering out most of this radiation, but not all sunglasses are equally effective. Along with two of my colleagues at the University of Illinois Eye and Ear Infirmary in Chicago, I recently did a study that showed which sunglasses do the best job.

Sunlight is made up mostly of waves of three kinds of radiation. Of these, infrared rays, which we cannot see, have the longest wavelength—the distance from one wave to the next. Wavelengths of infrared rays measure at least 700 nanometers (nm, or millionths of a millimeter); waves of visible light are 400 to 700 nm long; and ultraviolet rays, which are also invisible, have wavelengths below 400 nm.

Ultraviolet rays do the greatest damage to the eyes, followed by visible radiation, especially short-wavelength light. Infrared rays seem merely to intensify the damage caused by the other types of radiation.

Prolonged exposure to ultraviolet rays whose wavelengths are close to 400 nm can damage the retina, the area in the back of the eye that contains the organs of sight. Fortunately, the cornea, the eye's transparent outer covering, filters out almost all ultraviolet rays whose wavelengths range from about 200 to 300 nm. And the transparent lens of the eye absorbs ultraviolet rays whose wavelengths range from 300 to 400 nm.

The absorption of these rays alters an amino acid in the lens, improving the lens's ability to absorb such rays. This ability increases with age. A 10-year-old's lenses absorb about 10 per cent of the ultraviolet rays that reach them, while the lenses of a 20-year-old may absorb 80 to 90 per cent of this type of radiation.

However, laboratory studies on monkeys' eyes indicate that chronic doses of even low levels of ultraviolet radiation damage the retina. Furthermore, microscopic examination of human eyes shows that ultraviolet radiation may contribute to the development of a retinal disease called senile macular degeneration in the small number of people who are susceptible to the disease, most often seen after age 65. This can cause blindness.

In protecting the retina, the lens becomes a victim of ultraviolet light itself. Long-term absorption of ultraviolet light by the human lens contributes to the development of cataracts, a disease in which the lens becomes cloudy, often blocking vision significantly. Experiments have shown that animals developed cataracts when their lenses were exposed to prolonged, low doses of ultraviolet light. We also know that the incidence of cataracts among people varies with the amount of sunlight they receive. The incidence drops off with the distance from the equator. Fewer people in New York state, for example, get cataracts than do Florida residents.

Sunglasses minimize the risk of damage. To be most effective in bright sunlight, sunglasses should block out more than 95 per cent of the ultraviolet radiation between 300 and 400 nm, more than 80 per cent of the visible radiation, and most of the infrared.

In our evaluation of sunglasses, my colleagues and I drew up charts of lens efficiency showing that only a small percentage of the 90 pairs studied blocked the desired amount of ultraviolet, visible, and infrared radiation. About one-third of the lenses were extremely ineffective.

You can use our data to evaluate sunglasses if we studied your brand. A helpful technique in evaluating a brand of sunglasses not listed in our charts is to put them on and look at yourself in a mirror in bright light. If you can see your eyes easily, the lens is unlikely to be efficient at filtering out at least the recommended amount of visible light.   [Gerald A. Fishman]

Lenses That Block Out More Than 95 per cent of Ultraviolet Rays Between 300 and 400 Nanometers

Glass Lenses

American Optical
    Filterweld FW 3, 4, 5, 6 Green*†
    Filterweld Hazemaster Yellow
    Calobar D, ED Green*†
Bausch and Lomb
    Ray Ban 3 Green†
    Ray Ban G 15 Gray
    Ray Ban Mirror*
House of Vision Color Cote Green C†
Sun Cloud Mirror*†

Plastic Lenses

American Optical Aolite True Tone 5%, 10%,
    15%, 20% Green
Cool Ray Blue, Brown, Gray, Green,
    174 Green
Foster Grant Brown, Gray, 8257 Gray, Gray
    Clip-Ons
Jean Pierre Lamy Blue
Noir 107 Brown*†
Polaroid
    Rose, Blue, Brown, Orange, Gray, Green
Polaroid Mirror*
Sears Gray Clip-Ons, Brown

*Blocks more than 85 per cent of visible light at any wavelength from 400 to 700 nanometers.
†Blocks more than 85 per cent of infrared rays at any wavelength from 700 to 800 nanometers.

The Physics of the Fireplace

Few domestic scenes compare with the sight of a family gathered around a warm fireplace on a cold winter evening. And few household tasks are more miserable than a smoky struggle with sticks and wads of flaming newspaper in a vain attempt to get a fire going in a fireplace.

You can get the comfort without the struggle by understanding and employing the principles of combustion. Use a fire-starting technique named the three T's — for *t*ime, *t*urbulence, and *t*emperature.

The time it takes a fire to spread depends upon the heat of the fire, and this in turn depends upon the size of the fire. The small fire that you get when you ignite kindling generates so little heat that a weak current of air will blow it out. Therefore, you must protect the fire to give it plenty of time to spread.

Turbulence helps to blend combustible gases that rise from the burning wood with the slow-moving air around the fire.

The final T — temperature — must become high enough to keep the fire going. A log that seems to be burning well but is not hot enough to ignite the logs next to it will cool, and the fire will go out.

Putting the three T's technique to work begins with the selection of fuel. You will need dry kindling, varying in size from pencil-thin rods to sticks that are slightly thicker than your thumb. For best results, use about the same weight of slender sticks and thicker ones. You will also need some wood shavings or crumpled paper to ignite the kindling.

The next step in building a fire is arranging the fuel in the fireplace. First, lay a log at each end of the area in which you are going to build the fire. If you build the fire on the fireplace floor, put the logs next to the side walls. If you use a grate, put these logs at the ends of the grate. In either case, the logs should point straight out toward the room. Next, put a small pile of crumpled paper or wood shavings in the center of the area between the logs. Then crisscross the kindling into a lattice, beginning with the thinner sticks at the bottom center. Finally, open the chimney damper almost completely. You are now ready to light the fire.

The lattice will prevent the heated air from rising so rapidly that the fire does not have time to spread, and it will also promote turbulence. The variation in kindling sizes allows the temperature to become high enough so that the fire spreads from smaller to larger pieces.

As the fire spreads to the larger pieces of kindling, add logs parallel to the opening. Do not wait too long or the temperature of the kindling fire will drop below ignition temperature for the logs. On the other hand, adding logs too soon will choke off the fire. You will learn by experience how soon to add the logs.

Once your fire is going, start regulating the flow of air that it receives. Too much air makes a fire too hot, burning the wood rapidly and giving the fire an orange or yellow cast. Such a fire sends most heat straight up the chimney. Wood that receives too little air does not burn completely, creating smoke that tends to enter the room.

The typical fireplace does not have automatic controls to regulate airflow, but it does have a chimney damper. The damper is like the throttle in a car. When the damper is wide open, the fire roars; however, when the damper is almost closed, the fire burns slowly and fitfully.

Opening the damper almost completely before starting the fire allows the fire to get hot quickly, producing a strong updraft in the chimney. This draft helps the fire spread around the fuel and, in most cases, forces smoke up the chimney.

On a chilly day, cold, heavy air trapped in the chimney may push the

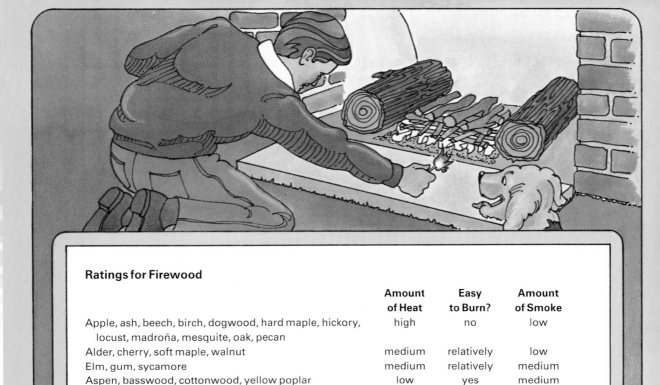

Ratings for Firewood

	Amount of Heat	Easy to Burn?	Amount of Smoke
Apple, ash, beech, birch, dogwood, hard maple, hickory, locust, madroña, mesquite, oak, pecan	high	no	low
Alder, cherry, soft maple, walnut	medium	relatively	low
Elm, gum, sycamore	medium	relatively	medium
Aspen, basswood, cottonwood, yellow poplar	low	yes	medium
Douglas fir, larch, southern yellow pine, tamarack	medium	yes	high
Cedar, cypress, pine (eastern white, ponderosa, sugar, western white), redwood, spruce, true fir	low	yes	medium

smoke back into the room. You can force this air back up the chimney by holding a burning newspaper near the open damper before lighting the kindling. It also helps to crack open a window briefly.

As the fire progresses, gradually close the damper until the opening is just wide enough to prevent smoke from entering the room.

You can take some steps to prevent heat from escaping through the hearth floor, the back of the fireplace, and up the chimney. To keep heat away from the hearth floor, do not use a grate. Instead, build the fire on two to three inches of ash. The ash retards the conduction of heat from the fire down to the hearth.

You can block the escape of heat through the back of the fireplace or up the chimney by stacking the logs so that they slope upward toward the back of the fireplace. Put the largest logs where the floor meets the back of the fireplace. These logs cut off conduction toward the back of the fireplace and tilt the plane of the fire so that heat radiates into the room, rather than up the chimney. Furthermore, this arrangement maximizes radiation, because it provides more burning area than does a row of logs laid flat. For even more burning area, use logs that are nearly as long as the opening at the front of the fireplace.

And to get even more heat, use hardwoods such as ash, beech, birch, maple, and oak. Hardwoods take a long time to ignite, but they burn slowly. Softwoods such as pine and spruce are easier to get going, but they burn more rapidly and tend to make smokier fires. However, softwoods make good kindling.

Do not use recently cut wood to build a fire, because the fire will use part of its heat just to drive moisture out of the wood. If you cut your own wood, store it for a year in a place where it is sheltered from rain but exposed to dry air and some sunlight.

The wise selection and storage of firewood and the application of physical principles to the task of getting heat out of the wood will produce a fire that is both pleasant to look at and pleasant to feel. [Pasquale M. Sforza]

Personal Computers: More for Your Dollar

Sales of personal computers surged in 1982 and the first half of 1983. Fewer than 2 million were in use in the United States in 1981, but 3.5 million were sold during 1982, and experts predicted 7 million sales for 1983.

Among the main reasons for this surge were the lower prices and higher capabilities of home computers, the least expensive machines. Some of these are battery-operated, but most plug into an electrical outlet.

The price of a typical home computer plummeted from $500 at the beginning of 1982 to less than $100 in May 1983. Texas Instruments, Incorporated, started the trend in August 1982 with a $100 rebate on its Model 99/4A—a $400 computer about the size of a portable typewriter.

Like all small portables, Model 99/4A is a complete computer with a main memory, which stores information; a central processing unit (CPU), which performs the arithmetic functions and logic processes; and a control unit, which coordinates the machine.

The computer user sends information to the machine through its keyboard, an ordinary typewriter keyboard that also has special computer keys. The machine sends data to the user via the screen of an ordinary TV set. For a permanent copy of a small computer's output, you can buy a printer for about $500.

A small computer can perform simple game programs, financial programs such as household budgeting and checkbook balancing, and other programs written by the user in BASIC, a computer language.

You can program the computer yourself, but this may take many hours. Fortunately, small computers accept ready-made programs fed from a cassette player that costs less than $50. Some machines also use cartridges that store programs in silicon chips no larger than a fingernail, and some use floppy disks that look like small phonograph records.

A typical home computer's memory unit can store only 16,000 bytes—letters and symbols of computer language—but you can buy an attachment that stores 32,000 bytes for about $300. This allows you to set up large databases such as mailing lists or to run more complex educational programs. Such a program, a computer language called Logo, teaches children logical concepts painlessly. They learn by teaching an image called a turtle how to move about the screen.

In 1983, several companies were manufacturing book-sized computers. The $800 HX-20, for example, made by Epson of Japan, measures about $8\frac{1}{2} \times 11 \times 2$ inches. It displays its output in four lines on a built-in screen. A book-sized machine can run programs written in BASIC and it can act as an electronic notebook, storing typed information for electronic delivery to a printing unit.

If you want to use large business programs, such as a payroll program, you will need the next larger size of computer. Most of these have from 64,000 to 512,000 bytes of main memory, and cost $3,000 to $6,000.

The prices of video game consoles, actually special-purpose computers, plunged from $300 to less than $100 between January 1982 and May 1983, and several manufacturers of video games introduced keyboards that convert consoles to home computers.

In January 1983, Apple Computer, Incorporated, of Cupertino, Calif., announced a concept that may influence the design of computers used in the home. Apple unveiled Lisa, a $9,995, professional-level computer that has a movable control called a mouse. Rolling the mouse along the table moves an arrow on the screen, enabling the user to select items shown on the screen. Lisa thus permits the user to by-pass the keyboard for common operations. No doubt the mouse system will soon become available in low-cost personal computers. [Harold C. Kinne]

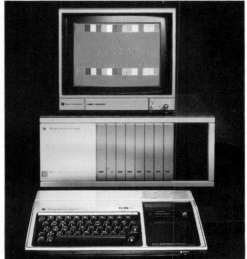

Modern personal computers include Apple's Lisa, *above left,* with a special handheld control; Radio Shack's TRS-80 Model 16, *left,* which runs three jobs at once; and Texas Instruments' 99/4A, *above,* which houses add-on components like books on a shelf.

Picking Out a
Pain Reliever

The death of seven people who swallowed poisoned capsules of Extra-Strength Tylenol in September 1982 raised questions about the safety of drugs sold from open shelving. The tragedy also aroused interest in why there are different kinds of pain relievers.

You can choose from a bewildering variety of pain-relieving *products*, but only two pain-relieving *drugs* are available in the United States without a prescription — aspirin and another chemical called acetaminophen. All the products contain one or both of the drugs. Bayer Aspirin, for example, includes only aspirin. Tylenol contains acetaminophen, but no aspirin. Excedrin contains both drugs. Because some people cannot take aspirin, acetaminophen products gained widespread use as a substitute in the 1950s.

Aspirin and acetaminophen work as pain relievers in tissues of the body where pain begins, rather than in the central nervous system — the brain and spinal cord. However, the brain is involved when the drugs reduce fever.

Pain arises as a result of inflammation, the response of tissue to injury. This response also involves heat, redness, and swelling. During the early stages of inflammation, cells of tissue form substances called prostaglandins that strengthen the response. Prostaglandins cause pain when another substance involved in inflammation, bradykinin, is also present.

Aspirin eases pain by stopping the production of prostaglandins. It does this by interfering with the operation of an enzyme that forms them. However, we do not know how acetaminophen prevents pain. Acetaminophen reduces prostaglandin production only slightly, but perhaps this is enough.

Both aspirin and acetaminophen have drawbacks. The main disadvantage of aspirin stems from its acidity — its chemical name is acetylsalicylic acid — in combination with the natural acidity of the stomach. When an ordinary aspirin tablet touches the mucous membrane that lines the interior wall of the stomach, small wounds form. Also, small doses of aspirin interfere with the production of thromboxane — a type of prostaglandin that promotes blood clotting. Therefore, aspirin almost invariably causes small, bleeding wounds in the stomach.

This bleeding is usually light and the wounds heal quickly. It does not threaten the health of most people, even though it can cause heartburn and a feeling of abdominal fullness and subsequent belching. However, bleeding in the stomach can lead to disastrous complications in patients who have an active peptic ulcer.

A number of nonprescription aspirin preparations counteract acidity. One of these is Bufferin, a mixture of aspirin and a substance called a buffer that greatly reduces the effect of aspirin's acidity. In addition, there are nonprescription tablets containing aspirin coated with substances that resist dissolving in stomach acid but not in the alkaline environment of the small intestine. These are known as *enteric* (intestinal) coated tablets. However, the coating retards absorption so that pain relief may be delayed.

Aspirin can also cause some hearing loss and tinnitus, ringing of the ears. These reactions disappear when the effect of the aspirin wears off. An extremely small number of people are allergic to aspirin.

Nevertheless, aspirin is almost trouble-free when taken in small doses by most people for average temporary pain, including headache.

However, doses of up to 20 tablets per day, such as are prescribed for arthritis, may magnify the drug's adverse effects. In addition to hearing reduction and tinnitus, heavy doses can cause toxic effects in the brain and spinal cord resulting in mental confusion and headaches.

Buffering or enteric coating is almost essential for such heavy doses. However, buffering hastens the excre-

The Punch in Pain Relievers

	Aspirin, mg	Acetaminophen, mg	Caffeine, mg	Other ingredients
Alka-Seltzer Effervescent Pain Reliever & Antacid	324			citric acid, sodium bicarbonate
Anacin/Maximum Strength Anacin	400/500		32/32	
Anacin-3 Analgesic Tablet		325		
Arthritis Pain Formula	486			buffering agents
Bayer Aspirin/Children's Chewable	325/81			
Bufferin: reg./Arthritis Strength	324/486			buffering agents·
Dristan Decongestant Antihistamine/Analgesic		325		antihistamine, decongestant
Ecotrin	325			enteric coating
Empirin	325			
Excedrin	250	250	65	
Extra-Strength Datril		500		
Ornex		325		decongestant
St. Joseph Aspirin for Children	81			
Sine-Aid Sinus Headache Tablet		325		decongestant
Tylenol: Children's/Regular Strength/Extra-Strength		80/325/500		
Vanquish	227	194	33	buffering agents

tion of aspirin in the urine. Consequently, the drug may leave the body so rapidly that too little remains to accomplish the desired effect.

Aspirin works as an anti-arthritic drug at least partially by limiting production of prostaglandins that contribute to pain and others that are at least somewhat responsible for inflammation. On the other hand, acetaminophen is a poor anti-arthritic drug, perhaps because it has only a slight effect on the production of prostaglandins. Physicians use it on arthritis patients only to strengthen the pain-reducing effect of other medications and to eliminate pain and other conditions associated with inflammation.

The advantage of acetaminophen is its lack of effect on the stomach, so people who have peptic ulcers can use it. Furthermore, acetaminophen does not prevent blood clotting, so physicians recommend it for patients whose blood clots poorly.

The greatest danger in using acetaminophen is that it can damage the liver. The liver changes acetaminophen into inactive substances which are then excreted into the urine. This liver activity, however, leads to the production of chemical substances that may damage the membranes of liver cells. Damage is especially likely to occur when a patient takes higher than recommended doses for a prolonged period. It is also risky when the liver is already damaged, for example, by excessive use of alcohol.

Many physicians advise their patients to take one aspirin tablet per day to decrease the tendency of their blood to clot. Some physicians believe this regimen can prevent or reduce the incidence of heart attacks, strokes, and clotting in the arms and legs. Larger doses may wipe out this advantage by reducing the production of prostacyclin, a prostaglandin that opposes thromboxane's clotting action.

Some people take aspirin at bedtime to help them sleep. There is no convincing evidence that aspirin can do this, unless pain is the cause of sleeplessness. There are antihistamine drugs that relieve headaches and allergy symptoms, and induce sleep. They may include aspirin or acetaminophen. The two drugs are also in cold medicines that dry the mucous membranes in the nose and throat.

Nonprescription pain relievers are available in tablets, capsules, powders, and liquids. The form of the drug does not alter its beneficial effects, and so most people buy the tablet, the least expensive form. Equal doses of pure aspirin and acetaminophen are almost equal in their ability to relieve pain and fever. Therefore a standard aspirin tablet that contains 5 grains, or 325 milligrams (mg), of aspirin is roughly equivalent to a 325-mg tablet of an acetaminophen such as Regular Strength Tylenol. To get more relief, you can take two or three of these tablets, or you can take a tablet such as Excedrin, which contains 250 mg of aspirin and 250 mg of acetaminophen.

Many people who have trouble swallowing tablets use capsules or liquids instead. Aspirin is not soluble in water, so it is not sold as a liquid. However, aspirin is the pain reliever in Alka-Seltzer Effervescent Pain Reliever & Antacid, a large tablet of compressed powder that dissolves in water. When the tablet dissolves, a chemical reaction converts the aspirin to sodium acetyl salicylate, which provides the beneficial effects of aspirin.

You may get more pain relief from a preparation of aspirin or acetaminophen that also contains caffeine, usually about the amount in a strong cup of coffee. Some medical researchers believe that caffeine strengthens the effect of both drugs. However, medical opinion on caffeine's effectiveness is sharply divided.

If you are unsure about which pain reliever to use, you can simplify your search by evaluating your needs, your medical condition, and the advantages and disadvantages of the various preparations. Obviously, if you have unusual or persistent pain or frequent fevers, you should consult a physician.

You should use the preparation that works best for you, subject to general medical precautions: Never use aspirin if you have an active peptic ulcer or a deficiency in blood clotting. Use aspirin with caution if you have a history of peptic ulcer. Use acetaminophen with caution if you have a liver disease or if you drink substantial amounts of alcohol.   [Thomas G. Kantor]

Get a Good Run
for Your Money

If you are thinking about taking up long-distance jogging or running to get yourself into shape, you should begin by obtaining your physician's approval. Then buy a good pair of running shoes.

Long-distance recreational running is a contact sport. When you run, your feet contact the ground with a force equal to two to three times your body weight. If the running surface is a street, a sidewalk, or a hard running path, the force can shock bones, muscles, and connective tissue severely. Furthermore, the impact can make your foot move within the shoe in a way that causes additional strain.

A good running shoe absorbs this shock and controls the foot as no other type of athletic shoe can. A running shoe's shock absorber is its heavily padded sole. The sole is made up of several layers: the outsole, or treads; the wedge, which reaches from the heel to the front of the arch; and the midsole, which is thickest at the heel and extends the length of the shoe.

An outsole made of natural rubber absorbs shock well and lasts a long time. The wedge and midsole contribute the most to shock absorption and should therefore be made of a material that cushions the foot but springs back quickly when weight is removed. The

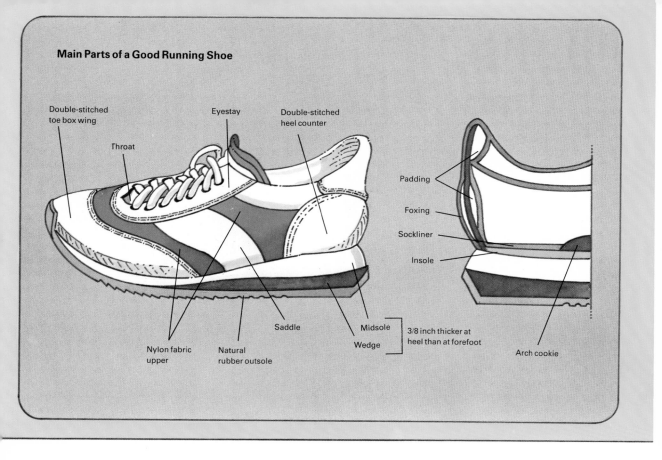

Main Parts of a Good Running Shoe

Double-stitched toe box wing

Eyestay

Double-stitched heel counter

Throat

Padding

Foxing

Sockliner

Insole

Saddle

Midsole

3/8 inch thicker at heel than at forefoot

Wedge

Nylon fabric upper

Natural rubber outsole

Arch cookie

wedge and midsole thickness should be ⅜ to ⅝ inch greater at the heel than at the forefoot.

The position of the foot is controlled by two components of the upper shoe called the heel counter and the toe box wing. The heel counter wraps around the heel of the foot, preventing excess side-to-side motion.

The toe box wing holds the ball of the foot on the sole and also prevents excess side-to-side motion. It is usually made of the same material as the heel counter. Both the toe box wing and the heel counter should be slightly firmer than a tennis ball and double-stitched to the shoe. The toe box wing should extend to the front of the arch. Nylon fabric is the best material for the rest of the upper shoe because it is washable, does not soak up water, and allows air to circulate through the shoe.

The shoe also may have a rubber liner or a wedge-shaped insert called an arch cookie. These inserts conform to the shape of the foot, providing additional support for common foot variations such as high or low arches.

Runners who have certain physical abnormalities—such as one leg being shorter than the other—need special inserts called orthotics.

Beginning runners need a great deal of cushioning and foot control, because their running style is probably not as efficient as that of experienced runners. The beginner therefore should wear training shoes, which are more cushioned and heavier than competition shoes. In fact, most amateur runners should use training shoes, even in races. The additional weight of the shoes will cost a runner just a few seconds, a trivial price to pay for the protection that the shoes provide. Overweight people and other heavy runners need stiff soles to absorb shock.

You should resist the temptation to use your running shoes as general-purpose athletic shoes. Running shoes are designed for constant forward motion. Using them in sports such as tennis and basketball that require quick lateral movements and sudden stops can cause injury. Use shoes designed for such sports. [Mike Moore]

Options for
the Soap Dish

If the only soap that cleans your hands well after gardening or changing a tire also irritates your skin, you have made uncomfortable contact with a fundamental fact about soaps and other detergents — the greater the cleaning power, the harsher the detergent.

However, understanding the simple mechanics and chemistry of detergents may help you find a soap that provides both cleanliness and comfort for your skin, and synthetic detergents that do the best job on your dishes, fabrics, woodwork, and walls.

Soaps and other detergents come as solids and liquids, and they have various chemical compositions. Each product is intended for use under certain conditions of water temperature, water chemistry, and soiling. However, most soaps and other detergents are fundamentally the same. At the molecular level, they work like mechanical implements. Detergent molecules penetrate grease and grip it from within like little harpoons. They pry dirt loose from soiled surfaces like tiny crowbars, and, like miniature pliers, wrap themselves around small pieces of dirt and grease.

These mechanical capabilities are due to the chemical makeup of detergent molecules. Soap molecules come from a fat molecule that looks like three long threads connected at one end. In the manufacture of soap, the threads react chemically with an alkali, usually sodium hydroxide, also known as caustic soda. The three threads break apart, and one sodium atom from the caustic soda joins one end of each thread to form a molecule of soap. Chemists call this molecule a sodium salt of a fatty acid.

When this molecule dissolves in water, the sodium atom, which is positively charged, drifts away from the molecule, leaving one end of the thread negatively charged. The other end is electrically neutral.

Water molecules are also neutral, but they have a positively charged region and a zone that is negatively charged. The positive region attracts and holds the negative end of a detergent molecule. The other end of the detergent molecule, although neutral, is chemically so similar to grease that it dissolves in grease and holds onto the grease from the inside.

Water's surface tension — the tendency of its molecules to cling to one another rather than to molecules of other substances — prevents it from penetrating soiled surfaces. Detergent molecules reduce surface tension, thereby enabling water molecules to "harpoon" grease.

A detergent's ability to clean depends greatly upon the length of its threads. The main part of each thread is made of a chain of carbon atoms with hydrogen atoms on the outside of the "links." A thread has an even number of carbon atoms, from 10 to 18. The shorter the thread, the more easily the molecule dissolves in water.

Toilet soaps are usually mixtures of the sodium salts of stearic (18 carbon atoms) and palmitic (16 carbons) acids. Stearic acid comes mainly from beef and mutton fat, while sources of palmitic acid include palm oil, cottonseed oil, beef fat, and lard.

Sodium stearate does not dissolve well in water that is cool enough for bathing, so bath soaps also contain substantial amounts of highly soluble molecules derived from coconut oil. These are the salts of lauric (12 carbons) and myristic (14 carbons) acids.

A special kind of bath soap, Castile soap, is popular in areas where the water is hard. Hard water contains dissolved calcium and magnesium, which combine readily with ordinary soap molecules to form insoluble salts. This chemical reaction prevents the soap from working well. Furthermore, when soapy water is rinsed away, the salts stay behind in forms such as bathtub rings. Castile soap is effective in hard water because its main salt — the sodium salt of oleic acid (also 18

Household Soaps and Detergents

Types	Commercial Examples
Shampoos	Alberto Balsam, Head and Shoulders, Prell, Suave, Vidal Sassoon
Toilet soaps	Camay, Cashmere Bouquet, Dial, Dove, Fiesta, Ivory, Lifebuoy, Safeguard, Sweetheart, Zest
Laundry soaps	
Granules	Ivory Flakes, Ivory Snow
Bars	Fels-Naphtha
Laundry detergents	
Granules	All, Fab, Oxydol, Purex, Tide
Liquids	Dynamo, Era, Heavy Duty All, Wisk, Yes
Dishwashing detergents	
Granules	Cascade, Calgonite, Electrasol
Liquids	Ajax, Dawn, Dove, Ivory, Joy, Lux, Palmolive
All-purpose cleaners	
Powders	Oakite, Soilax, Spic and Span
Liquids	
Bottle	Lestoil, Lysol Deodorizing, Mr. Clean, Top Job
Pump	Fantastik, Formula 409, Sensation
Aerosol	Big Wally

carbons) — is more water-soluble in the presence of dissolved calcium and magnesium than are the salts in ordinary soaps.

Toilet soaps contain combinations of various additives, including perfumes; dyes; cold cream; and antiseptics such as camphor, carbolic acid, iodine, and sulfur. None of these help soaps clean. However, pumice or sand added to soap increases its abrasive qualities and thus helps it clean.

Most people can use any toilet soap without irritation. However, if the soap you are using irritates your skin, you should try a soap that has a lower percentage of salts derived from coconut oil and palm oil. If the new soap also irritates your skin, an additive may be at fault. The next step therefore would be to use as pure a soap as you can find. If that does not work, visit your doctor — you may be allergic to soap. If that is the case, the doctor probably will recommend a synthetic detergent made for the skin.

"Hard" soaps are sodium soaps that are solid at room temperature. Hard soaps are the cleansers in soap chips, flakes, and powders for dishes and delicate fabrics.

On the other hand, soaps made from alkalis of potassium rather than sodium are usually liquid at room temperature. These liquid soaps are used in shampoos, shaving soap, and in squirt soap dispensed in public washrooms.

Soap-type shampoos are made of potassium salts of coconut oils, so they are extremely soluble. Other shampoos contain synthetic detergents.

One type of shampoo belongs to a class of synthetic detergents whose molecules have electrically neutral groups of atoms on their water-soluble ends. These groups include derivatives of sugar and of ethylene glycol. Water molecules attract these molecules because water, sugar, and ethylene glycol are chemically similar. These detergents are termed nonionic because their molecules are not ionic — that is, they are electrically neutral. The grease-soluble end of a nonionic detergent is the same as the long string of carbon and hydrogen atoms in soaps.

The nonionic shampoo contains a sugar detergent that dissolves readily but is not harsh. This product does not sting if it gets in your eyes.

Synthetic detergents generally are chemically similar to soaps, but they do not form insoluble salts with calcium and magnesium. The manufacture of synthetic detergents used widely for laundry begins with the same fats and oils used to make soaps. The resulting molecule — a sodium salt of a sulfate ester of a fatty alcohol — has a water-soluble end similar to the soluble end of a soap molecule. When the detergent dissolves, this end becomes negatively charged, so this type of detergent is called anionic, after the word *anion*, meaning a negatively charged atom or molecule.

Both soaps and synthetic detergents for your regular laundry contain additives. One class of additives called builders includes ammonia, borax, carbonates, and phosphates, which soften water; and silicates, which increase abrasion. Chlorine compounds and sodium perborate are bleaches. Brighteners are chemicals that emit light in the same way as glow-in-the-dark toys. Brighteners embed themselves in fabrics and emit blue light, brightening the fabrics. Many builders and other additives make some cleansers too harsh for the skin and even for delicate fabrics, so you should read the instructions on soap and detergent containers carefully.

Detergents for dishwashing machines are similar to laundry detergents but contain more builder. Most dishwashing and laundry soaps and detergents come in chips, flakes, and powders to help them dissolve more easily in hot water.

Liquid detergents for laundry machines and for washing dishes by hand contain water and substances that enable the detergent to dissolve in lower-temperature water. A more expensive product cleans fabrics in cold water. It contains a detergent that works well at low temperatures.

Powders and concentrated liquid detergents for walls, woodwork, and floors contain a high percentage of builder and are intended for use in hot water. These liquids may also contain solvents that are extremely harsh, so read the labels thoroughly before you use them.   [Richard D. Sands]

People in Science

Some people, when introduced to science, see problems that it can solve, and make a career out of solving them. Most of the rest of us see science as a fascinating phenomenon and are content to simply observe it in action. This section describes both approaches. It tells the story of a man who used his training in plant pathology to develop an agriculture that has kept millions of people from starving. It also describes a group of institutions that are designed to help the public learn how science works.

Norman E. Borlaug

By Noel D. Vietmeyer

By years of sweat and toil under the hot Mexican sun, this dedicated plant breeder sowed the seeds of the Green Revolution and saved millions from starvation.

Norman E. Borlaug is a spry, sparkling, effervescent character, normally clad in muddy boots and trousers, shirtsleeves, and a baseball cap. A plant pathologist and geneticist, he is not a typical academic scientist — he's happiest when close to the land. For most of his life, Borlaug has worked and lived in the open. To him, cities and offices seem like prisons; and a business suit, like a straitjacket. This casually dressed man, however, has done more to relieve world hunger than any other living person.

Historians of the future, assessing the great scientists of the 20th century, will have Norman Borlaug high on their list. In 1970, Borlaug was awarded the Nobel Peace Prize for his work in developing high-yielding varieties of wheat that produced 8 or 9 bushels of grain where only 1 had grown before. Since the 1960s, the wheats that he developed have saved millions from starvation.

For 39 of his 69 years, Borlaug has lived in Mexico, devoting his energies and talents to wheat. He serves as a consultant to the International Maize and Wheat Improvement Center — usually called CIMMYT, the initials of its Spanish name — a research center established jointly by the Mexican government and two United States foundations, the Ford Foundation and the Rockefeller Foundation. Until he officially retired in 1979, he directed CIMMYT's wheat-improvement program. But he was born and raised on a modest farm in the Saude community — population about 20 — near Cresco, Iowa. The town was known as Little Norway because many of its residents, including Borlaug's parents, were of Norwegian descent.

In his high school years, Borlaug became a star wrestler, suffering only a single defeat in his senior year. The wrestling coach and school principal, David Bartelma, believed that if you did your best on the playing field you would do your best in life. "Do your best or don't compete," was the message he drummed into his students, and these words have guided Borlaug throughout his life.

After Borlaug graduated from high school in 1932, during the Great Depression, his grandfather advised him to get a university degree. That was the best way to ensure work during hard times, said the elder Borlaug. However, no scholarship was available to a boy from a remote rural school. The bank where his parents kept their savings had gone out of business, taking their money with it.

Borlaug spent most of 1933 doing farm work, cutting fence posts, and trapping muskrats to bring in a little money. Then Bartelma came to his rescue. Another of Bartelma's students, George Champlin, had entered the University of Minnesota. That summer, at the principal's urging, Champlin offered to show Borlaug the Minnesota campus. "I'd never met Champlin before," recalls Borlaug, "but we drove to St. Paul in his beat-up Model A, and by the second day he had me sharing his living quarters and working as a waiter in the University Coffee Shop."

Borlaug visited the university registrar to see if he might be admitted but was told that the university did not consider him a high school graduate because some of his credits were not acceptable. "The only way I could get in was to pass a special examination," he recalls. "I was pretty nervous and proceeded to flunk it beautifully. I would have gone home right then, but Champlin wouldn't let me!"

That year, luckily, the University of Minnesota began a new division called the General College to teach remedial courses. Borlaug was admitted, made up his deficiencies, and about six months later transferred into the College of Forestry. Today, this student who barely squeezed in is one of the university's most famous alumni.

Borlaug graduated from the University of Minnesota in 1937 with a B.S. in forestry. However, the United States economy was still in trouble, and Borlaug was unable to find work. Somewhat reluctantly, he returned to the university for postgraduate studies in forest pathology. E. C. Stakman, a world-renowned plant pathologist on the faculty, had another idea. "Look here, Borlaug," he said, "for heaven's sake get your feet on the ground. Take plant pathology, and that will keep you out of the narrow specialization. You'll get a wide sweep of agronomy—genetics, soils, and plant diseases—and you'll be equipped for much more than trees."

So young Borlaug took up plant pathology, earning a Ph.D. in 1941. World War II had begun, and in 1942 he moved to Wilmington, Del., where he headed a microbiology research group at the laboratories of E. I. du Pont de Nemours & Company.

The author:
Noel D. Vietmeyer is a professional associate of the U.S. National Academy of Sciences. He wrote an article on physician-inventor J. Robert Cade for the 1982 edition of *Science Year*.

In experimental plots at the International Maize and Wheat Improvement Center in Mexico, plant breeder Norman E. Borlaug grows many varieties of grain.

It was not until 1944 that Borlaug, then 30 years old, started his work on crop breeding. The opportunity came because the Mexican government was concerned over the plight of the country's agriculture. Mexico had only a few agricultural scientists. Most farmers were illiterate, rural incomes were appallingly low, and the country had to import more than half its wheat. In 1940, Mexico sought help from Henry A. Wallace, Vice-President-elect of the United States. Wallace turned to the Rockefeller Foundation.

The Rockefeller Foundation and the Mexican government together created an Office of Special Studies. It began in 1943 as three hot rooms in an old government building on the outskirts of Mexico City. Jointly staffed by Mexicans and Americans, its chief goal was to provide research for graduates from Mexico's agricultural colleges. Stakman recommended young Borlaug to direct the project's wheat-improvement program, saying, "He has great depth of courage and determination. He will not be defeated by difficulty, and he burns with a missionary zeal."

After arriving in Mexico in 1944, Borlaug wrote to his wife in the United States, "The earth is so lacking in life force the plants just cling to existence. They don't really grow; they just fight to stay alive.... I don't know what we can do to help these people, but we've got to do something."

Borlaug decided to concentrate first on the most destructive fungus disease known, black stem rust. He'd first learned about rust from Stakman, who was world famous for developing new methods of combating it. Rust fungi clog the host plant's passageways, suck out food from the plant's cells, and cover fields with billions of reddish-brown spores that resemble iron rust. Diseased plants wither and die. "Rust is a shifty, changing, constantly evolving enemy," Stakman said. "We can never lower our guard. Rust diseases are the relentless, voracious destroyers of our food, and we must fight them by all means open to science."

From all over Mexico and from other countries, Borlaug gathered different varieties of wheat seed. He grew them and infected each plant with rust spores. Only 2 plants out of 5,000 showed resistance. Year after year, he laboriously crossed those two plants with varieties of wheat that had other desirable qualities.

Hybridizing wheat is incredible drudgery. Wheat plants are normally self-pollinating. Each head has 60 or more flowers, each of which has 3 stamens, or male reproductive organs, and 1 pistil, or female reproductive organ. When the stamens release their pollen, some of it falls on adjacent pistils on the same plant. To hybridize wheat, the breeder must prevent the plant from pollinating itself by plucking out each stamen with tiny tweezers while the stamens are green and before they shed their pollen. The wheat heads, which then have only female parts, are covered with a small envelope to prevent pollination by stray airborne pollen. The breeder makes the desired cross by inserting a wheat head of the chosen variety inside the envelope and shaking its pollen over the female pistils.

It is painstaking, tedious work. Borlaug's hands had to be rock steady. Hour after hour, he dragged a small stool from plant to plant down the long rows, hunched and tense, straining to pull off the more than 100 tiny stamens on each head. Muscles cramped, sweat running, the fierce Mexican sun burning his neck and ears, he worked from sunrise until dark, day after day. Often he slept in a sleeping bag on the ground or on a rough cot in the field to get an early start. He began wearing a baseball cap because its visor could be swiveled in the direction of the sun.

Each season, Borlaug and a small crew of technicians and young Mexican scientists removed the stamens from 2,000 to 6,000 plants and blended the genes with those of many other wheat plants. Carefully harvesting the resulting seeds, the scientists produced 120,000 to 360,000 seeds for planting the next season. By growing their plants in different parts of Mexico, they got two crops per year.

It was drudgery on a monumental scale. Other plant breeders found it hard to believe. Planted end-to-end, Borlaug's rows of wheat grown in a single year would have stretched 400 miles. He and his associates examined every plant and harvested the best. "Some of these kernels may be gold nuggets," he said. "Find them!"

By 1951, it began to look as if the battle against wheat rust had been won. The new varieties were resisting the disease. Then, suddenly, a new type of rust appeared and turned two of Borlaug's four

varieties into a mass of straw rotting in the sun. Two years later, another new rust wiped out one of the two remaining varieties.

Discouraged but not beaten, Borlaug went back to the beginning of the process. He crossed and recrossed the previously resistant types. He made thousands of new wheats and infected them with different types of rust. Four new resistant varieties resulted.

By 1957, 13 years after he had started, Borlaug was able to say that the black stem rust problem was finally under control — the shifty, changing, constantly evolving enemy was at bay, at least for the moment. Working with 40,000 wheats, he had created 4 varieties resistant to the disease. Soon, about 70 per cent of Mexico's wheat-land was planted with rust-resistant varieties, and the Mexican farmer's average yield almost doubled. A country that had to import half its wheat in 1943 was finally meeting the wheat demands of its large population by itself.

In 1960, the Office of Special Studies was closed, having achieved its goals, and Mexico's National Institute of Agricultural Research took over its activities. Borlaug carried on his work under the auspices of the Rockefeller Foundation. In 1964, he became director of the wheat program at CIMMYT, which was established that year.

Borlaug met his wife, Margaret G. Gibson, at the University of Minnesota. They were married in 1937 and endured difficult times.

Rust, the fungus disease that Borlaug helped to conquer, covers wheat plants with reddish-brown spores, *top left*. In the ongoing search for plants that resist rust, an aide collects the rust spores with a special vacuum cleaner, *top right*. He sprays fields with talcum powder, *above left,* which helps spread the spores on plants that the researchers hope will prove to be immune. Borlaug and co-workers study a rust specimen in a jar, *above right*.

To create dwarf hybrid wheat, Borlaug and his aides pluck stamens from wheat heads, *top,* cover the heads with protective envelopes, and shake pollen from dwarf wheat into the envelopes, *above right.* The resulting hybrid, *above,* on the left, has a bigger head than the regular wheat.

Margaret worked as a proofreader, and they struggled to make ends meet until the Du Pont job gave them a modest income. A daughter, Norma Jean, was born in the United States in 1943. Blue-eyed and blonde, she grew up in Mexico speaking Spanish like a native and now teaches Spanish in a Dallas high school. A son, William, born in Mexico in 1947, also grew up there.

When William was a child, his health was delicate, and Margaret Borlaug decided that physical exercise might build his strength. A neighbor had sons about William's age, and the two families organized some baseball games. Soon they co-founded the first Mexican Little League, the first Pony and Colt leagues, and the first all-Mexican boys' baseball tournaments. Borlaug became an enthusiastic baseball coach in his time away from the wheat fields. For 10 years, he coached and managed teams, winning 3 Mexico City championships and 1 national championship. Working with young athletes gave Borlaug many happy weekends and helped relieve the tensions of his work.

With rust overcome, Borlaug was turning his gaze to new vistas. Mexican wheat yields were still low by international standards. Fertilizing the fields should have helped, but Mexico's wheats were tall and spindly. Over the centuries, wheat in most countries had developed long, thin stems that enabled it to compete with weeds for sunlight. If those varieties were given much fertilizer, they became top-heavy and lodged, or toppled over, from the weight of their full heads. The more generous the fertilizer, the lower the yield.

However, some interesting Japanese wheats had been picked up by one of General Douglas MacArthur's agricultural aides in the late 1940s, during the U.S. administration of Japan after World War II. Japan is so short of arable land that its farmers heavily fertilize their tiny plots, mostly with human and animal manure. Japanese wheats are dwarf varieties with short, sturdy stems, great resistance to lodging, and the ability to use fertilizer efficiently. Agronomist Orville A. Vogel of the United States Department of Agriculture research station at Washington State University in Pullman was hybridizing some Japanese dwarf wheats with American wheats that had other superior characteristics. He sent Borlaug an envelope containing 60 seeds of his new experimental dwarf hybrids.

Borlaug crossbred Vogel's fertilizer-tolerant, Japanese wheats with his rust-resistant Mexican varieties. Initially, he gathered pollen from his Mexican varieties to pollinate the Japanese types, but rust demolished the Japanese plants before their seeds could mature.

Checking back in Vogel's envelope, Borlaug found eight seeds he had previously overlooked. He started again, this time using the Vogel plants to provide the pollen. It worked. Using those eight plants, he combined the genes for fertilizer responsiveness with those for rust resistance. He found, to his jubilation, that the resulting disease-resistant wheats not only utilized fertilizer without falling over, but also thrust up several stems from the base of each plant. Thus they became bushy, producing more heads than previous wheats. In addition, they yielded more grains per head.

Since the beginning of history, farmers had believed that the taller a crop grew, the better it was. Borlaug's results showed that this idea was wrong. His wheats were only about half the normal size, standing 3 feet instead of 4 or 5 feet tall, but they yielded twice as much. More of the plant's energy was going into the grain and less

Three varieties of grain involved in Borlaug's research, *below left,* are, left to right, traditional long-stemmed wheat, new shorter dwarf wheat, and even shorter triticale — a cross between wheat and rye. Triticale, *below,* has bigger heads, center, than either of its parents — rye, left, or wheat, right.

into unproductive stalk. The dwarf wheats were thus more efficient in their utilization of both fertilizer and water.

By 1965, only four years after their release to farmers, 95 per cent of Mexico's wheatland was planted with these dwarfs. Average wheat yields had increased from 11½ bushels per acre in 1943, before Borlaug began his work, to more than 30 bushels per acre.

Along with his wheat research, Borlaug established a training program. From 1944 to 1960, more than 100 young scientists from 12 nations learned his methods and absorbed some of his enthusiasm. Each was selected and supported by the Rockefeller Foundation. They became known as the "wheat apostles."

Ignacio Narváez, a Mexican plant geneticist who was one of the first wheat apostles, recalls, "I could see he [Borlaug] would not spare himself — or us. He was full of urgency and zest to drive on quickly, to get more and more food out of those lands. . . . we went about the work as though we were following him — like disciples."

When the wheat apostles returned to their own countries, many of them carried new wheat varieties with them. They could do so because Borlaug had always tried to breed adaptable wheats, even against the express wishes of Mexican officials. In keeping with what was then standard practice, they wanted him to concentrate on developing individualized types for Mexico's major wheat-growing areas. Instead, Borlaug sought varieties that would grow successfully throughout Mexico, from the lowlands to the mountain slopes and from the irrigated northern deserts to the rainy southern forests. Twice a year, he moved his wheat strains back and forth, selecting those that performed best in the two different regions. Now his foresight became clear. Conventional varieties of wheat were highly specialized in terms of climate, daylength, and other growing conditions, and a variety that succeeded in one area would not do well where conditions were different. But Borlaug's wheats were so adaptable that they flourished anywhere the winters were mild enough, from Turkey to Paraguay.

In 1965, India ordered 11,100 bushels of wheat seed from Mexico. Pakistan ordered 12,950 bushels. It was the beginning of a miracle for those nations, but also the start of a nightmare for Borlaug, who was handling the arrangements while his boss was on vacation.

The seed was to be shipped from Los Angeles on the last ship that would arrive in time for planting in mid-October. A truck convoy carrying the seed left Sonora, Mexico, bound for Los Angeles. Then the trucks disappeared. Borlaug began getting anxious calls from Narváez, who was handling the loading in Los Angeles. The ship was almost ready to sail, and Narváez did not know where the trucks were. Borlaug was frantic, but there was no word. It was July 1965. After a bureaucratic delay at the Mexican border, riots in the Watts section of Los Angeles had prevented the Mexican trucks from passing through to the harbor. At last, with only hours to

Borlaug has taught his
techniques to hundreds of
young scientists, known
as the "wheat apostles,"
who come to his research
center from many nations.

spare, the trucks reached dockside. Narváez called Borlaug to ask if
the paperwork was complete and loading could begin.

Borlaug knew that the Mexican bank might refuse to accept Pakistan's $98,000 letter of credit in payment for the seed because the
document had three misspelled names. If the wheat were shipped
and payment never arrived, the center would lose a lot of money.
Borlaug's nerves were frayed. "It got me in the stomach," he said.
"I can deal with a rust epidemic, but this business of crisis and
complication behind an office desk drives me frantic." Under strain,
he yelled into the telephone, "Get that wheat aboard the ship — send
it on its damn way." Later, Mexican and Rockefeller Foundation
officials reprimanded him for taking such a risk. But the decision
paved the way for the Green Revolution, and eventually Borlaug
could claim, "It was the best decision I ever made in my life."

Before Borlaug could feel such satisfaction, however, there were
other problems to overcome. While the ship was at sea, fighting
broke out between India and Pakistan. Borlaug heard a rumor that
India would confiscate Pakistan's share of the cargo when the ship
docked in Bombay. Hurriedly, he tried to get all the wheat unloaded
at Singapore and shipped to India and Pakistan in separate vessels.
It took Borlaug days of argument to get the shipping line to agree.

Arriving barely ahead of planting time, with no time left to check
the germination, the Mexican seed was rushed to the wheat-growing
areas of India and Pakistan. Borlaug should have been able to relax,
but soon an agonizing cable arrived from Narváez, who had followed
the seed to Pakistan, reporting that the planted fields looked bad.
"We have been struck a cruel blow," it said.

Borlaug flew to Pakistan and rushed into the fields. Everywhere, the seed had germinated poorly. The Mexican government seed organization had fumigated the seed so heavily to prevent insect damage in storage that 4 out of every 5 seeds had been killed. Disaster seemed almost certain.

In desperation, Borlaug recommended doubling the seeding rate, doubling the irrigation, and doubling or tripling the fertilizer. He hoped that the few remaining viable seeds would respond.

These measures brought results. One after another, the sparse seeds thrust up stems. The gaps in the rows filled out. Head after head appeared. The plants showed the versatility bred into them.

India's minister of agriculture, Chidambaram V. Subramaniam, and his counterpart in Pakistan, Malik Khuda Bakhsh, were aware of the problem with the test planting but were far-sighted enough to see beyond it. Borlaug credits them with saving the budding Green Revolution. In 1966, against the strenuous urgings of many of India's top scientists, Subramaniam ordered 20,000 tons of Mexican wheat seed, the biggest seed purchase in history. That fall, two shiploads set sail from Mexico. Borlaug and a special Indian commission supervised the harvest, cleaning, sacking, and shipping.

348

Together with seed from the first year's test crop, the Mexican wheat was planted on more than 1,000 square miles of farmland scattered across India. Then came a great drought. Disaster loomed once more, but the Mexican wheats outyielded the native wheats by 100 to 200 per cent, sometimes even more. The adaptability Borlaug had built into his wheat saved the program, and many lives.

In the following years, India's wheat yields increased up to 600 per cent. Mexican dwarf wheats covered the plains of northern India like a golden carpet. India's wheat production leaped from 400 million bushels in 1967 to more than 1 billion bushels in 1972 and to more than 1.3 billion bushels in 1982. Never had agriculture achieved such an increase.

After 1967, many countries made notable increases in wheat production, based largely on Mexican seed and methods. Yields in Argentina, Bangladesh, Brazil, Chile, Egypt, Guatemala, Iraq, Italy, Kenya, Morocco, Portugal, Spain, Syria, Tunisia, and other countries increased greatly, and in many nations doubled.

On Oct. 20, 1970, the world's news services reported, "The Nobel Committee of the Norwegian Parliament has decided to award the Nobel Peace Prize in 1970 to Dr. Norman E. Borlaug for his great

As a young man, *opposite page, far left,* Borlaug studied forestry. Later he helped found the first Mexican Little League and coached several teams to championships, including the 1959-1960 Aquilas, *opposite page, top right.* Norman and his wife, Margaret, *opposite page, bottom right,* have been married since 1937. At a family gathering in April 1983, three generations of Borlaugs pose for a group portrait, *above.* Later, Borlaug plays with his grandchildren in the backyard, *above right.*

King Olav V of Norway congratulates Borlaug at the 1970 Nobel Prize ceremony, when Borlaug was awarded the Nobel Peace Prize for his work in creating high-yielding varieties of wheat.

contribution toward creating a new world situation with regard to nutrition." Borlaug commented later that it was the first time a "dirty-handed" scientist had received the prize.

Margaret Borlaug first learned of the honor when a Norwegian reporter woke her with an early morning phone call. Norman had already been away working for an hour. Margaret drove out to the country to tell her husband the news, but he stayed in the wheat fields until the day's work with a team of wheat apostles was complete. It was, perhaps, the last private day of his life. Within hours — much against his will — he was an international celebrity.

Six weeks later, Borlaug received the famous prize from Aase Lionaes, chairman of the Peace Prize committee, in the presence of King Olav V of Norway. A contingent of Mexican farmers was in attendance, including one who had cashed in his life insurance so that he and his wife could attend the ceremony in Oslo. "Norman has changed our lives and is our beloved friend," the farmer said.

As with many scientific advances, the new wheats brought problems as well as promises. It became fashionable to criticize the Green Revolution that Borlaug's work had stimulated. Some of the faultfinding was just plain wrong. For example, opponents charged that the new wheats outperform traditional varieties only with large amounts of fertilizer, which few poor farmers can afford. Actually, the dwarfs yield more than the older wheats even when fertilizer is limited. The sturdy, short-stemmed wheats are also more efficient in their utilization of water and soil nutrients.

Other critics argued that large farmers benefited more than small ones from the Green Revolution because of their easier access to fertilizer, machinery, and other aids. The Green Revolution, they charged, had made rich farmers richer and poor peasants poorer. They apparently believed that advances in agriculture should also remove social and economic inequities that have accumulated since ancient times. Borlaug's comment is, "Oh, were it so simple."

Still others found fault with the loss of genetic diversity caused by the Green Revolution. In the past, farmers planted many different varieties of wheat that stored a wide range of genes. If disease struck one variety, it did not necessarily affect others. Today, so many farmers plant only the new dwarf wheat that if a new type of rust were to overcome its resistance, nearly all wheat crops would be wiped out. In addition, plant breeders would have nowhere to turn for rust-resistant genes. Borlaug responds that the risks of a disastrous rust epidemic are lower now than ever before because many countries have a dynamic breeding program and plant pathologists who constantly monitor farmers' crops for outbreaks of new disease.

But to appreciate the new seeds' importance to the world, one need only recall that massive famine was projected for much of Asia in the 1970s. That such mass misery and death never took place is due largely to the wisdom and dedication of Norman Borlaug. His miracle wheat not only ended the threat of starvation, but also gave needy countries 20 or 30 years of breathing time. Such countries as India and Pakistan now have enough to eat while they try to bring population into balance with food production.

Today, Borlaug has known fame, but he is untouched by it. He prefers to be called Norm and not to be introduced as a Nobel laureate. He still likes to work close to the land and maintains an active research group in Mexico. Crouching between rows, peering under curling leaves, fingering stems — that's where he prefers to be. His research projects today include crossbreeding wheat with rye to produce a new grain called triticale, and crossbreeding wheat with rice.

He is revered in his adopted country. His dedication and toil enabled Mexico to go from hunger to self-sufficiency and finally to exporting wheat in some years. Streets have been named for him, and throughout Mexico "Normando" means only one person.

The principles of his family and of his high school coach and principal are still evident in Borlaug. He is unassuming and self-effacing. Ask him about Borlaug, and he'll tell you about R. Glenn Anderson, the Canadian plant breeder who headed CIMMYT until his death in 1981; and about Bartelma, Stakman, Narváez, and the others who have worked with him. Ask him about his accomplishments, and he'll tell you about the population problem, which threatens to overwhelm even Borlaug's giant achievement. But talk to him about wheat and you won't be able to talk about anything else. No wonder that to all the world Norman Borlaug is "Mr. Wheat."

Science on Display

By Edward G. Nash

**The new science museums are giving more and
more people the opportunity to learn about
the exhibits by becoming part of them.**

Bobbing a bit, the ball floats in midair. From a distance, the effect appears mysterious. Close up, you can see that the ball is supported by a powerful stream of air rising from a cone on the floor.

A brother and sister remove the ball and play a game with it. They bounce it lightly off, and throw it through, the air jet. They try to land it, with little success, back on top of its invisible support.

With their game, the children are inadvertently illustrating a principle of Daniel Bernoulli, an 18th-century Swiss mathematician, which describes the relationship between the speed and pressure of a flowing gas. Bernoulli's principle is fundamental to understanding how airplanes fly, and why a baseball curves. The ball, the cone, and the supporting stream of air are in The Exploratorium, located in a corner of the city of San Francisco. It is one of the best of a new breed of science museums.

"Sometimes, I go out on the floor to see what's wrong with an exhibit that isn't working properly. Often, a 12- or 14-year-old will come up and explain the exhibit to me because I look puzzled." Frank F. Oppenheimer, founder and director of The Exploratorium and a physicist, muses on the pleasures of running a science museum. He speaks of a kind of sharing of discovery, without reference to age, occupation, or training. "Visitors are always explaining things here to one another, friend to friend, parent to child, or child to parent—it's another kind of teaching."

For most of us, knowledge of science trickles down from above, from informed to uninformed—teacher to student, or book to reader. In the new science museums, or science-technology centers as their staffs like to call them, the path to scientific understanding is more horizontal. You walk it by yourself, at your own pace.

But you won't be alone, not in The Exploratorium, nor in Chicago's Museum of Science and Industry, nor Philadelphia's Franklin Institute Science Museum, nor in any of dozens of science-technology centers in the United States and Canada. More than 40 million people visited these science-technology centers in 1982.

And you had better be prepared for noise. "The noise level here reminds me of the streets of New York City," says a staff member, looking around the cavernous Palace of Fine Arts that houses The Exploratorium. Left over from the 1915 Panama-Pacific International Exposition, the building is essentially a single, 100,000-square-foot room, a curved city-block long, near San Francisco's Golden Gate Bridge. It is alive with the shouts and laughter of children, and the clanks, whirs, beeps, and other miscellaneous noises of exhibits that invite participation. Visitors, of whatever age, learn. They explore the processes of science. Looking at things is quiet; discovery can be noisy.

The visitor, when he operates the machines, or sets up his own experiments with light, sound, electricity, or some other facet of the physical world, becomes a component of the science-technology center. "It is participatory science," says geophysicist J. Tuzo Wilson, director of the Ontario Science Centre in Don Mills, a Toronto suburb. "Children find it more exciting; they learn more. They like things that they have to do themselves; things that allow them to measure their own ability."

This collaboration between museum and visitor sets the new centers apart from the older museums. "The classical museum is about things," says William D. Pattison, associate professor of geography and education at the University of Chicago and a student of museums and their role in society. "They are filled with paintings, bones, rocks, machines—all objects. The art museum celebrates the beauty of art; the natural history museum, the diversity of nature;

The author:
Edward G. Nash is editor of *Economic Perspectives*. He is a former senior editor of *The World Book Year Book* and *Science Year*.

the history museum, the achievements of humankind. But the science center provides access to scientific thought and procedure. It is an invitation to participate in the processes of inquiry."

The classical museum with its collections has a purpose, of course. Such a museum is a repository, a kind of gigantic attic or storehouse where scientists can read the records of life on earth. Extremely valuable, difficult or impossible to replace, the collections are not generally accessible to the public. At Chicago's Field Museum of Natural History, for example, scarcely 2 per cent of its many collections are on display.

"The Ontario Science Centre started out that way in 1969," says Wilson. "The staff began collecting all sorts of things — old cars, fire engines. But it was hard to do because so much had been collected elsewhere. Finally, we got rid of it. Now our exhibits are made up of nuts and bolts and other common things you can get in a hardware store. We decided to be a 'hands-on' museum, a kind of public science laboratory."

That hands-on quality is another break with traditional museums. There are barriers in most museums — glass cases, guards, and alarms protect the exhibits from the public. But in The Exploratorium, for example, everything is open to the visitor. There are no exhibit cases. Even the museum workshops are open to visitors.

The Exploratorium has more than 500 hands-on exhibits; the Ontario Science Centre has 400. Such exhibits must be able to handle constant, sometimes rough, treatment. "We've been braver here than most [museum] people," says Oppenheimer, "in having things out in the open and allowing them to be manipulated. We've learned how to do that and since the exhibits are many and varied, nobody is bored with them. So there is almost no deliberate breakage. Occasionally somebody mischievously unplugs an exhibit. Sometimes they fool around and invent things to do that we didn't know the exhibits were capable of."

Another way the new science centers are unlike the natural history museums is that they do little in the way of scientific research. There are few curators of the classical mold, poring over the accumulated specimens, naming organisms, classifying things. Chicago's Museum of Science and Industry, the biggest and oldest of North America's science-technology centers, retired its curators in 1940, says Victor J. Danilov, the museum's president and director. "We had curators in the beginning, too," says Wilson, "But they went when we sold the collections." The largest group on Wilson's staff are the craftsmen, artists, and designers who make and maintain the exhibits.

Nonetheless, there is the occasional scientific discovery. "We haven't limited the sophistication of the exhibits," says Oppenheimer, "and all kinds of new phenomena that are puzzling even to me and my physicist colleagues arise as we develop the exhibits. There's one now, a new exhibit by a young man who's not a scien-

An exhibit designer assembles a new exhibit on prisms for The Exploratorium in San Francisco.

tist. He has built a tube, closed at one end and having a signal generator and amplifier at the other. A liquid — kerosene — lies along the bottom of the tube. We expected a certain simple wave behavior in the kerosene when you send a sound signal into the tube. But we get all sorts of things happening that we're at a loss to explain.

"The sound sets up standing waves — we expected that. But there are little lines of bubbles and, if you turn the sound up, they become little sprays. How this effect is generated in the liquid we don't know. We'll put something into the kerosene and do some more experiments." Work on The Exploratorium's exhibits has produced a few scientific papers and will probably produce more when Oppenheimer and his staff get around to writing them up.

The lack of organized research, and of systematic collections, prevented many centers from being accredited as full-fledged museums by the American Association of Museums (AAM) in the early 1970s, although many of these institutions were already members of the AAM. In 1975, after some years of negotiation, the AAM modified its accreditation criteria to include any institution that "maintains and utilizes exhibits and/or objects for the interpretation of scientific and technological information," whether or not such an institution maintains collections. Meanwhile, in 1973, the science-technology units formed their own group — the Association of Science-Technology Centers (ASTC) — to serve "museums dedicated to communicating to the public a better understanding and appreciation of science and the derived technology." There were 17 full and 5 associate members. By 1982, ASTC had 152 members, including 17 institutions located overseas.

"The science center movement is very young," notes Bonnie VanDorn, ASTC's executive director. "More than half of ASTC's members are less than 20 years old."

"Museums, in general, are creations of Western European civilization," says Pattison. In the 17th century, European philosophers and scientists such as England's Francis Bacon, France's René Descartes, and Germany's Gottfried W. Leibniz suggested that what we would now call science museums be established. They were to educate and entertain the public about the achievements of science and technology. The first public science museum was the Ashmolean Museum, founded at Oxford University in England in 1683. It was based on the natural history collections of the scholar Elias Ashmole.

The Industrial Revolution of the 1700s and the early 1800s spurred the establishment of more such museums. A society for public education in technology was formed in London in the 1760s. A similar group, The American Society for Promoting and Promulgating Useful Knowledge, was formed with the support of Benjamin Franklin in Philadelphia in 1776. These societies displayed models of the machines that were in the process of revolutionizing industrial production in Europe.

After the French Revolution ended in the late 18th century, the French government opened displays in Paris to educate artisans and the general public and to inspire inventors. Ultimately, the displays became part of the Musée National des Techniques, the first museum of technology, established in 1794.

. In 1851, the Royal Society of Arts in London sponsored "The Exposition of the Industry of All Nations," the first major international exhibition. Vast amounts of machinery, manufactured goods, curiosities, and rarities from all over the world were assembled in London for the exhibition. Its focal point was the Crystal Palace, a glass building that covered 18 acres. These collected materials became the basis of the South Kensington Museum of Industrial Arts — later called the Victoria and Albert Museum. It was the forerunner of the Science Museum, Great Britain's national museum of science and technology.

Many science centers and museums had their beginnings in World's Fairs. Chicago's Museum of Science and Industry occupies the sole surviving building from the 1893 World's Columbian Exposition. It opened as a museum just in time for the 1933 Century of Progress Exposition. The Exploratorium is in an old fair building.

A bolt of artificial lightning strikes a model factory in a demonstration of nature's forces at the Deutsches Museum in Munich, West Germany.

Both New York City's Hall of Science and Seattle's Pacific Science Center are housed in science buildings erected for World's Fairs held in those cities in the 1960s.

The notion of a hands-on museum came with the establishment of the Deutsches Museum in Munich, Germany, in 1903. Its founder, Oskar von Miller, an electrical engineer, wanted to show "the development of various branches of natural science and technology by means of original apparatus and machines, as well as by means of models and arrangements for demonstration, in a manner easily understood by all classes of people."

Von Miller was a pioneer in exhibition techniques. The new museum had, alongside more traditional displays, such innovations as operating models, a walk-through coal mine, scientific demonstrations, cutaway models — and displays that the visitor could operate. He called them "experimental exhibits" and said that they "must be designed with the greatest simplicity. They are operated by the average museum visitor. . . . They must be built sturdily. . . .and must produce the desired results quickly and often continuously." Von Miller's instructions continue to be carried out today. As one modern museum technician put it: "If they can break it, we didn't build it right."

Chicago's Museum of Science and Industry directly owes its existence to the Deutsches Museum. In 1911, Julius Rosenwald, a Chicago businessman and philanthropist, took his family to Munich on vacation. His 8-year-old son was fascinated by the exhibits at the Deutsches Museum, especially those he could operate himself. In the 1920s, Rosenwald, then chairman of Sears, Roebuck and Company, pushed for the founding of a similar museum in Chicago. The Museum of Science and Industry, sparked by Rosenwald's determination, and $7 million of his money, opened its doors in 1933.

After half a century of development, the range of the 2,000 exhibits now housed in the Museum of Science and Industry's 608,000-square-foot building on Chicago's South Side is enormous. The museum has long had a close relationship with industry. Many exhibits are sponsored by corporations such as American Telephone and Telegraph Company on communications, Santa Fe Industries on rail transportation, and International Business Machines on computers. They mix a small amount of commercial message with hefty chunks of technological information. Alongside these are new exhibits on the physical and life sciences, such as moving models of the phenomenon of continental drift.

In the attempt to keep abreast of science and technology, "we revise or replace about 10 per cent of our exhibits each year — high for a museum," says Danilov. Among the latest is the computer exhibit. The exhibit gives a history of computers and a brief, basic explanation of how they work. But at the heart of the exhibit are a number of computer keyboards at which visitors can interact with a computer, undertaking a series of simple operations, answering questions, or solving problems presented on the display screens.

To watch museum visitors, young and old, talk with the computer is to understand the extraordinary value of science-technology centers. By allowing people to participate, an exhibit can eliminate the mystery, and the accompanying fear, that often surround a scientific or technological advance. Many people are afraid of computers. They are convinced that the machines are beyond their understanding. But by sitting down and working with one, they soon learn that a computer is a tool, not a master.

Chicago's Museum of Science and Industry's two most popular exhibits are echoes of the Deutsches Museum — a walk-through model of a coal mine and a German submarine, captured during World War II and resting, a fish out of water, on the grass outside the museum.

"It's a three-dimensional magazine," says Pattison. And, in a time when many two-dimensional magazines are folding, the Museum of Science and Industry remains Chicago's most popular tourist attraction. Nearly 4 million visitors crowd into the museum each year, about 10 per cent of the total attendance at science-technology centers in the United States.

Unlike Chicago's Museum of Science and Industry, The Exploratorium celebrates no achievements of industry. But it too has a connection with the Deutsches Museum. Oppenheimer had long been concerned with popular science education, and was convinced that U.S. science museums were inadequate. In 1965, he "went to London for a year and saw the South Kensington [science] museum. It woke me up. Then I went and studied what was happening in Munich and Paris."

After his European tour, he opened The Exploratorium in San Francisco. "This place isn't like any of those European museums," he says, "although it has taken ideas from a lot of museums."

The Exploratorium has many exhibits based on those ideas. With odd-looking devices and machines arranged in sections by subject matter on a concrete floor under a high, metal-girded roof, the museum looks like a cluttered airplane hangar. It has none of the high-tech science-fiction glamour, none of the design sheen of other science centers. Just after The Exploratorium opened in the early 1970s, a visitor recalls thinking, "This place will be really wonderful once they get shaped up and organized." Returning 10 years later to essentially the same, though greatly expanded, scene, he realized that The Exploratorium had, in its own special way, been organized from the beginning.

That organization resembles the thinking of its founder. "I got interested in binocular vision," says Oppenheimer, "and how one tells distance. I would hold up my hands at different distances from my face and I would ask little kids, 'How do you know one hand is farther from my face than the other?' They would say, 'I see it is.' But what of the science behind 'I see it is'? People didn't really understand perception. So, a section on perception was a starting point." Now the museum has exhibits on depth perception, color vision, spatial orientation, and other aspects of light perception.

"Then you go on — because if you talk about the eye, you have to talk about the structure of the eye, the lenses, the nerves. And, of course, the eye doesn't do everything alone; it's the constant interaction of the eye and the brain — and experience. It is the different roles played by the things that are wired into the brain and the things that have been experienced in different cultures. All of this can come out in the exhibits."

The Exploratorium has always had artists working on exhibits. One result is the Sun Painting — an exhibit in which sunlight, captured by a sun-tracking mirror on the roof, strikes an angled, flat

A "whisper disk," at left, greets visitors to the Science Circus area of Discovery Place/Nature Center in Charlotte, N.C., *left.* Here, visitors can observe nature in the jungle, *below left,* or learn about static electricity, *below,* in a very direct way.

Visitors participate in the Sun Painting at The Exploratorium by moving mylar strips that intercept the prism-dispersed sunlight.

A youngster steps from the giant heart, *left,* at the Museum of Science and Industry in Chicago. She has just observed its parts and heard its beat. An experiment with soap films, *below,* is a feature of the "hands-on" exhibits at the Science Museum in London.

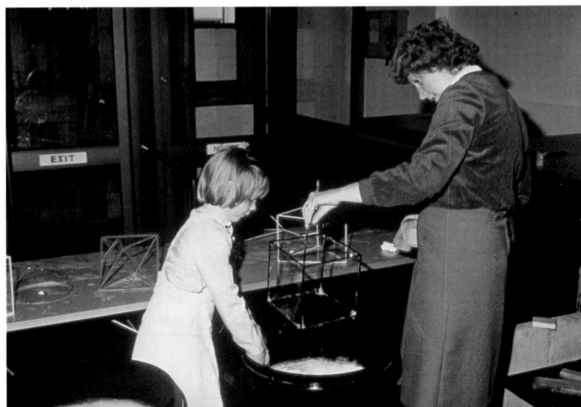

A remote arm, *right,* of the type used to handle radioactive materials is operated by a youthful visitor to the Ontario Science Centre near Toronto. Young people are also permitted to use the computers, *below,* at the Lawrence Hall of Science in Berkeley, Calif. A child at the Birla Industrial & Technological Museum in Calcutta, India, *below right,* operates knobs that show how an automobile engine works.

mirror near the museum's entrance. The light then travels horizontally through an array of prisms. These break the light into its component colors. This, in turn, is picked up by hanging strips of mirrorlike mylar and bounced onto an 8- by 15-foot screen. As people move through the light, or brush against the mylar strips, the Sun Painting shimmers and changes, intimately involving the viewer in the product. Another exhibit, the Vidium, uses microphones to pick up the speech, songs, shouts, and claps of participants and translate them into images on an oscilloscope. These are sound paintings.

"The idea is not necessarily that art and science are the same," says Oppenheimer, "but that they both start with nature. They both start from noticing and fiddling around with patterns and trying to rearrange them. They both tell what's possible. The artist tells what's possible in human experience and the physicist what's possible in nature, what you can look for." One Exploratorium display, for example, uses plastic overlays to dissect drawings by artist Saul Steinberg. In this way, science may help the visitor understand the intuitiveness of the artist's perception.

Sensory illusions are prominent in The Exploratorium, partly because they are entertaining, and partly because they force the participant to think about the relationship of the senses and the "real" world. One innovative program developed by The Exploratorium and San Francisco's Garden-Sullivan Hospital employs spatial, visual, and movement illusions to sensitize the parents of learning-disabled children. The exhibits are used to temporarily and partially disorient the adults in ways that make them experience some of the difficulties their children have to cope with.

Disabled children themselves can benefit from the museum's exhibits. Exploratorium staff members remember a day when terrifying shrieks — almost inhuman sounds — in the exhibit area brought them running from their offices to see what was the matter. They found a young mother, oblivious to the horrifying noise, joyously watching her stone-deaf son *see* his own sounds on the screen of the Vidium and understand for the first time that he could make sound, even though he could not hear it.

The Exploratorium's exhibits have proved so successful that Oppenheimer and his associates have published a two-volume manual called the *Cookbook*. It contains detailed instructions and drawings for the building and maintenance of many of the museum's devices. Hundreds of copies have been sold, many to other science centers.

One satisfied *Cookbook* user is Discovery Place/Nature Center, in Charlotte, N.C., which has adapted a number of The Exploratorium's creations for its own use. Two-thirds of the 150 exhibits at the 72,000-square-foot museum, which opened in October 1981, are hands-on exhibits. They include a "touch tank" in the aquarium, where visitors may touch marine organisms such as starfish and sea urchins. Among the newest exhibits is a laser pinball

Science-interested patrons of a shopping mall in downtown Philadelphia can take time out from their shopping to visit a traveling exhibit from the Franklin Institute.

machine, in which the participant bounces beams of light — not balls — off angled prisms to hit a target.

Many of the staff members at Discovery Place are former teachers. And each year, other teachers from Charlotte-area schools work and study at the Center to improve their teaching skills and scientific understanding. The nearby city and county school systems also use Discovery Place for a number of required courses in such subjects as human growth and marine biology.

Most science-technology centers have school programs and teacher-training courses. They view themselves as important adjuncts to the local educational systems, with materials, equipment, and expertise no single school could hope to match.

Lawrence Hall of Science, a unit of the University of California, Berkeley, is a science center that has long specialized in research on science education. It has an extensive computer-literacy program, aimed at both children and adults. It is also the home of a number of curriculum development and teacher-training programs, such as Project EQUALS, which is designed to improve mathematics training for women and girls.

Most science centers are private institutions, financed primarily by private contributions, and government and corporate grants. Those that are not usually have even closer relations with local school systems. Fernbank Science Center in Atlanta, Ga., for example, is an integral part of the DeKalb County school system. In addition to its observatory, planetarium, and exhibit hall, Fernbank owns a 65-acre forest in north Georgia that serves as an outdoor museum for visitors and students.

The Ontario Science Centre, founded by the provincial government to celebrate Ontario's centennial in the 1960s, is also fully supported by the government and thoroughly integrated into the province's school system. With 1,000 exhibits, 38 special-purpose minitheaters, computer terminals, laboratories, and science materials, it provides a rich atmosphere for learning. In a special program, exceptional high school students are brought together in the Centre for a semester of intense study in mathematics, the physical or life sciences, or communications. The Centre also works closely with teachers' organizations to provide professional development programs.

Many people go to science centers, but some science centers also go to the people. Traveling exhibits move from school to school. Some centers set up branches in other parts of their communities. The Franklin Institute Science Museum, for example, operates a storefront science center in a shopping mall in Philadelphia.

But few such "outreach" programs are as extensive — in mileage as well as in exhibits — as those of the Ontario Science Centre. Ontario is a sprawling province — from east to west slightly longer than the distance from Philadelphia to Minneapolis, Minn., and stretching more than 900 miles from Windsor, near Detroit, north to Hudson Bay. Since 1973, the Centre's traveling museum, called Science Circus, has visited almost every community in Ontario, including some on Hudson Bay that can only be reached by air.

Typically, Science Circus sets up in a shopping mall, church hall, or community center, where schoolchildren visit it in the daytime, and their families visit it in the evening. Science Circus has some 40 exhibits, covering a broad spectrum of scientific subjects. The Centre also runs two smaller traveling shows: Body Works, dealing with growth and health; and Seeing Brain, which has optical illusions and other exhibits on perception and vision. A fourth traveling museum, featuring high technology, was being developed in the summer of 1983.

In 1982, the Ontario Science Centre became the first North American host to a science and technology exhibit from the People's Republic of China. "China: 7,000 Years of Discovery" highlighted such Chinese achievements as gunpowder, paper, the compass, and movable type. Traveling with the exhibit were 17 artisans, who demonstrated techniques for papermaking, printmaking, and silk weaving.

The exhibit, which will tour Chicago, Seattle, and Atlanta in 1983 and 1984, was co-sponsored by the Ontario museum. "It was a cooperative arrangement," Wilson says, "partly a barter deal. We built copies of some of our exhibits for display in a new science center in Beijing, China. This year, we are sending 10 of our staff to China to help them set it up."

China is not the only country looking to North America for advice and help in setting up science centers. Wilson estimates that about 20 countries presently have plans for new science centers. "Museums in the industrialized nations, like us," says Chicago's Museum of Science and Industry's Danilov, "are being deluged with requests for help in starting science centers." The International Committee of Science and Technology Museums has decided to use The Exploratorium's *Cookbook* to develop an *International Cookbook* that can be used by developing nations to start their own science and technology museums.

"India has three science museums—in Bombay, Bangalore, and Calcutta," notes Danilov, "and is building a fourth in New Delhi. It is also planning a string of satellite science centers that will be serviced by the four bigger ones." Malaysia, Sri Lanka, and Hong Kong have plans for science centers, as do countries in the Middle East and South America.

New science-technology centers continue to spring up in North America as well. Vancouver, Canada, opened its Arts, Sciences, and Technology Centre on Jan. 15, 1982. It offers some 60 participatory exhibits, including a walk-in kaleidoscope—a small mirrored room that produces multiple receding reflections of its visitors.

On Feb. 2, 1982, the Museum of Scientific Discovery opened in 10,000 square feet of space in the Strawberry Square shopping mall in Harrisburg, Pa. Some exhibits were adapted from The Exploratorium's *Cookbook*, others were donated by local businesses. "We billed ourselves as a regional museum and as a factor in revitalizing the city," says director Roger A. Smith. "And that has been the case. Suburbanites who haven't been to Harrisburg in years are coming in to check out the museum."

There are new and growing science centers in Regina, Sask., and Richmond, Va., where the Commonwealth of Virginia acquired a vacant railroad station to house its museum. "Atlanta wants something bigger and more technological than Fernbank," says Danilov, "and industry there is talking about taking over a whole convention hall for a science center. Phoenix is thinking about one, and there are plans in Palo Alto, Calif., and New Orleans."

Not only is the science center phenomenon growing, it is changing. "It is certainly true," says Danilov, "that science centers are more concerned today with the social consequences of technological and scientific advances. We need to look at the possible harm from such changes as well as at the benefits." Pattison wonders if there was a turning point in such thinking at science centers in the early 1970s, with the rising concern about the environment.

Despite changes in emphasis, however, certain things will remain true of these institutions. "Whatever else they are about," says Pattison, "museums are about the responsibilities of citizens to take care of their heritage, their environment, and their future."

World Book Supplement

Revised articles on subjects in science and technology reprinted from the 1983 edition of *The World Book Encyclopedia.*

Center for American Archeology, Northwestern University

Archaeologists Dig for Remains of Past Human Cultures. They work like detectives and treat the things they find as clues to the lives of the people who used them. Objects made up to 8,000 years ago have been uncovered in diggings at the Koster farm site in Illinois, *above.*

ARCHAEOLOGY

ARCHAEOLOGY, AHR *kee* AHL *uh jee*, is the scientific study of the remains of past human cultures. Archaeologists investigate the lives of early people by studying the objects those people left behind. Such objects include buildings, artwork, tools, bones, and pottery. Archaeologists may make exciting discoveries, such as a tomb filled with gold or the ruins of a magnificent temple in the midst of a jungle. However, the discovery of a few stone tools or grains of hardened corn may reveal even more about early people.

Barbara Voorhies, the contributor of this article, is Associate Professor of Anthropology at the University of California at Santa Barbara.

Archaeological research is the chief method available for learning about societies that existed before the invention of writing about 5,000 years ago. It also provides an important supplement to our knowledge of ancient societies that left written records. In the Americas, archaeology is considered a branch of *anthropology*, the scientific study of humanity and human culture. European archaeologists, however, think of their work as most closely related to the field of history. Archaeology differs from history in that historians mainly study the lives of people as recorded in written documents.

Archaeologists look for information about how, where, and when cultures developed. Like other social scientists, they search for reasons why major changes have occurred in certain cultures. Some archaeologists try to understand why ancient people stopped hunting and started farming. Others develop theories about what caused people to build cities and to set up trade

An Army of Life-Sized Statues of soldiers and horses form an amazing collection of *artifacts* (movable objects made by people). The clay figures were found in 1974 near the tomb of Shih Huang Ti, who ruled China in the 200's B.C.

routes. In addition, some archaeologists look for reasons behind the fall of such early civilizations as the Maya in Central America and the Romans in Europe.

What Archaeologists Study

Archaeologists examine any evidence that can help them explain how people lived in past times. Such evidence ranges from the ruins of a large city to a few stone flakes left by someone making a stone tool long ago.

The three basic kinds of archaeological evidence are (1) artifacts, (2) features, and (3) ecofacts. *Artifacts* are objects that were made by people and can be moved without altering their appearance. Artifacts include

such objects as arrowheads, pots, and beads. Artifacts from a society with a written history may also include clay tablets and other written records. *Features* consist mainly of houses, tombs, irrigation canals, and other large structures built by ancient peoples. Unlike artifacts, features cannot be separated from their surroundings without changing their form. *Ecofacts* are natural objects found with artifacts or features. Ecofacts reveal how ancient people responded to their surroundings. Examples of ecofacts include seeds and animal bones.

Any place where archaeological evidence is found is called an *archaeological site*. To understand the behavior of the people who occupied a site, archaeologists must

A Roman Bath uncovered at Caesaria, near Hadera, Israel, is an example of an archaeological *feature*. Unlike artifacts, features cannot be separated from their sites without changing form.

Whale Bones, *foreground,* were among the *ecofacts* found in diggings on Bathurst Island in the Canadian Arctic. Such natural objects reveal how ancient people related to their surroundings.

371

study the relationships among the various artifacts, features, and ecofacts found there. For example, the discovery of stone spearheads near the bones of an extinct kind of buffalo at a site in New Mexico showed that early human beings had hunted buffalo in that area.

If objects are buried deep in the ground, their position in the earth also concerns archaeologists. The scientists study the layers of soil and rock in which objects are found to understand the conditions that existed when the objects were placed there. In some places, archaeologists discover many levels of deposits called *strata*. The archaeological study of strata, called *stratigraphy*, developed from the study of rock layers in geology.

How Archaeologists Gather Information

Archaeologists use special techniques and equipment to gather archaeological evidence precisely and accurately. They also keep detailed records of their findings because much archaeological research destroys the remains being studied.

Locating Sites is the first job of the archaeologist. Sites may be aboveground, underground, or underwater. Underwater sites include sunken ships as well as entire towns that have been submerged because of shifts in land or water level.

Some large sites are located easily because they are clearly visible or can be traced from descriptions in ancient stories or other historical records. Such sites include the pyramids in Egypt and the ancient city of Athens in Greece. Some less obvious sites have been discovered accidentally by nonarchaeologists. In 1940, for example, four children in search of their dog found the Lascaux Cave in southwestern France, which has prehistoric wallpaintings. Many important discoveries have been made by archaeologists who searched tirelessly over many years for a specific site or type of site. Working in this way, an English archaeologist

Aerofilms Ltd.

Aerial Photography can discover unsuspected sites. The lines of a defensive ditch in the English field above indicate the remains of an ancient Roman fort and campsite.

named Howard Carter discovered the treasure-filled tomb of the ancient Egyptian king Tutankhamon in 1922.

Archaeologists use systematic methods to discover sites. The traditional way to find all the sites in a region is through a *foot survey*. In this method, archaeologists space themselves at measured distances and walk in preset directions. Each person looks for archaeological evidence while walking forward. Archaeologists use this method when they want to know where sites do not occur as well as where they do. For example, they might use it to confirm that sites in a particular region occur on hilltops but never in valleys.

Pat Baker, Western Australian Maritime Museum

An Underwater Site may contain cargo from sunken ships. Such cargo has added to our knowledge of ancient Greek and Roman times. Archaeologists working off the west coast of Australia use a vacuum device to scoop up coins and other small objects, *left*.

Archaeologists use scientific methods to help discover underground sites. Aerial photography, for example, can reveal variations in vegetation that indicate the presence of archaeological evidence. Plants that are taller in one area of a field may be growing over an ancient grave or irrigation ditch. Plants that are shorter in another area may be growing in shallow ground over an ancient building or road. In addition, simple metal detectors can be used to sense metal artifacts that have been buried as deep as 6 feet (1.8 meters).

Surveying Sites. Archaeologists begin to study a site by describing it. They make detailed notes about the location of the site and the kinds of evidence visible on its surface. They also take photographs of the site.

Archaeologists make maps of most sites they find. The type of map drawn depends on the importance of the site, the goals of the study, and the amount of time and money available. In some cases, simple maps are made after pacing off distances or using a measuring tape. In other cases, archaeologists use special instruments to survey the site carefully and draw precise, detailed maps.

After making a map, the scientists collect artifacts from the surface of the site. They divide the surface into small square areas and examine one area at a time. The

Center for American Archeology, Northwestern University

Computers can greatly speed up the process of evaluating artifacts and ecofacts. This team is studying the printout of a computer used to classify objects found at a site in Illinois.

locations where artifacts are found are recorded on the map. Some surface artifacts can give information about when or how a site was used.

Excavating Sites. Archaeologists dig carefully for buried objects in a process called *excavation*. The method of excavation depends partly on the type of site. For example, archaeologists working in a cave might divide the floor and the area in front of the cave into small square units and then excavate each unit separately. Archaeologists working on a temple platform might dig a trench into the front part of the platform and extend the trench into the ground next to the platform. At large sites, excavation may be limited to certain areas. Other considerations that frequently determine the excavation method include the climate and soil at the site.

Tools used in excavation range from tractors and other heavy equipment to small picks and paint brushes. In some cases, the scientists strain soil through wire screens to recover extremely small objects. In other cases, they analyze soil in a laboratory to detect either grains of pollen or chemical changes caused by human remains.

Working Underwater. Archaeologists who work underwater use many methods adopted from land archaeology. Aerial photography over clear water may reveal the outlines of sunken harbors and towns. A method called *sonar scanning* helps detect underwater objects by the reflection of sound waves. In addition, divers use metal detectors to uncover metal objects. Photographic maps of sites can be made from submarines or by divers carrying underwater cameras. Archaeologists work at underwater sites in submersible decompression chambers. They use balloons to raise large objects to the surface for further study.

Recording and Preserving Evidence. Archaeologists describe, photograph, and count the objects they find. They group the objects according to type and location. For example, broken pieces of pottery, called *potsherds*,

Donald Frey, Institute of Nautical Archeology

Sorting Artifacts is an important task of the archaeologist. The archaeologists above are separating pieces of glass by color in hope of rebuilding some of them into their original objects.

**The Seriation
of Pottery**

Archaeologists use a method called *seriation* to show cultural development. In seriation, all objects of one type are arranged in a series that reflects changes in style through the years. The example below shows how pottery developed in the Tehuacán Valley of Mexico.

WORLD BOOK illustration by Bill Anderson

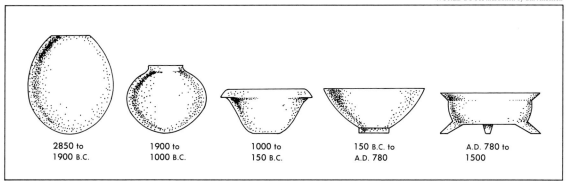

2850 to 1900 B.C.	1900 to 1000 B.C.	1000 to 150 B.C.	150 B.C. to A.D. 780	A.D. 780 to 1500

are bagged together by excavation unit and level. This collection then goes to the field laboratory to be cleaned and labeled.

At the field laboratory, special care must be taken to preserve objects made of such materials as metal and wood. For example, rust on a metal object must be removed without damaging the surface. Water-soaked wooden objects may crack or lose their shape when exposed to the air. These objects must be kept wet until specialists called *conservators* can preserve them.

How Archaeologists Interpret Findings

Archaeologists follow three basic steps in interpreting the evidence they find: (1) classification, (2) dating, and (3) evaluation.

Classification. Archaeologists can interpret their findings only if they can detect patterns of distribution of artifacts in space or through time. To find these patterns, archaeologists must first classify artifacts into groups of similar objects. The two main systems of classification are *typology* and *seriation.*

In typology, objects are grouped according to what they look like, how they were made, and how they were used. Each group of objects is called a *type.* For example, all the pottery jars from a site that look alike represent one type, and other jars represent other types.

In seriation, all objects of one type are arranged in a series that reflects changes in style. These changes either developed gradually as time passed or as a culture spread to other areas. In many cases, the age of the objects must be known to determine which is the first and which is the last member of a series.

Dating. Archaeologists use various methods to determine the age of ancient objects. These methods can be divided into two major types: (1) relative dating and (2) absolute dating.

Relative Dating gives information about the age of an object in relation to other objects. Thus, relative dating methods produce only comparisons, not actual dates. For example, archaeologists can determine the relative ages of bones found at a site by measuring their fluorine content. Fluorine from underground water gradually replaces other elements in bones, and so older bones contain more fluorine.

Absolute Dating determines the age of an object in years. There are many absolute dating methods. The method used in a specific case depends mainly on the type of object being dated.

The most widely used method of dating the remains of ancient plants, animals, and human beings is *radiocarbon dating.* This technique is based on the fact that all living things constantly absorb two kinds of carbon atoms, carbon 12 and carbon 14. Atoms of carbon 14, also called *radiocarbon,* are unstable and change into nitrogen atoms at a known rate. After an organism dies, therefore, the ratio of carbon 14 to carbon 12 also decreases at a known rate. As a result, archaeologists can compute the age of a specimen by measuring the amounts of carbon 12 and carbon 14 present. The traditional method of measurement is accurate as far back as 50,000 years. A newer method that uses a device called a *particle accelerator* is accurate up to 60,000 years even with the tiniest specimens. See RADIOCARBON.

Archaeologists use *potassium-argon dating* to find the age of certain rock formations in which archaeological objects are discovered. These rocks contain radioactive potassium 40, which changes into argon 40 gas at a

© Norman Owen Tomalin, Bruce Coleman Inc.

Yearly Growth Rings on a cut tree, *above,* reveal its age. Archaeologists can date wooden objects by matching rings in the objects with those on trees from the same area.

constant rate. Scientists measure the amount of each element present and then calculate the age of the rock. This method was used to date rock formations found with bones and tools in eastern Africa. The rock was found to be $1\frac{3}{4}$ million years old, which indicated that the bones and tools were that age also.

The best-known method for dating wood is called *dendrochronology*. This technique involves counting the yearly growth rings visible on cross sections of cut trees. Archaeologists match the pattern of tree rings with those of ancient wooden objects to determine the age of the objects. Dendrochronology is the most accurate of all dating methods, but it can be used only with wooden objects up to about 8,000 years old.

Evaluation. Archaeologists evaluate artifacts and features to learn such information as how and where the objects were made and used. In some cases, the scientists learn by direct experimentation. In Central America, one archaeologist stored nuts for a year in underground chambers to support his theory that the Maya used the chambers to keep nuts. Artifacts and features can also help explain the social lives of ancient people. For example, the size of houses can show how many people lived in one household. The number and value of objects found in graves can indicate differences in social class.

The evaluation of ecofacts reveals such information as what food people ate and whether they grew crops or gathered wild plants. Ecofacts can even explain ancient migration patterns. A seed of grain not native to the area where it is found may reveal how and when eating habits were carried from one place to another.

Archaeologists evaluate evidence with the help of specialists from other fields. Zoologists help identify animal bones and butchering techniques. Botanists analyze seeds to learn about ancient agricultural practices. Such specialists as geologists, architects, and engineers also work with archaeologists. In some cases, other specialists operate computers that greatly speed up the evaluation process.

History

Beginnings. The idea of studying the past through ancient objects has developed gradually. But the most intense interest has occurred in the past 200 years. During the 1700's, some wealthy Europeans began to study and collect art objects from the times of ancient Greece and Rome. This interest in classical art is called *antiquarianism*. These first diggers looked only for treasures and threw away ordinary objects.

Also during the 1700's, European scholars began to debate how long human beings had lived on the earth. Their interest resulted partly from recent discoveries of primitive stone tools together with the bones of extinct animals. These scholars also knew about the huge mounds and ruined cities in the Americas that pointed to ancient human life there. They realized that human beings had a prehistoric past, but they could not decide when and where this past had begun.

The 1800's brought a more scientific approach to the study of the past. The great length of human prehistory became widely accepted due to advances in geology and biology. By the early 1800's, geologists had determined that rock formation resulted from extremely slow processes, such as erosion and volcanic activity. This view, known as *uniformitarianism*, led most scholars to believe

The Griffith Institute, Ashmolean Museum, Oxford

The Tomb of King Tutankhamon of Egypt was discovered in 1922 by the English archaeologist Howard Carter. Carter, *left*, and his sponsor, Lord Carnarvon, stand at the tomb's entrance.

that the earth was much older than previously thought. Then, in 1859, the British biologist Charles R. Darwin proposed the theory of *biological evolution* in his book *The Origin of Species*. This theory suggested that human beings, like other animals and the earth itself, had developed slowly over a great period of time.

By the mid-1800's, archaeology had become a separate field of study, and evidence of human prehistory was accumulating rapidly. Important discoveries included prehistoric lake dwellings in Switzerland, ancient cave paintings in France and Spain, and part of a prehistoric human skull found in Germany. During the late 1800's, archaeologists began to use scientific techniques of excavation that made it possible to determine sequences of cultural development. In an excavation at Naqada, near Qus, Egypt, a British scholar named Sir Flinders Petrie became one of the first diggers to look carefully for all remains, not just for treasures. Others who undertook large-scale excavations at that time included the British nobleman Sir Austen Henry Layard, at Nineveh in what is now Iraq, and the German businessman Heinrich Schliemann, at Troy in what is now Turkey.

European archaeologists of the late 1800's focused their studies on the ancient European and Middle Eastern civilizations described by classical and Biblical authors. American archaeologists, however, could find almost no written records of the civilizations they studied. Partly for this reason, they turned to anthropology for methods of interpreting their discoveries. For example, they studied artifacts produced by contemporary American Indians to help interpret objects from past societies.

The 1900's. The scope of archaeology expanded greatly during the 1900's. Archaeologists began to explore the past civilizations of Central and South America, China, Japan, Southeast Asia, and other areas. By the early 1900's, archaeologists were using stratig-

ARCHAEOLOGY

Important Dates in Archaeology

1797 The British geologist John Frere found flint tools at Hoxne, England, and reported that they belonged to a period "beyond that of the present world."

1853-1854 A drought revealed Swiss lake villages dating back at least 5,000 years.

1870 Heinrich Schliemann, a German businessman, began excavations on the site of Troy in what is now Turkey.

1879 Prehistoric wallpaintings were found in a cave at Altamira, Spain.

1894 Sir Flinders Petrie of Great Britain excavated the royal cemetery at Naqada, near Qus, Egypt.

1900 The British archaeologist Sir Arthur Evans began excavating Knossos, capital of the Minoan civilization of Crete.

1922 Howard Carter of Great Britain created worldwide interest in archaeology when he found King Tutankhamon's tomb in Egypt.

1925 Flint points found at Folsom, N. Mex., showed that people lived in North America thousands of years ago.

1939 Basil Brown of Great Britain discovered the remains of an Anglo-Saxon treasure ship at Sutton Hoo, near Ipswich, England.

1952 The British archaeologist Dame Kathleen Kenyon led excavations at Jericho, Jordan, that proved it to be one of the oldest known communities.

1964-1975 Excavations at Ebla, near Aleppo, Syria, revealed an ancient kingdom that flourished as a commercial and cultural center about 2400 B.C.

raphy and seriation to date their finds. During the mid-1900's, new techniques made dating much easier and more accurate. The most significant of these techniques was radiocarbon dating, developed in the 1940's by an American chemist named Willard F. Libby.

Great advances in underwater archaeology also occurred during the mid-1900's. Previously, underwater excavation had been both difficult and expensive. The aqualung and other diving devices invented during the 1940's enabled divers to move more freely.

Recent Developments. Since the 1950's, the primary aim of archaeologists has been to develop general theories that explain the changes in human societies revealed by archaeological evidence. For example, archaeologists today look for reasons behind the development of farming in Mexico about 6500 B.C. and the growth of cities in the Middle East about 3000 B.C. Many archaeologists undertake projects to study a problem rather than just a site. During the 1960's, for example, the American archaeologist Richard MacNeish studied plant remains from many cave sites in Mexico to document the domestication of corn.

Contemporary archaeologists have also developed many new research techniques. They use sampling methods based on the principles of statistics and probability. In this way, they can study sites quickly and without extensive excavation. New scientific methods also aid in the discovery of underground sites. For example, archaeologists can locate buried remains by using a magnetometer to measure slight irregularities in the earth's magnetic field. This method led to the discovery of an ancient city buried 15 feet (4.6 meters) below the ground in Italy.

A major concern among archaeologists today involves the preservation of archaeological sites that have not yet

been studied. Many such sites are threatened by construction projects, the expansion of agriculture, and other types of development. The United States enacted laws during the 1960's and 1970's that require federal agencies to identify and preserve places that might be of historic importance. On an international scale, archaeologists seek to halt the illegal sale of archaeological objects. They urge that developed nations enact and enforce laws to prohibit the import of ancient objects unless an export certificate has first been obtained from the country of origin.

Careers in Archaeology

Most careers in archaeology require a master's or doctor's degree. In college, most students who wish to become archaeologists major in anthropology but also take courses in history, languages, biology, computer science, statistics, and geology. In addition, their studies may include experience in excavation. In graduate school, students generally select a geographic area that becomes their research specialty.

Archaeologists are employed in three main fields: (1) teaching, (2) museum work, and (3) government service. Most archaeologists who teach at colleges and universities also carry out research and publish their findings. Archaeologists who work in museums conduct research, preserve and restore ancient objects, and use those objects to educate the public. Archaeologists employed by governments identify and study archaeological remains located on public property or endangered by public construction projects.

In the United States, most archaeologists belong to the Society for American Archaeology. *American Antiquity* and *Archaeology* are the leading journals for archaeologists.

BARBARA VOORHIES

Related Articles in WORLD BOOK include:

BIOGRAPHIES

Breasted, James H.	Piranesi, Giovanni B.
Carter, Howard	Schliemann, Heinrich
Evans, Sir Arthur J.	Ventris, Michael G. F.

EGYPT

Egypt, Ancient	Necropolis	Rosetta Stone
Hieroglyphic	Obelisk	Sphinx
Mummy	Pyramids	Valley of the Kings

GREECE

Acropolis	Corinth	Knossos	Parthenon
Aegean	Elgin Marbles	Mycenae	Sparta
Civilization	Ephesus	Olympia	Troy

ITALY

Appian Way	Herculaneum	Pompeii
Forum, Roman	Pantheon	Rome (Ancient City)

MIDDLE EAST

Assyria (picture:	Ebla	Persia, Ancient
An Excavation)	Mesopotamia	Phoenicia
Babylonia	Moabite Stone	Sumer
Dead Sea Scrolls	Nineveh	Ur

THE AMERICAS

Aztec	Inca	Machu Picchu
Cliff Dwellers	Indian, American	Maya
Easter Island	(The First Americans)	Mound Builders
Folsom Point	Kensington Rune Stone	

OTHER RELATED ARTICLES

Angkor	Anthropology	Archaeoastronomy

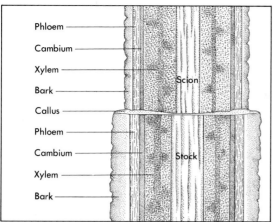

Phloem
Cambium
Xylem
Bark
Callus
Phloem
Cambium
Xylem
Bark

Scion

Stock

WORLD BOOK illustrations by Patricia J. Wynne

Grafting involves joining a *scion*—a bud or cutting from one plant—to a *stock*—the root system of another plant. A *callus* then develops, forming the *cambium* of a new plant. The cambium produces the *phloem* and *xylem,* which carry food and water.

GRAFTING

GRAFTING is the process of uniting parts of two plants to form a single plant. Plant growers reproduce many trees and bushes by means of grafting. They also use grafting to improve and repair plants.

Grafting requires two plant pieces: a *scion* (pronounced *SY uhn*) and a *stock*. The scion consists of a bud, branch, or cutting from a stem. The stock, or *rootstock*, is the piece to which the scion is grafted. The stock provides the root system and may also include part of a stem. For grafting to be successful, the scion and the stock should belong to the same species or to species that are closely related.

Each part contributes its own characteristics to the graft. The scion determines the kind and quality of fruit, nut, or flower that will be produced by the grafted plant. The stock nourishes the grafted plant and affects its size and productivity.

Uses of Grafting

The primary use of grafting is to *propagate* (reproduce) existing varieties of plants. Most fruit trees, including nut trees, are propagated by grafting. Grape and rose vines may also be grafted. In addition, rare varieties of such flowers as magnolias, dahlias, and peonies may be propagated by grafting.

Grafting can propagate hybrids, which do not grow true to variety if raised from seed. For example, seeds from McIntosh apples almost never produce trees with typical McIntosh fruit. However, a McIntosh scion will produce apples with the same characteristics as its parent. Grafting can also propagate seedless fruit, such as navel oranges and seedless grapefruit.

Grafting can be used to change the variety of fruit a plant produces. For example, a grower can graft different apple scions to one stock and thus make a single tree bear many kinds of apples. However, grafting does not create new kinds of fruit or flowers, even when the scion and stock belong to different species. For example, a Bartlett pear scion grafted to quince stock will produce Bartlett pears.

Grafting can change a plant's growing habits. A graft that uses established roots as the stock saves growing

Some Methods of Grafting

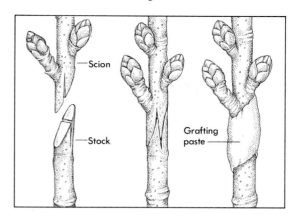

Scion

Stock

Grafting paste

In Whip Grafting, a scion and a stock of about the same diameter are joined. The scion and stock are cut diagonally, and then a notch is made in each piece. The pieces are fitted together and sealed with grafting paste to keep them from drying out.

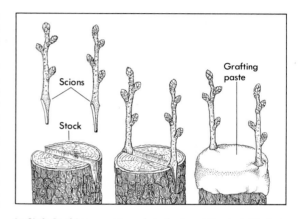

Scions

Stock

Grafting paste

In Cleft Grafting, a cut is made in the top of the stock. The bottoms of two smaller scions are trimmed, and a scion is wedged into each end of the opening. The exposed areas of the stock and scions are then covered with grafting paste.

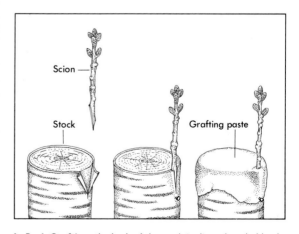

Scion

Stock

Grafting paste

In Bark Grafting, the bark of the stock is slit and peeled back. The scion is trimmed, fitted in place, and secured with a nail. The exposed surfaces are then covered with grafting paste. Several scions can be grafted around the stock in this way.

377

time. Orange and lemon trees, among others, not only grow faster, but also bear fruit earlier when they have been grafted.

Grafting can also produce hardier, disease-resistant plants. Stocks that grow in poor soils or survive low temperatures can support scions that suffer under those conditions. Pear varieties that 'are attacked by a disease called fire blight can be grafted to quince stock, which reduces the chance of infection.

Plant growers also use grafting to repair injured parts of trees. For example, scions can be grafted in place of broken branches.

Kinds of Grafting

Commonly used grafting methods include *whip grafting, cleft grafting,* and *bark grafting.* In all methods, the *cambium* of the scion and the stock must touch. The cambium is a thin layer of growing tissue between the bark and the wood.

Scion and stock unite as new cells grow from their cambium. While these cells form, the scion and stock must remain firmly in place. Gardeners wrap most graft joints with tape or rubber bands, or they use a nail to hold the graft in place. For a successful graft, the plant tissues must not dry out. If scions are cut more than a day before they are to be used, they should be kept cold and moist. After joining the scion and stock, the gardener spreads a preparation called grafting paste over the joint to prevent drying.

Whip Grafting is used when the scion and stock have about the same diameter. To make a whip graft, cut scions in winter and graft them as soon as possible. Slice off the bottom of the scion and the top of the stock on a slant. Make a slash about $\frac{1}{2}$ inch (1.3 centimeters) deep in each piece. The projecting tongue on one piece should fit snugly into the slash on the other, with the cambium meeting. Tie the joint and cover it with grafting paste. When the scion begins to grow after about a month, cut away the tying materials.

Cleft Grafting is done in midwinter, when the plant is dormant. This type of graft is used when the scion has a smaller diameter than the stock. To make a cleft graft,

USDA

Grafting Produces Healthy New Growth in a fairly short time. The above photograph was taken one year after these olive scions were cleft-grafted onto 30-year-old olive stock.

saw the stock straight across. Split the sawed-off stock across the center to a depth of a few inches. Smooth the surface with a sharp knife. Trim two scions to a wedge shape at the bottom. On each side of the split or cleft, insert a scion so that its cambium touches the cambium of the stock. Spread grafting paste over the surfaces.

Bark Grafting takes place in spring when the stock begins to grow and the bark peels more easily. Cut several scions in winter and store them until spring. When you are ready to graft, saw the stock straight across and peel back its bark in several places just enough to make room for a scion. Pare the bottom of each scion diagonally for about $1\frac{1}{4}$ inches (3.2 centimeters) on one side and about $\frac{1}{2}$ inch (1.3 centimeters) on the opposite side. Insert each piece between the bark and wood of the stock with its long cut against the wood. Drive a nail through the bark and bottom of the scion and into the wood to hold the scion in place. Cover the graft with grafting paste.

Other Kinds of Grafting include *bud grafting, bridge grafting,* and *inarching.* Bud grafting, or *budding,* uses a bud rather than a stem cutting for a scion. The grower makes a T-shaped cut in the bark of the stock to receive the bud. The bark is peeled back and the bud inserted and pressed down into the cut. Bridge grafting is used to repair injuries in which large sections of bark have been destroyed. Scions are joined to the stock above and below the damaged area. Inarching is the grafting of two complete plants side by side. The gardener removes a small area of bark on each plant and ties the two together. After the plants have joined, the root and lower stem of one is cut away.   GEORGE C. MARTIN

ALZHEIMER'S DISEASE is a brain disorder characterized by loss of memory and judgment. It rarely occurs before the age of 40, but its frequency increases as people grow older. It affects 20 to 30 per cent of people 85 years old.

In the early stages of Alzheimer's disease, people forget recent events but can recall past events clearly. They may try to conceal their memory loss by writing notes to themselves to help remember names and other details. As the disease progresses, the memory loss steadily increases and other abilities become impaired, including judgment, speech, and muscle coordination. Outbursts of rage or tears often occur, usually for no apparent reason. In severe cases, the victims become completely incapable of caring for themselves. The disease gradually weakens the body, making it subject to various infections. Most victims die from pneumonia or other infections.

Alzheimer's disease results from the progressive destruction of brain cells. The cause of this destruction is unknown. The brain tissue of Alzheimer's patients shows an excess of aluminum and a deficiency of a certain protein. However, physicians do not know if these abnormalities cause the disease or are effects of it. Research indicates that heredity plays a major role in 25 to 35 per cent of the cases that begin before age 70. Heredity seems less important in cases that begin at older ages.

Alzheimer's disease cannot be cured, but proper care can help minimize its effects. Doctors recommend adequate rest, relief from stress, and immediate treatment of infections or other physical ailments that may weaken the body.   LEONARD L. HESTON

AMYOTROPHIC LATERAL SCLEROSIS, or ALS, is a rare and incurable disease of the nervous system. It is sometimes called *Lou Gehrig's disease,* after a famous baseball player who died from it. ALS gradually destroys the nerves that control the muscles. Weakness, paralysis, and eventually death result. Physicians advise ALS patients to remain active as long as they can, but no treatment can halt the disease.

ALS develops when certain nerve cells in the brain and spinal cord *degenerate* (break down) and die. These cells, called *motor neurons,* make the muscles work by sending them *impulses* (nerve messages). As the motor neurons degenerate, they lose the ability to transmit impulses. The muscles they control gradually stop working and then waste away. Physicians do not know what causes the motor neurons to degenerate and die.

Small twitches occur as the dying neurons send irregular impulses to the muscles. The arms and legs grow increasingly weak, and victims have trouble walking and performing simple tasks with their hands. They lose weight and gradually become paralyzed as their muscles grow useless. Talking and swallowing may become difficult. Death occurs when the muscles that control breathing stop functioning. In most cases, this happens within two to five years after the first symptoms appear.

ALS is painless and does not affect the mind. It occurs among all races and social classes throughout the world. The disease afflicts almost twice as many men as women. Most victims develop the first symptoms in their 50's. 	MILTON ALTER

DYSENTERY, *DIHS uhn TEHR ee,* is a disease involving inflammation of the lining of the large intestine. The inflammation, which is caused by microscopic organisms, produces abdominal pain and diarrhea. The bowel movements may contain mucus and blood. Some cases of dysentery include fever or vomiting.

Diarrhea causes people with dysentery to lose fluids and salts necessary to their bodies. The disease can be fatal if the body becomes dehydrated.

Dysentery strikes people of all ages throughout the world, but some forms of the disease occur more frequently in tropical countries. It can be particularly dangerous to infants, the elderly, and people in weak physical condition.

Causes and Symptoms. Most dysentery is caused by bacteria called *shigella* or by a one-celled animal called an *ameba.* Shigella produce *shigellosis,* also called *bacillary dysentery.* Shigellosis begins suddenly and involves high fever and severe diarrhea. If untreated, the disease may disappear in a few weeks. However, some cases result in fatal dehydration.

Amebas cause *amebic dysentery,* which begins gradually and rarely produces high fever. It can cause diarrhea for years, however, and may produce *ulcers* (open sores) in the lining of the large intestine. Later, the infection may spread to the liver. Amebic dysentery seldom is fatal.

Spread. The organisms that cause dysentery are transmitted through the *feces* (solid body wastes) of infected individuals. Some people, known as *carriers,* spread the disease but have no symptoms of it.

The bacteria and amebas enter the body through the mouth, in most cases in food or water. Flies and unwashed hands can transfer feces to food. Fruits and vegetables must be thoroughly washed if they have been treated with fertilizer containing human feces.

Epidemics of dysentery have occurred where people live in overcrowded conditions and have poor sanitation. In the past, the disease was common in such places as hospitals, prisons, and army camps. During some wars, more soldiers died from dysentery than in battle. Improved sanitation during the 1900's has greatly reduced the number of cases of dysentery. However, epidemics of the disease still occur in developing countries.

Diagnosis and Treatment. Physicians diagnose dysentery after finding shigella or amebas in samples of the patient's feces or intestinal tissues. Treatment includes replacing fluids and body salts that the patient has lost. Physicians also use certain antibiotics to speed recovery from dysentery. 	JAMES L. FRANKLIN

GAUCHER'S DISEASE, *goh SHAYZ,* is a severe hereditary disorder that affects the spleen, liver, bones, and, in some forms of the disease, the brain and nerves. It results from the abnormal accumulation of a chemical compound called *glucosylceramide,* which forms as the body replaces worn-out tissues. In most people, the compound is broken down by an enzyme called *beta-glucosidase.* Victims of Gaucher's disease do not produce enough normal beta-glucosidase. As a result, glucosylceramide builds up in certain cells in the affected organs. These swollen *Gaucher cells* damage the organs.

There are three major forms of Gaucher's disease. Type 1, the most common form of the disease, can begin at any age. It is characterized by damage to certain bones and joints, and by enlargement of the spleen and liver. Its symptoms, which vary from mild to severe, include bone pain, fractures, difficulties in walking, anemia, bruises, and blood clotting problems. Many victims have a shortened life span. In such cases, death results from complications of the disease, especially from pneumonia or blood disorders. Type 1 disease primarily affects Jewish people of central and eastern European ancestry.

Type 2 is a rare disorder that generally appears during the first 6 months of life. Its symptoms include severe mental retardation and loss of muscle control, as well as enlargement of the spleen and liver. Most victims die by age 2. This type of Gaucher's disease has not been linked to any particular group of people.

Type 3 begins during later childhood. It includes all the symptoms of type 1 disease, along with mental retardation, poor coordination, and muscle weakness. Most victims die from disease-related complications between the ages of 15 and 30. Type 3 occurs mainly among persons of northern Swedish ancestry.

A person inherits two genes—one from each parent—that control the production of beta-glucosidase. Gaucher's victims inherit an abnormal form of the gene—called the *Gaucher gene*—from each parent. A person who inherits one normal gene and one Gaucher gene is a *carrier* of the disease. Carriers do not have the disease. But if two carriers have children, each child has one chance in four of inheriting the abnormal gene from each parent and thus of developing Gaucher's disease. 	ROBERT J. DESNICK

379

NASA

Argonne National Laboratory

Radiation Is a Vital Form of Energy. All life on the earth depends on natural radiation from the sun, *left.* Artificially produced radiation has many uses in science and industry. A researcher behind protective glass, *right,* works with radioactive material by remote control.

RADIATION

RADIATION is one of the chief forms of energy. We live in the midst of a continuous flow of radiation. Natural radiation comes from rocks and minerals in the earth and from the sun and other objects in space. Artificially produced radiation is widely used in communications, industry, medicine, and research.

Most scientists believe the amount of radiation to which we are exposed is not harmful. But larger doses of radiation cause biological and chemical changes in living tissue. Illness and even death can result if a person receives excessive amounts of radiation.

Radiation consists of *electromagnetic waves* or *high-energy particles.* Electromagnetic waves are changing patterns of electric and magnetic energy that move rapidly through space. They include infrared rays, light, microwaves, radio waves, X rays, and gamma rays. High-energy particles are tiny bits of matter that have been accelerated to great speeds. Much of the radiation given off by radioactive substances is made up of high-energy particles called *nuclear radiation.*

The Importance of Radiation

All life on the earth depends on radiation from the sun. Without heat from the sun, the earth would soon become so cold that nothing could live on it. Without sunlight, we would starve. Green plants use sunlight in making their own food, and our food comes from plants

or from animals that eat plants. Almost all our sources of energy originate from solar radiation. See SUN (How the Sun Affects the Earth).

In addition to enjoying the benefits of natural radiation, people have learned to produce radiation for a variety of practical purposes. This section gives only a sampling of the many uses of radiation.

In Industry, radiation is used in the preparation of certain industrial chemicals. Manufacturers use nuclear radiation to measure and test materials on production lines. For example, the thickness of a hot strip of steel can be measured by placing a source of radiation beneath the steel and a radiation detector above it. The amount of radiation that penetrates the steel indicates its thickness. Nuclear power plants produce heat energy in a reaction called *nuclear fission.* The heat is used to power steam turbines that generate electricity (see NUCLEAR ENERGY).

In Communications. Radio waves make possible almost instantaneous communication between any two places in the world. Artificial satellites that circle the earth send radio, telephone, and television signals by means of radio waves. Microwave relay stations built on hills and ridges transmit business information and telephone messages across great distances. Thin, flexible fibers of glass or plastic called *optical fibers* can transfer

John W. Poston, the contributor of this article, is Associate Professor of Nuclear Engineering and Health Physics at the Georgia Institute of Technology.

messages from one place to another by means of light waves. These fibers can transmit telephone conversations, television programs, and other types of communication. See FIBER OPTICS.

In Medicine, physicians use X rays to make photographs of the bones and organs of the human body. Dentists X-ray teeth to reveal cavities. In a type of therapy called *short-wave diathermy*, electromagnetic waves are passed through parts of the body to produce localized heating. Diathermy helps relieve such conditions as arthritis and muscle strain. Beams of high-energy particles sterilize *sutures* (threads for stitches) and other medical equipment. Cancer cells can be destroyed by controlled exposure to radiation.

In Scientific Research, archaeologists determine the age of many ancient objects by measuring the amount of radioactive carbon they contain (see RADIOCARBON [Radiocarbon Dating]). In a process called *neutron activation analysis*, scientists bombard a sample of a substance or object with particles called *neutrons*. Some of the atoms in the sample become *radioactive*—that is, they give off particles and rays of high energy. The scientists can then identify the elements present in the sample by studying the radiation *emitted* (given off) by the radioactive atoms. See RADIOCHEMISTRY.

In Military Operations, a thin beam of light from a device called a *laser* guides some types of bombs toward their targets. Certain small weapons have telescopic sights that send out infrared rays. The rays are reflected by objects they strike. These reflections enable soldiers to aim the weapons accurately in the dark. Radar uses radio waves to detect enemy aircraft, missiles, ships, and soldiers. Much of the fear of nuclear weapons stems from the deadly radiation that they produce.

Kinds of Radiation

There are three major kinds of radiation: (1) electromagnetic radiation, (2) nuclear radiation, and (3) cosmic radiation.

Electromagnetic Radiation consists of electromagnetic waves, which travel through space at the speed of light—186,282 miles (299,792 kilometers) per second. Electromagnetic waves differ widely in *wavelength*. Wavelength is the distance between the crest of one wave and the crest of the next. The main types of electromagnetic radiation, in order of increasing wavelength, are gamma rays, X rays, ultraviolet light, visible light, infrared rays, microwaves, and radio waves. Electromagnetic radiation with short wavelengths has higher energy than does radiation with long wavelengths. See ELECTROMAGNETIC WAVES.

Scientists formerly believed that electromagnetic waves consisted of a continuous flow of energy. But electromagnetic radiation actually occurs in the form of individual packets of energy called *photons* (see PHOTON). When photons travel through space, they appear as continuous electromagnetic waves. However, when photons of radiation strike a substance, they behave as if they were separate particles of energy. Each photon has a certain amount of energy.

Except for gamma rays, all electromagnetic radiation is generated by the movement of *electrons*, negatively charged particles in the atoms of a substance. For example, visible light, ultraviolet light, and X rays originate from changes in the *energy levels* of electrons. Electrons in an atom are restricted to a certain set of motions, each of which is called an energy level. When an electron moves from a higher to a lower energy level, the electron emits a photon.

Gamma rays result from the rearrangement of particles that make up the *nucleus* (central core) of an atom. The major types of particles in the nucleus are *protons* and *neutrons*. Nuclear changes are the most energetic changes that occur in an atom. Therefore, gamma rays have more energy than any other form of electromagnetic radiation.

Nuclear Radiation consists of high-energy particles and rays given off from the nuclei of certain types of atoms. Such atoms are radioactive. Radioactive atoms emit radiation in the form of *alpha particles, beta par-*

Weston Controls

A Hot Strip of Steel is measured for the desired thickness by radiation as the steel rolls through a production line. A source of radiation is beneath the steel, and a radiation detector is above it. The amount of radiation that penetrates the steel indicates its thickness.

Bell Laboratories

A Microwave Relay Station transmits telephone messages by radio waves. Radio waves make possible almost instant communication between any two places.

© Dan McCoy, Rainbow

A CAT Scanner X-rays internal organs, such as the brain. A computer uses the X-ray data to form an image of the organ on a screen.

RADIATION

ticles, or gamma rays. An alpha particle is the nucleus of a helium atom. It consists of two protons and two neutrons that behave as a single particle. A beta particle is a high-speed electron. After the nucleus of a radioactive atom gives off an alpha or beta particle, the arrangement of protons and neutrons in the nucleus changes. This rearrangement produces gamma rays. See RADIOACTIVITY.

Many radioactive substances occur naturally in the rocks and minerals of the earth's crust. In addition, physicists artificially produce radioactive elements by bombarding atoms with high-energy protons, neutrons, and other accelerated particles. These particles are produced in such devices as *nuclear reactors* and *particle accelerators*. The accelerated particles themselves are also classified as nuclear radiations. See NUCLEAR REACTOR; PARTICLE ACCELERATOR.

Cosmic Radiation consists of high-energy particles that come from the sun and other objects in outer space. These particles, also known as *cosmic rays*, include electrons, protons, helium nuclei, hydrogen nuclei, and the nuclei of such heavier elements as carbon and oxygen. Cosmic rays travel at tremendous speeds. Large quantities of the rays originate from exploding stars called *supernovae* and extremely dense stars known as *pulsars*. The sun releases cosmic radiation during spectacular eruptions called *solar flares*.

Every second, about three to six cosmic rays strike each square inch (6 square centimeters) of the earth's atmosphere. However, only a few of these particles reach the earth's surface. See COSMIC RAYS.

The Effects of Radiation

How Radiation Affects Matter. When electromagnetic waves strike a substance, they transfer some of their energy to the substance. Ordinarily, this energy causes electrons in the substance to vibrate. These vibrations generate heat, which raises the temperature of the substance. Some forms of electromagnetic radiation, such as visible and ultraviolet light, can cause electrons to jump to higher energy levels within atoms. These electrons then emit light when they return to lower energy levels.

The Deadly Effects of Long-Term Gamma Radiation can be seen in this picture of a forest. In an experiment, the trees in the center were exposed to gamma rays for about six months.

The process by which certain materials give off light after absorbing radiation is called *luminescence* (see LUMINESCENCE).

In some cases, photons of electromagnetic radiation have enough energy to knock electrons completely out of the atoms of a substance. Such an occurrence is known as the *photoelectric effect*. Each electron is removed by the action of a single photon, which disappears in the process. The photon transfers its energy to the electron. The electron can then escape from the atom. Atoms that have lost electrons become positively charged particles called *ions*. The process of removing electrons from atoms is known as *ionization* (see ION AND IONIZATION).

Certain types of radiation are classified as *ionizing radiations* because they produce trails of ions as they travel through a substance. Ionizing radiations include the high-energy particles of nuclear radiation and cosmic radiation. These particles collide with atoms as they pass through a material. In these collisions, they knock electrons out of atoms, forming ions. The particles of radiation produce ionization until all their initial energy has been consumed. An electron leaves a thin trail of ions, but such heavier particles as alpha particles and protons form dense groups of ions. In addition, many of the electrons knocked out of atoms have sufficient energy to cause further ionization.

Two types of electromagnetic radiation, X rays and gamma rays, are also classified as ionizing radiations. Their high-energy photons can penetrate deep into a substance, where they produce ionization through the photoelectric effect and similar processes. Although the photons are absorbed, the electrons that they knock loose move rapidly through the substance, forming additional ions.

How Radiation Affects Health. Overexposure to ultraviolet light from the sun causes sunburn (see ULTRAVIOLET RAYS [Harmful Effects]). But most nonionizing radiations do not ordinarily have enough energy to endanger living things. However, all types of ionizing radiation can cause serious biological damage. The ionization produced by such radiation disrupts the normal chemical processes of living cells, causing the cells to grow abnormally or to die. The seriousness of the biological damage depends on the density of the ions formed. Cells can repair the damage produced by only a few ions, but they generally do not recover from a high density of ionization.

The various types of ionizing radiation produce different degrees of biological damage. The *relative biological effectiveness* (RBE) of a particular radiation indicates the extent to which it damages cells compared with equal doses of other ionizing radiations. For example, the dense tracks of ions formed by alpha particles cause about 20 times as much damage as do the thin ion trails generated by electrons. Thus, alpha particles have an RBE of 20, and electrons have an RBE of only 1.

The amount of radiation absorbed by a substance is measured in units called *rads*. A rad is defined as a dose of $\frac{1}{100}$ *joule* of radiation energy per kilogram of material (see JOULE). Another unit, called the *rem*, measures the biological damage produced in the human body by different types of ionizing radiation. The number of rems of radiation equals the number of rads multiplied by the RBE of the radiation involved. Another common unit is the *millirem*, which is $\frac{1}{1,000}$ of a rem. The average annual

Jim Curry Associates, Inc.

Working Near Radiation, a technician wears a *dosimeter* on his collar. The dosimeter measures the amount of radiation to which he is exposed in his job at a nuclear power plant.

radiation dose received by a person in the United States is about 180 millirems. Most of this dose is due to natural radiation and medical and dental X rays. A small amount comes from the testing of nuclear weapons. The rest comes largely from such items as color TV sets, smoke detectors, and airport baggage X-ray machines. The operation of nuclear power plants accounts for only a tiny amount of the total radiation dose.

A person can receive a dose of up to 25 rems of radiation without showing any immediate effects. A dose of 100 rems may produce *radiation sickness* (see RADIATION SICKNESS). People exposed to doses between 300 and 800 rems experience severe radiation sickness. Radiation doses of more than 800 rems are fatal.

Other effects of exposure to radiation may not become evident until later in life. These effects include a shortened life span and an increased probability of developing cancer and cataracts. Radiation can also damage a person's genes. Damaged genes can transmit harmful traits to the person's offspring.

Protection Against Radiation. People who work with radiation and those who receive radiation treatments must be specially protected from exposure to dangerous amounts. The simplest means of protection is to increase the distance between the person and the source of radiation. As this distance increases, the intensity of the radiation decreases. If the distance is doubled, for example, a person receives only one-fourth as much radiation. Another easy safeguard is to limit the period of exposure to the radiation.

Shields of absorbing material also offer protection against radiation. Lead is the most effective shield against the types of radiation to which people are most commonly exposed—medical and dental X rays and nuclear radiation. For example, before X-raying a patient's teeth, a dentist covers the patient with an apron that contains a thin layer of lead. The lead absorbs most

of the radiation, protecting the patient from excessive exposure. Larger quantities of radiation require greater shielding. For instance, thick concrete shields protect workers who conduct experiments with high-energy radiation in laboratories.

People who work with radiation also take extra precautions. For example, workers use mechanical hands or remote-control devices to handle radioactive substances. In addition, everyone who works near radiation wears a *dosimeter,* a device that measures the doses of radiation received over a period of time. Workers check their dosimeters regularly to detect any excessive exposure.

Detecting and Measuring Radiation

Radiation can be detected and measured by the effects it produces. For example, most forms of radiation cause chemical changes on the surface of photographic film. Scientists study these changes to determine the kind of radiation and its intensity. In addition, various instruments detect electronic vibrations, heat, or luminescence produced by radiation.

Scientists use several devices to study ionizing radiations. These devices include (1) bubble chambers, (2) geiger counters, (3) scintillation counters, and (4) solid-state detectors.

Bubble Chambers are metal vessels filled with a special liquid under pressure. As a particle of ionizing radiation passes through a bubble chamber, it leaves a track of tiny bubbles. Scientists examine the type of track to identify the radiation. See BUBBLE CHAMBER.

Geiger Counters. A typical geiger counter consists of a metal tube filled with a gas at low pressure. A thin wire projects into the center of the tube. A high voltage is set up between the walls of the tube and the wire. When ionizing radiation enters the geiger counter, it generates a brief pulse of electric current. Each particle or photon produces a single pulse. Thus, the number of pulses indicates the intensity of the radiation. A geiger counter produces the same size of electric pulse, regardless of the type of radiation. See GEIGER COUNTER.

Scintillation Counters emit a flash of light when a crystal in the device absorbs a particle or photon of ionizing radiation. A special tube called a *photomultiplier tube* senses the flash of light and produces an electric signal in response to it. The strength of this signal is proportional to the energy of the radiation involved.

Solid-State Detectors also produce signals that are proportional to the energy of the radiation. A solid-state detector consists of a piece of silicon or germanium that gives off an electric signal in direct response to an ionizing particle or photon.

History

Early Theories and Discoveries. Since the 1600's, scientists have made many discoveries about radiation. One of the earliest debates regarding radiation concerned the nature of light. In 1666, the English scientist Sir Isaac Newton theorized that light consists of tiny particles. About the same time, a Dutch physicist named Christian Huygens suggested that light is made up of waves. Scientists argued about these two theories for more than 100 years. Then, in 1801, the English physicist Thomas Young showed that light exhibits certain properties similar to those of water waves and sound waves. Most scientists eventually came to accept Young's experiments as proof of the wave theory of light.

In 1864, a British scientist named James Clerk Maxwell formulated a theory that described the relationship between electric and magnetic fields. He stated that these fields act together in producing radiant energy in the form of electromagnetic waves, which travel at the speed of light. In fact, Maxwell theorized that light itself consists of such waves. In the late 1880's, the German physicist Heinrich Hertz confirmed Maxwell's theory by producing electromagnetic waves in the laboratory.

Henri Becquerel, a French physicist, discovered natural radioactivity in 1896. Becquerel found that uranium gives off invisible rays that darken a photographic plate. In 1898, the French physicists Marie and Pierre Curie discovered two new radioactive elements and named them *polonium* and *radium*. Between 1899 and 1903, a British physicist named Ernest Rutherford found that some radioactivity consists of high-energy particles. He identified two kinds of these particles, which he named *alpha particles* and *beta particles*.

The Quantum Theory. In 1900, a German physicist named Max Planck proposed a theory of electromagnetic radiation based on his studies of the light emitted by certain hot objects. Planck suggested that radiation consists of tiny packets of energy called *quanta*. Quanta were later named *photons*. In 1905, another German physicist, Albert Einstein, expanded Planck's theory to explain the photoelectric effect. Einstein theorized that all electromagnetic radiation consists of photons, which are separate bundles of electromagnetic energy. If a photon of sufficient energy strikes a piece of matter, it can interact with an atom and cause it to emit an electron.

In the photoelectric effect, photons act in a localized manner characteristic of particles rather than of waves. Thus, Einstein's ideas revived the particle theory of light. Scientists now know that radiation has features of both particles and waves. Both types of features can be observed, but not in the same experiment. If scientists set up an experiment to investigate the photoelectric effect, the photons of radiation behave as individual particles. But if a stream of photons is passed through a narrow slit, the photons appear as continuous electromagnetic waves.

In 1913, the Danish physicist Niels Bohr proposed the theory that electrons travel in certain orbits in an atom. He showed that atoms emit photons of radiation when their electrons drop from an outer orbit to an inner one. In 1924, the French physicist Louis de Broglie suggested that electrons themselves have properties of both particles and waves. Later experiments showed that electrons and other atomic particles of matter are associated with waves called *matter waves*.

Recent Developments. During the 1930's and 1940's, the development of particle accelerators and nuclear reactors enabled scientists to harness high-energy radiation. The first full-scale nuclear power plant began operation in 1956. During the 1960's and 1970's, high-energy radiations were increasingly used in industry, medicine, and research. This increased use led to growing concern about the biological effects of radia-

tion, the danger of radiation accidents, and the disposal of radioactive wastes. During this time, the field of *health physics* grew rapidly. Health physics is the branch of science that deals with the protection of people against harmful radiation. The science also studies the uses of radiation for human benefit.

For many years, scientists have known that large amounts of high-energy radiation are dangerous. But some scientists believed that frequent exposure to small amounts of radiation was not harmful. In the late 1970's and early 1980's, several studies indicated that repeated exposure to low doses of ionizing radiation could cause serious health problems. As a result of these findings, many people are demanding strict regulation of the production and use of high-energy radiation. Scientists are conducting further studies to determine the effects of low levels of radiation on people and on the environment.   JOHN W. POSTON

Related Articles in WORLD BOOK include:

Outline

I. The Importance of Radiation
    A. In Industry   D. In Scientific Research
    B. In Communications   E. In Military Operations
    C. In Medicine

II. Kinds of Radiation
    A. Electromagnetic Radiation   C. Cosmic Radia-
    B. Nuclear Radiation   tion

III. The Effects of Radiation
    A. How Radiation Affects Matter   C. Protection Against
    B. How Radiation Affects Health   Radiation

IV. Detecting and Measuring Radiation
    A. Bubble Chambers   C. Scintillation Counters
    B. Geiger Counters   D. Solid-State Detectors

V. History

Questions

Why does life on the earth depend on radiation from the sun?

How does ionizing radiation damage living cells?

Why is photographic film often used to detect radiation?

How do physicists artificially produce radioactive elements?

What was Max Planck's theory about radiation?

How do photons of radiation remove electrons from atoms?

Why are patients covered with a lead apron before they are given dental X rays?

How does a scintillation counter detect ionizing radiation?

How is most electromagnetic radiation generated? How are gamma rays produced?

What are some of the ways that radiation is used in medicine?

Additional Resources

ASIMOV, ISAAC. *Inside the Atom.* Rev. ed. Harper, 1974.

JENKINS, ERIC N. *Radioactivity: A Science in Its Historical and Social Context.* Wykeham, 1979.

MOCHE, DINAH. *Radiation: Benefits/Dangers.* Watts, 1979.

UPTON, ARTHUR C. *Radiation Injury: Effects, Principles, and Perspectives.* Univ. of Chicago Press, 1969.

Index

This index covers the contents of the 1982, 1983, and 1984 editions of the *Science Year*, The World Book Science Annual.

Each index entry is followed by the edition year in *italics* and the page numbers:

Botany, *84*-235, *83*-234, *82*-230

This means that information about Botany begins on the page indicated for each of the editions.

An index entry that is the title of an article appearing in *Science Year* is printed in boldface italic letters: ***Archaeology.*** An entry that is not an article title, but a subject discussed in an article of some other title, is printed: **Plate tectonics.**

The various "See" and "See also" cross references in the index are to other entries within the index:

Neuroscience, *84*-292, *83*-292, *82*-286.

See also **Brain.**

Clue words or phrases are used when the entry needs further definition or when two or more references to the same subject appear in *Science Year*. These make it easy to locate the material on the page:

Toxic waste disposal: environment, *84*-270, *83*-271, *82*-252; *Special Report*, *84*-82

The indication *"il."* means that the reference is to an illustration only, as:

Flashlight fish: *il, 84*-66

Index

A

Index

Index

Index

Maya: archaeology, *84*-222, *83*-219, *82*-217; *Special Report, 83*-12
Mead, Margaret: *Close-Up, 84*-217
Meadura (Ethiopia): Afar, *Special Report, 84*-108
Mean density: Saturn, *82*-17
Measles: *Close-Up, 84*-277
Meat-eating bee: zoology, *84*-320
Meat production, *82*-91
Medfly: *Special Report, 83*-70
Medical school, *82*-371
Medicine, 84-278, *83*-278, *82*-268; alcoholism, *82*-112; awards, *84*-312 *83*-312, *82*-309; *Close-Ups, 83*-284, *82*-272; dentistry, *84*-278, *83*-278, *82*-268; internal, *84*-279, *83*-279, *82*-269; magnetism, *Special Report, 84*-175; medical school, *82*-371; monoclonal antibodies, *82*-167; plant chemicals, *82*-128; rhinoceros, *82*-30; smell, *Special Report, 83*-195; surgery, *84*-284, *83*-285, *82*-275. See also Disease; *Public Health.*
Medicine man, *82*-129
Melanoma: drugs, *84*-243
Memory: neuroscience, *84*-293, *82*-228; psychology, *82*-305
Memory (computer): *Consumer Science, 84*-326, *82*-338; electronics, *84*-263
Menstrual synchrony, *83*-195
Mental retardation: *Close-Up, 83*-274
Mercury (element): hazardous wastes, *Special Report, 84*-87
Mesolithic Period: Old World archaeology, *84*-218
Meson: *83*-204
Mesoscale convective complex: meteorology, *84*-254
Mesothelioma: environment, *84*-270
Messenger RNA: immunology, *82*-267; molecular biology, *82*-281
Metabolism: *82*-289
Metallothionein: genetics, *84*-273
Metal-oxide-semiconductor field effect transistor: physics, *82*-295
Metals: color, *Special Report, 84*-138; condensed matter, *84*-303; hazardous wastes, *84*-87. See also Mining.
Metalworking: chemistry, *Close-Up, 83*-238
Meteorite: extinction, *Special Report, 82*-44; geology, *84*-248, *83*-246; paleontology, *84*-250, *83*-250
Meteorology, 84-251, *83*-253, *82*-278; *Special Report, 83*-115. See also Climate; Weather.
Methane: astronomy, *82*-219; zoology, *84*-318
Methanol: catalysts, *82*-203
Microcomputer, *84*-28
Microelectronics: bionics, *Special Report, 84*-28
Microprocessor: robotics, *Close-Up, 84*-262
Microtectite: paleontology, *84*-250
Microwave energy: physics, *82*-294
Middle Stone Age: Old World archaeology, *84*-218
Migration: *World Book* Supplement, *83*-378; ecology, *84*-257; zoology, *84*-317

Milky Way: galactic astronomy, *84*-226; universe mapping, *Special Report, 84*-142
"Millisecond pulsar": galactic astronomy, *84*-226
Mimas: Saturn, *Special Report, 82*-16
Mind. See Brain; *Psychology.*
Mind-altering drugs, *82*-114
Mining: ecology, *82*-240; environment, *83*-271
"Missing link": anthropology, *84*-216
Mithochondria: genetics, *82*-257; molecular anthropology, *Special Report, 84*-125
Molecular anthropology: *Special Report, 84*-113
Molecular Biology, 84-287, *83*-288, *82*-281
Molecular hybridization: molecular anthropology, *Special Report, 84*-122; oncogenes, *Special Report, 84*-161
Momentum: nuclear physics, *82*-298
Monkey: zoology, *82*-318
Monoclonal antibodies: immunology, *84*-276; neuroscience, *82*-287; *Special Report, 84*-172
Mononucleosis, *84*-75
Monopole: magnetism, *Special Report, 84*-180; particles and forces, *84*-300
Monozygotic twins: alcoholism, *82*-123; nutrition, *82*-290
Montane vole: botany, *83*-234
Monticello: archaeology, *84*-221
Mood: psychology, *82*-305
Moon: geology, *84*-248
Moons of Saturn: astronomy, *83*-223; *Special Report, 82*-12
MOSFET: physics, *82*-295
Moth: botany, *83*-234
Mount Saint Helens: agriculture, *82*-210; geology, *83*-246; *Special Report, 82*-69
Mountains, formation of: geology, *84*-249; plate tectonics, *Special Report, 84*-183
Multiple sclerosis, *84*-292
Music: *Consumer Science, 82*-342
Mutation: anthropology, *82*-214; antibodies, *83*-166; molecular biology, *83*-290, *82*-283; oncogenes, *Special Report, 84*-163; sickle cell, *83*-91
Mutualism, *84*-69
Myc oncogene, *84*-162

N

Naloxone: internal medicine, *82*-269
NANB. See Non A/non B hepatitis.
Narrow-line quasar, *82*-225
Nasopharyngeal carcinoma: herpes, *Special Report, 84*-77
National Aeronautics and Space Administration (NASA): Saturn, *Special Report, 82*-12; solar system astronomy, *84*-223; space exploration, *84*-313, *83*-313, *82*-311
National computer network, *82*-340
National Institutes of Health: animal welfare, *Special Report, 82*-90

Natural history: *Books of Science, 83*-232, *82*-229
Natural selection: scrub jays, *Special Report, 84*-23
Nature study: *Special Report, 83*-355
Neanderthal Man, *84*-216, *82*-214
Neovascularity: surgery, *84*-287
Nepenthes: carnivorous plants, *Special Report, 83*-45
Neptune: astronomy, *83*-225
Nerve grafting, *83*-292
Nerve impulses: Medfly, *Special Report, 83*-80; neuroscience, *82*-286
Nervous system. See Brain; *Neuroscience.*
Neurofibrillary tangles: neuroscience, *83*-293
Neuron: owl, *Special Report, 83*-40
Neuroscience, 84-292, *83*-292, *82*-286. See also Brain.
Neurotransmitter, *82*-116
Neutrino: cosmology, *82*-226; particles and forces, *84*-301
Neutron: particle decay, *Special Report, 83*-198; physics, *82*-299
Neutron star: galactic astronomy, *84*-226; physics, *82*-300; X-ray astronomy, *82*-146
New Waste Calcining Facility: energy, *84*-266
New World Archaeology, 84-221, *83*-219, *82*-217
Nitric acid: acid rain, *Special Report, 84*-43
Nitrogen fixation: agriculture, *82*-211; ecology, *83*-261
Nitrogen narcosis, *82*-291
Nitrogen oxide, *84*-43
NMR spectroscopy: magnetism, *Special Report, 84*-174
Nobel Prizes: chemistry, *84*-310, *83*-310, *82*-308; medicine, *84*-312, *83*-312, *82*-309; physics, *84*-312, *83*-312, *82*-309
Non A/non B hepatitis, *82*-164
Nongravitational forces: Halley's Comet, *Special Report, 83*-62
Nonionic detergent: *Consumer Science, 84*-335
Nova: galactic astronomy, *84*-228
Nuclear fission: fusion, *Special Report, 83*-144; particle decay, *Special Report, 83*-198
Nuclear fusion: particle decay, *Special Report, 83*-198; plasma physics, *82*-300; *Special Report, 83*-145
Nuclear magnetic resonance (NMR): chemistry, *83*-237; magnetism, *Special Report, 84*-174; medicine, *Close-Up, 83*-284
Nuclear moment: physics, *82*-303
Nuclear physics. See *Physics (atoms and nuclei).*
Nuclear power: environment, *83*-270; fusion, *Special Report, 83*-144
Nuclear reactor: energy, *84*-265; fusion, *Special Report, 83*-144
Nucleon: physics, *82*-298
Nucleotide: genetics, *82*-257
Nucleus: atoms and nuclei, *84*-296, *83*-296; fusion, *Special Report, 83*-144; genetics, *82*-255; magnetism,

Index

Index

Substantia innominata: internal medicine, *84*-282

Sulfur dioxide: acid rain, *Special Report,* *84*-43; environment, *83*-270

Sulfuric acid: acid rain, *Special Report,* *84*-43

Sun: astronomy, *82*-222. See also headings beginning **Solar.** . . .

Sun pitcher: carnivorous plant, *Special Report,* *83*-45

Sundew: *ils.,* *83*-49, 54

Sunglasses: *Consumer Science,* *84*-322

Sungrazers, *83*-66

Sunspots: geology, *83*-247; solar system astronomy, *84*-223

Super Proton Synchrotron, *84*-300, *83*-298

Supercluster, *84*-230, *83*-230

Superconducting cable: energy, *84*-269

Superconductivity: *84*-176

Superfund: *Close-Up,* *84*-272; environment, *83*-272, *82*-254; hazardous wastes, *Special Report,* *84*-84

Supergiant star: astronomy, *84*-227

Supernova: astronomy, *84*-226, *83*-226; quasar, *Special Report,* *83*-181; X-ray astronomy, *82*-144

Suppressor T cell, *84*-275

Surface antigen: hepatitis, *82*-157

Surface mining: ecology, *82*-240

Surgery: drugs, *83*-245; medical school, *82*-375. See also **Medicine (surgery).**

Suture zone: geology, *83*-249

Swamp forest: ecology, *82*-242

Symbiosis: *il.,* *82*-231

Symbiotic star: astronomy, *83*-227

Synchrotron radiation: extragalactic astronomy, *84*-231; physics, *83*-298

Synthetic blood: bionics, *Special Report,* *84*-38

T

T lymphocyte: immunology, *84*-275, *83*-276; public health, *84*-308

Tamper-resistant package, *84*-244

Tampons: public health, *82*-307

Tandem mirror concept (TMC): fusion, *83*-150

Technology: *Books of Science,* *84*-234, *83*-233, *82*-229

Tectite: geology, *84*-247

Teleconnections: meteorology, *84*-251

Telescope: X-ray astronomy, *82*-139

Television: *Consumer Science,* *83*-328; electronics, *83*-262, *82*-244; videodisc, *Special Report,* *83*-130

TERCOM navigational system, *84*-263

Termite: zoology, *84*-318

Terrain: geology, *83*-249

Terrane: plate tectonics, *Special Report,* *84*-183

Territorial budding: scrub jays, *Special Report,* *84*-24

Tertiary Period: extinction, *82*-42

Tethys: astronomy, *83*-224

Tetracycline: anthropology, *82*-214

Thalassemia, *84*-292

Thermoplastic technique, *84*-95

3C273 (quasar): extragalactic astronomy, *84*-230

Thromboxane: drugs, *84*-245

Thule culture: archaeology, *83*-221

Thunderstorm: *il.,* *83*-253, *82*-279

Thylakoid, *84*-198

Thyrotropin releasing hormone, *83*-293

Time depth recorder (TDR): *il.,* *84*-316

Tires: *Consumer Science,* *82*-352

Titan: Saturn, *Special Report,* *82*-19

Toad: ecology, *84*-257

Toilet soap: *84*-333

Tokamak: energy, *84*-265; fusion, *83*-151; physics, *82*-300

Tolerance: alcoholism, *82*-115

Tolstoi, Edward: deaths, *84*-242

Tool, prehistoric: Afar, *Special Report,* *84*-108; archaeology, *82*-215, 217; *il.,* *82*-215

Tooth bonding: *ils.,* *83*-278

Tooth decay: dentistry, *84*-278, *83*-278; nutrition, *84*-295

Topical magnetic resonance (TMR): *Close-Up,* *83*-284

Topo (robot): *Close-Up,* *84*-262

Topsoil: ecology, *82*-240

Torus: fusion, *Special Report,* *83*-151; plasma physics, *82*-300

Toxic shock syndrome, *82*-307

Toxic waste disposal: environment, *84*-270, *83*-271, *82*-252; *Special Report,* *84*-82

Toxicity test: animal welfare, *82*-88

Tracking and Data Relay Satellite, *84*-313

Transcription: molecular biology, *82*-281

Transforming growth factor, *84*-283

Transition metal trichalcogenide, *84*-304

Transportation: magnetism, *84*-178

Transposon: genetics, *84*-274; molecular biology, *84*-289

Trichalcogenide: condensed matter, *84*-304

Tricontonal: agriculture, *84*-213

Tris-(bipyridine) ruthenium (II) dication: chemistry, *84*-233

Tritium: energy, *84*-265; fusion, *Special Report,* *83*-145

Tritium Systems Test Assembly: energy, *84*-265

Tropical reef: extinction, *82*-48; zoology, *82*-316

Tumor: monoclonal antibodies, *82*-167; surgery, *84*-286

Turbulence: *Consumer Science,* *84*-324

Turfgrass: *Consumer Science,* *83*-330

Twins: alcoholism, *82*-123; nutrition, *82*-290

2-D electrophoresis, *83*-347

2,4,5-trichlorophenoxyacetic acid: environment, *84*-271

Tylenol: *Close-Up,* *84*-244

U

Ultraviolet radiation, *84*-322

Underwater research: oceanography, *82*-291; sunken treasure, *82*-97

Unified force: magnetism, *Special Report,* *84*-181

Universe: extragalactic astronomy, *84*-229; *Special Report,* *84*-140; X-ray astronomy, *Special Report,* *82*-140

Upwelling, *83*-120

Uranium: energy, *84*-266; geochemistry, *82*-258

Uranus: astronomy, *83*-225

Urban-cowboy rhabdomyolosis: medicine, *Close-Up,* *82*-272

Utah arm: bionics, *84*-28

Uterine cancer, *84*-281

V

Vaccine: agriculture, *83*-212; *Close-Up,* *84*-277; hepatitis, *82*-153; herpes, *Special Report,* *84*-79; immunology, *84*-276; public health, *83*-310, *82*-308

Vacuum fluorescent (VF) tube, *82*-244

Vane, John R.: science awards, *84*-312

Varicella zoster virus, *84*-74

Vasopressin: neuroscience, *82*-288

Veal production, *82*-91

Venera: astronomy, *83*-222

Venereal disease: herpes, *Special Report,* *84*-70

Vent, ocean: geology, *83*-249; oceanography, *83*-256

Venus: astronomy, *83*-222

Venus's flytrap: botany, *84*-236; carnivorous plants, *Special Report,* *83*-49; *il.,* *83*-51

Verapamil: drugs, *82*-239

Vertical axis wind turbine, *83*-267

Very Long Baseline Interferometry (VLBI): quasar, *Special Report,* *83*-173

Very low mass star, *83*-228

Vestibular system: *Close-Up,* *84*-302

Vesuvius: *Close-Up,* *84*-219

Video game: *Consumer Science,* *84*-326, *83*-328

Video high-density system, *83*-136

Videodisc: *World Book* Supplement, *82*-336; *Special Report,* *83*-128

Videotape recorder: videodisc, *83*-130

Vinogradov, Ivan M.: deaths, *84*-242

Viperfish: *il.,* *84*-62

Viral oncogene probe: *il.,* *84*-159

Viroconium: archaeology, *83*-218

Virus: genetics, *83*-275; hepatitis, *82*-153; herpes, *Special Report,* *84*-70; immunology, *84*-276; medicine, *82*-273; molecular biology, *82*-281; monoclonal antibodies, *82*-176; oncogenes, *Special Report,* *84*-158. See also **Cancer; Microbiology; Vaccine.**

Vitamins: nutrition, *84*-296, *83*-294

Index

Acknowledgments

The publishers of *Science Year* gratefully acknowledge the courtesy of the following artists, photographers, publishers, institutions, agencies, and corporations for the illustrations in this volume. Credits should be read from top to bottom, left to right, on their respective pages. All entries marked with an asterisk (*) denote illustrations created exclusively for *Science Year*. All maps, charts, and diagrams were prepared by the *Science Year* staff unless otherwise noted.

Cover
Walter Frerck, Odyssey Productions

Advisory Board

7   University of Pennsylvania; Harvard University; University of California; Argonne National Laboratory; University of Michigan; Missouri Botanical Garden; California Institute of Technology.

Special Reports

10   P. A. Hinchliffe, Bruce Coleman Ltd.; Institute of Human Origins; John Zielinski*

11   Mark Rosenthal; Rob Wood, Stansbury, Ronsaville, Wood, Inc.*, Brookhaven National Laboratory

12   © John W. Fitzpatrick and Glen E. Woolfenden

15   Britt Taylor Collins*; © John W. Fitzpatrick and Glen W. Woolfenden

16-17   © John W. Fitzpatrick and Glen E. Woolfenden

18   Patricia Wynne*

20   Britt Taylor Collins*

24   © John W. Fitzpatrick and Glen E. Woolfenden

26   John Zielinski*

29   Motion Control

31   Ronald Kalstein, Moss Rehabilitation Hospital

32   Mike Inderreiden; Anne Cusack, *Chicago Tribune*

34   Terry D. Newfarmer, University of Utah

35   Brad Nelson, University of Utah Medical Center; John Zielinski*; Brad Nelson, University of Utah Medical Center; John Zielinski*

36   University of Utah; Philip Katz, Harold L. Schwartz, Henry Brenman, D.D.S., and Louis Lowry, M.D., Thomas Jefferson University

37   Otologic Products, Surgical Products Division, 3–M Company (Ruben Berrerez, University of Iowa Hospitals and Clinics); John Zielinski*

40   F. Fanaki, Environment Canada; Eddie Adams, Gamma/Liaison; John Bora, Photo Researchers; World Book photo by Fred Leavitt*; National Film Board of Canada; J. C. Suares

43-46   Stephen Boswick*

48   Westfälisches Amt für Denkmalpflege, Münster, West Germany

49   Oak Ridge National Laboratory; © Lars Overrein; © Lars Overrein

50   John Goerg, New York State Department of Environmental Conservation

51   Stephen Boswick*

52   Carl Skalek; Oak Ridge National Laboratory

54   Ivan Polunin, Bruce Coleman Inc.

55   P. A. Hinchliffe, Bruce Coleman Ltd.

57   Ron Church, Tom Stack & Assoc.

58   Carré, Jacana

59   Fritz Goro, *Life* Magazine, © Time Inc.

60   Greg Harlin*; P. M. David, Photo Researchers; Oxford Scientific Films from Animals Animals

62   Oxford Scientific Films from Animals Animals

63   Oxford Scientific Films from Animals Animals; Tim Rock, Animals Animals

64   New Zealand Tourist and Publicity Department

66   Dave Baird, Tom Stack & Assoc.

67   Mike Price, Bruce Coleman Ltd.; George Whiteley, Photo Researchers

70   Leonard Morgan*

73   © 1983 Carroll H. Weiss; Center for Disease Control

75   © 1973 Carroll H. Weiss; © 1983 Carroll H. Weiss

76   Jon Mummaw, Milton S. Hershey Medical Center

77   Leonard Morgan*

78   Kenyon S. Tweedell, University of Notre Dame; Robert Furrow, D.V.M., Food Safety Inspection Service, USDA

79   © 1983 Carroll H. Weiss; John L. Ziegler, M.D.

80   Leonard Morgan*

82   Walter Frerck, Odyssey Productions

86   United Press Int.; Scott Dine, Picture Group

87   Environmental Protection Agency

89   Leonard Morgan*

90   David R. Frazier

92   Center for Disease Control

93   Kevin Twombly, Picture Group

94   Leonard Morgan*; Office of Nuclear Waste Isolation

96   Battelle Memorial Institute

98   Jon Kalb; Tim White

102-103   Yoshi Miyake*

104-106   Jon Kalb

107   Institute of Human Origins; Tim White

109   Yoshi Miyake*

110   Jon Kalb

112-115   Laura Lizak*

117   L. L. T. Rhodes, Animals Animals; L. L. T. Rhodes, Animals Animals; Mark Rosenthal; Mark Rosenthal; Laura Lizak*

118   David Pilbeam, Harvard University

120-124   Laura Lizak*

126   Ethyl Corporation

129   Trudy Rogers*

130   Trudy Rogers*; GTE Lighting Products, Sylvania Lighting Center; © Harold and Erica Van Pelt, National Gemstone Corporation; © Harold and Erica Van Pelt; © Harold and Erica Van Pelt, Pala International

131   © Harold and Erica Van Pelt, National Gemstone Corporation; Trudy Rogers*; © Harold and Erica Van Pelt; © Harold and Erica Van Pelt, Pala International; Trudy Rogers*; Trudy Rogers*; Trudy Rogers*

132   Ken Firestone; Alan D. Briere, Tom Stack & Assoc.; Gary Randall, Tom Stack & Assoc.; Trudy Rogers*

133   Trudy Rogers*; Karen M. Koblik

134   Lee Boltin; Free Chin

135-136   Trudy Rogers*

137   Roberta Dimmer

138   John Deeks; Trudy Rogers

140-143   Rob Wood, Stansbury, Ronsaville, Wood, Inc.*

144   Rob Wood, Stansbury, Ronsaville, Wood, Inc.*; © Association of Universities for Research in Astronomy, Inc., Kitt Peak National Observatory; Harvard-Smithsonian Center for Astrophysics

146-149   Rob Wood, Stansbury, Ronsaville, Wood, Inc.*

150   Harvard-Smithsonian Center for Astrophysics

151   Rob Wood, Stansbury, Ronsaville, Wood, Inc.*

154-165   James Teason*

168   Steve Boswick*

171   Steve Boswick*; Martin Dohrn, Bruce Coleman Ltd.; R. and N. Blakemore; Jeff Foott, Bruce Coleman Ltd.

173   Steve Boswick*

174   Brookhaven National Laboratory

175   Fermi National Accelerator Laboratory

176   Nuclear Division, Union Carbide Corporation/Oak Ridge National Laboratory

177   The Cleveland Clinic Foundation

178   Japanese National Railways

179	Japanese National Railways; Steve Boswick*
180	Steve Boswick*
182-185	Tim Evans*
186	Tim Evans and Yoshi Miyake*; U.S. Geological Survey; U.S. Geological Survey
187	Tim Evans*; U.S. Geological Survey
188	Tim Evans*
189	David L. Jones, U.S. Geological Survey
190-193	Tim Evans*
197-206	Susan Pyle*

Science File

210	Jose Ochoa, M.D., Dartmouth Medical School; Walker Montgomery, University of Georgia; © Zoological Society of San Diego
211	Stanford University, Kitt Peak National Observatory, NASA
212-214	Agricultural Research Service, U. S. Department of Agriculture
216	University of California at Berkeley
217	Institute for Intercultural Studies
219	© Jonathan Blair, National Geographic Society.
220	© Dean Conger, National Geographic Society; © Lincoln Potter, Gamma/Liaison
221	© Bill Deane, National Geographic Society
222	Norb Bielat*; Brigham Young University
223	Wide World
224	Kitt Peak National Observatory
225	Chip Clark, Smithsonian Natural History Museum
226	S. Djorgovski, *Nature*
227	NASA
228	© Len Norris, *Vancouver Sun,* from Rothco
229	Y.-H. Chu, University of California at Berkeley and Cerro Tololo Inter-American Observatory
230	Jet Propulsion Laboratory
231	Jack W. Sulentic, Jet Propulsion Laboratory/University of Alabama
232	Fred Lawrence Whipple Observatory, Smithsonian Institution
235	Nancy Allin and G. L. Barron, University of Guelph
236	Cornell University
237	Los Alamos National Laboratory
239	Lawrence Livermore National Laboratory
241	Wide World; Rockefeller University; Ingbert Grüttner, Rockefeller University
242	Canadian Broadcasting Company from Wide World; Wide World; Wide World
243	Drawing by Joseph Farris; © 1978 The New Yorker Magazine, Inc.
244	Steve Hale*
246	NASA
248	Jet Propulsion Laboratory
250	Johns Hopkins University; Robert T. Bakker
255	Jet Propulsion Laboratory
258	Walker Montgomery, University of Georgia
260	Seiko Time Corporation
261	© Jeff Nadler
262	Robotics International Corporation
263	International Business Machines
264	Sharpshooters
265	Princeton Plasma Physics Laboratory
268	Lawrence Berkeley Laboratory, Universtiy of California; Norb Bielat*
270	Coastal Environments, Inc.
271	Stan Alost, *State-Times* and *Morning Advocate,* Baton Rouge
274	School of Veterinary Medicine, University of Pennsylvania

276	National Cancer Institute
279	© Berni Rich, Score Photographers
280	BCD Products, Inc.
281	Axionics Inc.; Stanford University
282	Emory University of School of Medicine and The Upjohn Company
283	*Medical World News*
284	John F. Burke, M.D.
285	Norb Bielat*; National Eye Institute; Retinal Vascular Department, Ingalls Memorial Hospital
286	Russell W. Bessette, D.D.S., M.S.
288	Luka Milas, M. D. Anderson Hospital and Tumor Institute
289	A. G. Matthysse, K. V. Holmes and R. H. G. Gurlitz, Agricultural Research Service, U.S. Department of Agriculture
290	Sidney Harris
291	Weizmann Institute of Science
292	Michael G. Rossmann et al., Purdue University
293	James Glisson
294	Jose Ochoa, Dartmouth Medical School
295	U.S. Department of Agriculture
297	Lawrence Berkeley Laboratory, University of California
298	Gesellschaft für Schwerionenforschung MBH; Norb Bielat*
299	CERN
300	Stanford University, Norb Bielat*; Stanford University (Norb Bielat*)
302	R. Mackson, FPG
303	Drawing by Chas. Addams; © 1983 The New Yorker Magazine, Inc.
304	Norb Bielat*; International Business Machines
307	Jon Hoffmann, Photographers International
309	Norb Bielat*
313	NASA
315	Tass from Sovfoto
316	Gerald L. Kooyman, Scripps Institution of Oceanography; Scripps Institution of Oceanography; Norb Bielat*
317	Thomas Eisner and Stephen Nowicki
318	Sea World
319	© Zoological Society of San Diego
320	Anthony Taber

Science You Can Use

323-325	Mike Hagel*
327	Mike Hagel*; Apple Computer Inc.; Radio Shack, A Division of Tandy Corporation; Texas Instruments
329-334	Mike Hagel*

People in Science

336	Nancy Rodger, Exploratorium; Ted Streshinsky*; © Bruce Roberts, *Southern Living*
337	Ted Streshinsky*; Ontario Science Centre; Ted Streshinsky*
338-347	Ted Streshinsky*
348	Norman E. Borlaug; Norman E. Borlaug; Les Wollam*
349	Les Wollam*
350	Norman E. Borlaug
352	Steven Goldblatt, Franklin Institute Science Museum
356	Nancy Rodger, Exploratorium
358	Deutsches Museum, Munich
361	© Bruce Roberts, *Southern Living*
362	Nancy Rodger, Exploratorium
363	WORLD BOOK photo; John Stevenson
364	Ontario Science Centre; Lawrence Hall of Science; Birla Industrial and Technological Museum
366	Franklin Institute Science Museum